Lethal Wor

LETHAL WORK

A History of the Asbestos Tragedy in Scotland

RONALD JOHNSTON
and
ARTHUR McIVOR

TUCKWELL PRESS

First published in Great Britain in 2000 by
Tuckwell Press
The Mill House
Phantassie
East Linton
East Lothian EH40 3DG
Scotland

ISBN 1 86232 178 7

British Library Cataloguing in Publication Data
A catalogue record for this book is available
on request from the British Library

Typeset by Carnegie Publishing Ltd, Chatsworth Road, Lancaster
Printed and bound by The Cromwell Press, Trowbridge, Wiltshire

This book is dedicated to all those who have died, and those currently suffering from, asbestos-related diseases

Contents

     Red Road Building Site, Glasgow, for the Corporation of
     Glasgow, May 1967

     Bibliography   241

     Index   249

Illustrations

Tables and Graphs

Abbreviations

AOHP	Asbestos Oral History Project
ARC	Asbestosis Research Council
CAA	Clydeside Action on Asbestos
CSA	Clyde Shipbuilders' Association
DHSS	Department of Health and Social Security
DSS	Department of Social Security
FIR	Factory Inspectors Report
GMWU	General and Municipal Workers' Union
GP	General Practitioner
GSS	Glasgow Scientific Services
HMWC	Health of Munitions Workers' Committee
HSC	Health and Safety Commission
HSE	Health and Safety Executive
HSWA	Health and Safety at Work Act
IFRB	Industrial Fatigue Research Board
IHRB	Industrial Health Research Board
NHS	National Health Service
NWETEA	North West Engineering Trades Employers' Association
RIDDOR	Reporting of Injuries and Dangerous Occurrences Regulations
SCWS	Scottish Co-operative Wholesale Society
SIEA	Scottish Insulation Employers' Association
SMA	Socialist Medical Association
SOHS	Scottish Occupational Health Service
SPAID	Society for the Prevention of Asbestosis and Industrial Diseases
SSP	Statutory Sick Pay
STUC	Scottish Trades Union Congress
STUC, GC	Scottish Trades Union Congress, General Council
TGWU	Transport and General Workers' Union
T&N	Turner & Newall
TAC	Turner's Asbestos Cement
TUC	Trades Union Congress
WSCSU	West of Scotland Cancer Surveillance Unit

Acknowledgements

We would like to acknowledge our thanks to a great many people for their assistance during the preparation and writing of this book. Our greatest debt is to all those asbestos victims in Scotland who allowed us to interview them, completed our questionnaires, shared freely their memories (even though these were often painful to recall) and insights, and responded patiently to our often naïve and sometimes intrusive questioning. Their stoic courage has been inspirational. We would also like to especially thank the officers and volunteers of the pressure group Clydeside Action on Asbestos (CAA), particularly Ian McKechnie, Phyllis Craig, Harry McCluskey, Jimmy Dempsey, Andy Rae and John Rooney. CAA provided our first entry into this topic, allowed free access to their massive asbestos archive, distributed our questionnaires and organised the initial group of client interviews. They also provided much invaluable advice, guidance and feedback, as well as a place to work and cups of tea to lubricate the research process. The Clydebank Asbestos Group also provided useful material and contacts, whilst several trade unions assisted our project in a number of ways, including the Scottish Trades Union Congress, the General and Municipal Workers' Union and the Transport and General Workers' Union (Glasgow). We are also grateful to the recently formed Scottish Trade Union Research Network (and its coordinator, Mike Donnelly) for providing an early opportunity to air the results of our research and publicise our interim findings. We would also like to thank the Health and Safety Executive Statistics Unit in Bootle, Merseyside, for collating and releasing series of statistics relating specifically to Scotland, which are published here for the first time.

Invaluable financial assistance to aid research, interviewing and transcription was provided by three sources: the Nuffield Foundation, the University of Strathclyde and the Thriplow Trust. Without such support this book would certainly have taken much longer to produce and might not have appeared at all.

We would also like to express our appreciation to the many archivists, librarians and individuals who have helped us in our search for pertinent source material, including the National Library of Scotland; the Mitchell Library (and Archives), Glasgow; Glasgow University Archive and Business Records Centre; and the Central Library, Aberdeen. Special thanks, though, to Carole McCallum, Library Archivist, and Audrey Canning, Archivist, Willie Gallagher Collection, Glasgow Caledonian University; and to Pat Malcolm, local librarian, Clydebank Central Library. Useful material was also provided by the Aberdeen Newspapers' Group. We are similarly grateful for additional material, advice and guidance provided by Jim Cameron, Alan Dalton, Willie Dewar, Andy Higgison, Robin Howie, William Kenefick, Owen and Margaret Lilly, Phil Taylor, Pat Whitelaw, Murdoch Nicolson, Dr Ian Symington, Professor O. L. Lloyd (Scottish Occupational Health Service), Chris Orr and Frank Maguire, the Scottish lawyer who has campaigned vigorously for changes in the law to benefit asbestos-disease sufferers. Special thanks also to James Murdoch and Francis Devine who wrote the evocative poems that start and finish the book.

A host of other specialists provided freely of their time and offered guidance and advice for which we are deeply indebted. Geoffrey Tweedale merits a special mention because he openly shared with us the Scottish material that he discovered during his monumental study of the major UK asbestos multinational company Turner & Newall. On the latter, readers should refer to Geoff's pioneering book, *Magic Mineral to Killer Dust* (Oxford, 2000). Geoff also kindly read and commented on some of our earlier work and on the complete draft of this book, as did Tommy Gorman, a Scottish welfare rights worker and long-standing Scottish asbestos expert and campaigner. Tommy provided freely and warmly of his time and his expertise on the asbestos issue, acted as a sounding board for many ideas, assisted in locating illustrations and kindly gave us access to his unpublished dissertation. We have also benefited greatly from discussions and feedback on our work from a long-time colleague, Charles Woolfson, as well as support from the recently formed European Centre for Occupational Safety, Health and the Environment. We would also like to express our thanks and appreciation to our publisher, John Tuckwell, for his enthusiasm for the project, meticulous copy-editing, providing many helpful suggestions and for guiding this book rapidly through the various stages from the original idea to the final product. Of course, we alone are responsible for misjudgements, errors and weaknesses in the text.

Last but not least, we would like to thank our families and partners for bearing with us whilst preoccupied with this project, and for offering encouragement and constructive criticism and assistance in many ways. Our partners, Margot and Janne, and our children, Kieran, Sandra, Alison and Tom, have, as always, been an inspiration and source of unstinting support. Researching this book has drawn us into close contact with a great many courageous people who have been severely disabled by inhaling asbestos dust. Many of these stoically face certain death from the mesothelioma strangling their lungs, and several of our interviewees have already succumbed to this modern-day plague. This experience has made us acutely aware of how lucky we are to be healthy and to have healthy children. This book is dedicated to all sufferers of asbestos-related diseases in Scotland. If it succeeds in raising awareness of how asbestos has curtailed and destroyed people's lives and gets policy makers thinking about how the lifestyles of such victims and their dependants deserve to be improved, it will have fulfilled its primary purpose.

Introduction

IN PASSING

Hello Jack! Want a lift up Kilbowie Hill?
Aye thanks, a'hm going up to the doctor's
I've a bit of a chill
or something.

Hello Jack! Going up the hill?
Aye thanks, a'hm going back to the doctor's
This is more than a chill,
'am ill.

Hello Jack! Found out yet what's making you ill?
Aye, it's that bloody asbestos, the merchants of death
knew it could kill,
and said nothing.

Today Jack got a lift o'er Kilbowie Hill,
no hacking cough, no breathless pause,
cause Jack isn't ill
anymore.

A parting hymn, a pious prayer.
We said farewell to Jack until
the curtains drew quietly to a close,
and everything was still,
except a sob,
from Jill.

James Murdoch (2000)

Asbestos destroys people's lives. Incredibly, asbestos-related diseases now account for some 400 deaths every year in Scotland, with many more being severely disabled. This number is still increasing, due to the long latency period of this disease, and according to one cumulative estimate something in the region of 20,000 Scots will have died through exposure to asbestos by 2025. Asbestos is now one of the most deadly occupational diseases and by any standards this constitutes a major tragedy of epidemic proportions.

This book is a history of the unfolding asbestos tragedy in Scotland. We aim here to outline the dimensions of the problem, identify the causes and analyse the impact upon people's lives and the community of this public health disaster. We would stress at the outset that this is a *social* history – going back to the 1870s when the first Scottish companies began manufacturing asbestos – of this most virulent of industrial diseases. Here we are particularly concerned to show how individuals in particular jobs in specific communities came into contact with asbestos, and how it affected their lives and those of their dependants, both physically and socially.

The research on which the book is based has been undertaken over the past two years. It has been both a hard book to write and a most rewarding experience. Sources have been difficult to locate, not least because many of the companies involved have since disappeared as de-industrialisation progressed and few have left records to consult. From the outset, therefore, we determined to speak directly to those survivors who had been involved in the industry and designed an oral history project to accumulate personal testimony. We interviewed over 30 former asbestos workers and their partners, as well as several key 'gatekeepers' – including trade union and asbestos pressure group officials and the principal solicitor involved in compensation litigation in Scotland. Our respondents were drawn from a number of sources, including the databases of the main asbestos pressure groups on Clydeside (Clydeside Action on Asbestos and the Clydebank Asbestos Group) and the Transport and General Workers' Union. We also consulted surviving documentary evidence relating to the asbestos industry in Scotland. Particularly rich has been the material collected and archived by Clydeside Action on Asbestos since the mid-1980s. These records include the papers of the asbestos activist John Todd and much of the microfilmed archive of the major asbestos company in the UK, Turner & Newall (T&N). The T&N papers are available, quite uniquely, because they were copied and brought into the public domain as a result of the legal case taken up in the USA by the Chase Manhattan Bank against T&N in 1995. These papers include material on the industry in Scotland, particularly relating to the Turner's Asbestos Cement Company in Clydebank and Newall's Insulation. Other sources that have been quarried for this book include newpapers, government reports – including the Factory Inspectors and Health and Safety Executive – trade union and employers' association records, including those of the Scottish Trade Union Congress and, on the employers' side, the records of the Scottish Thermal Insulation Engineers' Association.

Much has been published on the asbestos issue in the UK, so what does this book add to this quite voluminous literature? Surprisingly little so far has been published on the Scottish experience and in our view this merits separate and more detailed analysis. There is a specifically Scottish story to tell because Scottish law, culture and society provide a quite different context, and the country includes several asbestos 'blackspots', with very high incidences of asbestos-related diseases, including Clydeside, Rosyth, Aberdeen and Leith. Moreover, we hope that our methodology – integrating conventional research in the archives with oral interviewing – will provide a fresh approach and some new perspectives on the sometimes deadly interaction between work and health. The book is infused with this participant oral testimony. Specifically, our respondents have provided many insights into the mechanisms of exposure and the culture of disregard for health in employment which prevailed for much of the twentieth century as well as the effects of asbestos disease on people's lives. The culpability of employers and management in asbestos manufacturing, shipbuilding and construction in this tragedy is also evident, whilst the preventative legislation and the policing mechanisms – the Factory Inspectorate and, latterly, the Health and Safety Executive – are also shown to be inadequate. We try to set the asbestos disaster in context, locating it within the broader tapestry of prevailing working conditions and attitudes, the state of medical knowledge at the time and the existence of a wide range of other toxic substances, industrial diseases and dangerous practices in Scottish workplaces in the twentieth century.

We hope that our book has contemporary relevance as well as being of historical interest. Certainly, the history of this disaster tells us much about attitudes and policies within Scottish society today in relation to occupational health and safety. The deficiencies within the medical and social services designed to deal with asbestos victims are also clearly evident and there is a critical need to introduce reforms to tackle the disgrace of disability-induced poverty and social exclusion. The lessons of the past, in other words, need to be absorbed and acted upon. In this respect, the new Scottish Parliament provides a unique opportunity.

The first chapter provides an overview of the origins and development of the asbestos industry and the uses of asbestos in Scottish industry and construction since the 1870s. Here we also define the asbestos-related diseases and investigate the occupational and geographical patterns of mortality within Scotland. However, it is important that asbestos be seen in context as only one of a long catalogue of occupational health hazards that have afflicted Scottish workers throughout the nineteenth and twentieth centuries. The next chapter takes us outside the asbestos story and into a commentary on the dangers and hazards that Scottish workers have had to face in the workplace over the past century or so. Chapter 3 investigates the long exposure of workers in their workplaces to asbestos dust, focusing in some depth on three case studies of the asbestos factories, shipbuilding and construction. Chapter 4 explores the protracted process whereby the hazards of asbestos were discovered and legislation passed to regulate the dangers and protect workers. The successes and the inadequacies of the state and civil compensation systems are also discussed here. In Chapter 5 we evaluate the changing attitudes and policies of the employers, management, trade unions and the workers themselves in Scotland towards the asbestos problem, and comment on the role of the main asbestos pressure groups, including Clydeside Action on Asbestos. In the final chapter we analyse the social and personal impact of disability and death caused by asbestos – examining the ways in which asbestos has blighted people's lives and affected the community in twentieth-century Scotland. Whether the evidence we provide and the interpretations we develop from our material are convincing is for the reader to determine.

CHAPTER ONE

The Asbestos Tragedy

Peter realised something was wrong on a Saturday morning in mid-May, a fine day for working in the garden. He lived in a small village in Lanarkshire, and the big garden was his pride and joy. Peter was a foreman electrician, and often whilst at work during the week he would go over in his head the weekend tasks that lay ahead: tidy up the back path, trim the hedge, weed the potato patch. Normally he could easily spend a good four hours in the garden on a Saturday, and his wife would sometimes bring out cups of tea and sandwiches which they would have together in the hut. This day was different, though, for he had only managed to weed one row before he had to stop for a breather. This puzzled him a bit. A lifetime non-smoker, he had always prided himself on being a fit man. 'Surely', he thought, 'this cannae be old age already?' He was only 63. The following week he felt even worse and went to his doctor. 'Did you ever work with asbestos?' the doctor asked him. He thought for a minute. 'Asbestos?' Well, way back during his apprenticeship he had worked with the old fuses that were fitted with asbestos flashguards, and he had sometimes used asbestos tape to join cable; he could also remember working beside joiners who sawed asbestos boards in the prefabs, and he himself used to cut holes in asbestos panelling though which he fed cables; and as he thought, more and more run-of-the-mill instances came into his mind. 'Yes', he finally replied, 'everybody in the building trade has been exposed to asbestos. There was none of us that was in the building trade that hasnae been.' Three weeks later he was diagnosed as having a lethal cancerous tumour called mesothelioma. This, he was told, was without any doubt caused by his exposure to asbestos at work.[1]

Around about the same time a 65-year-old joiner from Glasgow also came to realise that his recent breathing difficulties and racking cough were not just a sign of advancing old age. He and his wife had been counting off the days to his retirement, and they had lots of

1. Interview A 13. The passages cited are the respondent's own words.

5

plans. He had his workshop out the back where he would make furniture, and they would socialise even more than they did. The cough, though, had been getting worse, and eventually he was persuaded to go to the doctor. He also had never smoked, so he presumed that the dark avenue leading to lung cancer would be ruled out. But to his amazement the doctor asked him if he had ever worked with asbestos. He had to think for a while, then it came to him. During the War the company he worked for had found it more and more difficult to get wood, so they had started using asbestos boarding instead. He and his work-mates had cut and shaped the stuff using their joiners' tools, and sometimes the dust got so bad that you couldn't see who was working at the next bench. This information seemed to satisfy the doctor and she recommended that he go for some tests. These revealed that his exposure to asbestos during the Second World War had caused severe lung damage that was going to get progressively worse. His dreams of a long and happy retirement had suddenly been shattered. [2]

These experiences are being repeated all over Europe, as tens of thousands of ordinary people are becoming aware that their health has been damaged by exposure to asbestos at work many years ago.[3] The death toll from asbestos-related diseases is absolutely staggering. At present, around 3,500 die each year from asbestos exposure in the United Kingdom, and it has been estimated that in the UK alone asbestos will have killed around 250,000 men and women between 1995 and 2029.[4] In the late 1990s, almost 400 deaths per year were occurring in Scotland alone as a consequence of asbestos-related diseases.[5] In other words more than one person per day dies in Scotland as a result of asbestos, and that number is still increasing. This is the product of historic exposure, both in the workplace and the environment, and of ongoing problems even after extensive statutory regulations. Recent research, for example, has demonstrated that even in the 1980s the workplace performance of approved respirators was considerably poorer than laboratory performance, resulting in life-threatening levels of exposure to asbestos fibres in

2. Interview A 8.
3. See J. Peto, 'The European Mesothelioma Epidemic', *British Journal of Cancer*, vol. 79, 1999, pp. 666–72.
4. J. Peto *et al.*, 'Continuing increase in mesothelioma mortality in Britain', *The Lancet*, vol. 345, 4 March 1995, pp. 535–9.
5. *Aberdeen Evening Express*, 17 February 1998.

stripping operations.[6] Many of these deaths will be clustered in areas where shipbuilding and heavy engineering were dominant, and where asbestos was used extensively. The West of Scotland is one of these clusters, and this is due primarily to the fact that at one time more ships-per-head of population were launched on Clydeside than in any other industrial region in the world. One of the legacies of this proud record is that Clydebank, the birthplace of the giant Cunard liners, has now the highest rate of asbestos-related deaths anywhere in Europe.

In Scotland, shipyard workers were particularly at risk of contracting asbestos-related disease, and a recurring theme in the evidence is the callousness with which victims and their families were treated by employers and the legal system. The case of Charlie Coyle is an example. Coyle worked for Newall's Insulation – the largest UK asbestos thermal insulating contractor – as an asbestos sprayer between 1945 and 1954. In 1954 he was diagnosed with advanced pneumoconiosis and suspended. He then took up a legal case against Newall's for compensation for negligence. The solicitors for Turner & Newall (the parent company and biggest asbestos manufacturer in Britain) fought the case quite ruthlessly – employing delaying tactics, denying liability and shedding doubt upon the extent of the victim's incapacity. At that time, Scottish law decreed that if a claimant died, the case virtually died too, so the company solicitors knew exactly what they were doing, informing Turner & Newall (T&N):

> The man has a very poor expectation of life and if he does succumb the claim will not be any more expensive, and without his evidence the solicitors will be in greater difficulties. In short, I do not think tactically we have anything to lose by leaving the matter in abeyance.[7]

With a relatively inexperienced solicitor representing Coyle, the process was allowed to be strung out for over a year. In the event Charlie Coyle died in November 1956. T&N's solicitors then pressurised Charlie Coyle's solicitor and widow into accepting an *ex*

---

6. We are grateful to the occupational hygienist and asbestos expert Robin Howie for this information. See R. Howie, 'Asbestos, the Way Forward Learning from Past Mistakes' in T. Gorman (ed.), *Clydebank: Asbestos, the Unwanted Legacy* (2000).

7. Cited in T. Gorman, 'A Case Study of the Settlement Process', in G. A. Peters and B. J. Peters, *Sourcebook on Asbestos Diseases* (vol. 20), p. 365; see also G. Tweedale, *Magic Mineral to Killer Dust* (Oxford, 2000), p 110.

gratia payment of £500 in a final out-of-court settlement with the company officially refusing to accept any liability for Coyle's death. 'A hard fight' was threatened if the case went to court. £500 was a minuscule price to pay for a man's life, cut short at the young age of 48. Had the case gone to court when Charlie Coyle was still living, it had been estimated that the settlement would have been nearer to £4,000. Not surprisingly, T&N expressed their satisfaction with such a favourable outcome.[8]

The issue of asbestos has been at the forefront of media attention for some time, and several books have been written on the topic, as well as radio and television programmes. A recent book by G. Tweedale called *Magic Mineral to Killer Dust* exposes how T&N continued to expose their workers to the dangers of asbestos dust long after the directors were aware of these dangers. At a more local level an edited volume called *Clydebank and Asbestos: the Unwanted Legacy* (Clydebank, 2000) looks at how this shipbuilding community on the Clyde – in which T&N built an asbestos cement factory – became the asbestos-disease capital of Europe. There have also been several medical papers on the subject of asbestos in the West of Scotland, and a report by the victim support group Clydeside Action on Asbestos gives an excellent account of how sufferers of asbestos-related disease have had to fight for recognition and compensation.[9] The media and academic attention surrounding asbestos is set to continue, as the long latency period of asbestos diseases means that it is only now that the consequences of working with the hazardous mineral are really beginning to be realised, and it has been estimated that asbestos deaths will peak over the next 20 years. Therefore, as Scotland with its new Parliament and its drastically changed industrial structure moves into the new millennium, this ghost from the old heavy industries of the past is set to spoil the feast for some time to come.

8. For more detailed accounts of the Charlie Coyle case see T. Gorman, 'A Case Study' and G. Tweedale, *Magic Mineral*, pp. 109–11.
9. H. De Vos Irvine, 'Asbestos and Lung Cancer in Glasgow and the West of Scotland,' *British Medical Journal*, 1993, June 5; 306, p. 689; J. Lenaghan, *Victims Twice Over* (Glasgow, n.d., c. 1994). See also R. Johnston and A. McIvor, 'Pushed into Social Exclusion', *Scottish Affairs*, No. 32, Summer 2000.

The history of asbestos in Scotland

Asbestos – which comes from the Greek word meaning inextinguishable – is a fibrous mineral which has been mined since prehistory. There are several types of asbestos, although chrysotile, or white asbestos, is the most common. Chrysotile, like all asbestos, is characterised by having curly needle-like fibres that are damaging to lung tissue. However, by far the sharpest and most invidious of asbestos is crocidolite known as blue asbestos.[10]

TABLE 1:1. TYPES OF ASBESTOS

Type of asbestos	Colour
Chrysotile	White
Amosite	Grey brown
Anthophyllite	White
Crocidolite	Blue
Tremolite	White
Actinolite	White

As industrialisation increased its pace in the late nineteenth century, the use of asbestos increased too, and its unique qualities were more and more in demand. The fibres could be spun or woven into cloth which could be used as insulation; they could be added to cement to make pipes, wall boarding, fire-resistant roofing sheets, etc; they could be impregnated into rubber, or used as friction material, or in countless other industrial processes. Because of its cheapness, its sheer flexibility, and its usefulness, asbestos was dubbed 'the magic mineral', and vast deposits in Canada, Russia, and later South Africa, were exploited and shipped to ports in the industrial world. Much of this, as can be seen from Graph 1:1 below, came to the UK. A proportion of it was shipped directly to Scotland, peaking at over 6,000 tons per year in the mid-1950s imported directly through the Glasgow docks.[11]

Scotland has had a long association with the asbestos industry. Scottish entrepreneurs were amongst the pioneers in developing the manufacture of asbestos products, with the first companies appearing

10. J. Lenaghan, *Victims*, p. 10.
11. Derived from the Annual Statistical Statements of the Clyde Navigation Trust. We are grateful to Robin Howie for this material.

Lethal Work

GRAPH 1:1. ANNUAL IMPORTS OF ASBESTOS — THOUSANDS OF
TONS — INTO THE UK, 1930–70

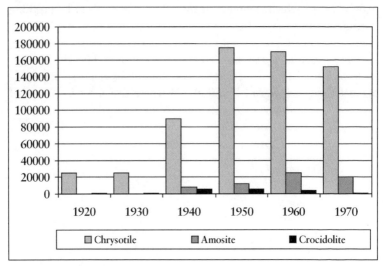

Source: Clydeside Action on Asbestos

in the 1870s. One account suggests that it was two Scottish businessmen who first introduced the mineral to the UK, establishing the Patent Asbestos Manufacturing Company in Glasgow to process asbestos imported initially from Canada in 1871.[12] Later that same year an engineer read a paper in Glasgow to the Institute of Engineers and Shipbuilders in Scotland on the uses of asbestos in steam engines.[13] Thereafter growth was rapid as the potential of the manufactured mineral began to be realised. By 1885 there were at least 19 asbestos manufacturers and distributors in Glasgow.[14] There were also some dotted around Lanarkshire. For example, the Phoenix Asbestos Manufacturing Company opened its new works at Baskmill in Hamilton in 1894 on the site of what had been Robertson's Asbestos Ltd.[15] The number of companies increased, and at the turn of the century 52 were listed as 'asbestos manufacturers' in the *Glasgow*

12. A. L. Summers, *Asbestos and the Asbestos Industry* (1919), p. 10.
13. St-J. Vincent Day, 'On Asbestos', Institution of Engineers and Shipbuilders in Scotland, 5 December 1871 (Glasgow, 1872).
14. *Post Office Directory of Glasgow, 1884–85*, p. 888.
15. Articles of Association of Phoenix Asbestos Manufacturing Company, (Glasgow City Archives, SRA, T-BK 167/2).

Post Office Directory.[16] The importance of the industry in Clydeside in this early period is suggested by the fact that of 18 asbestos companies (probably the largest) listed in a UK Trade Directory in 1884, six were located in Glasgow.[17] These six – the Scottish Asbestos Company, the Glasgow Asbestos Company, the United Asbestos Company, James Wotherspoon and Sons, William Hollywood, and John Bell – were probably the industry leaders in Scotland in the late nineteenth century.

TABLE I.2. ASBESTOS MANUFACTURERS IN GLASGOW, 1884–85

Argyle Rubber Co.	Irwell India Rubber and Gutta Percha Works
John Bell	Lincolne and Co.
Campbell, Achnach and Co.	John C. Mackay and Co.
Clydesdale Rubber Co.	George MacLellan and Co. (Glasgow Rubber Works)
Downie and McClure	James McNeill and Co.
Glasgow Asbestos Co.	Peter Robertson
J. T. Goudie and Co.	The Scottish Asbestos Co. Ltd
J and R. Hatch	The United Asbestos Co. Ltd
William Hollywood	James Wotherspoon
Thomas Ironmonger and Co.	

Source: *Post Office Directory of Glasgow, 1884–85* (1885), p. 888.

The Scottish Asbestos Company (founded in 1877) was one of the pioneers, exploiting the market for engine packing and insulation, producing asbestos blocks, rope and millboard for these purposes from its Levenshields works in Nitshill, near Glasgow. The 40-inch-square asbestos boards that the company manufactured in various thicknesses were used in buildings: in walls, ceilings, floors and partitions as a fire retardant. The company also manufactured flexible mattresses for boiler coverings, asbestos tape, powder, putty, cement and paint. A dry form of its product was supplied ready to be mixed with water and applied directly to boilers and pipes as an insulator. The company also owned asbestos mines, and so was able to supply its own raw material. So dominant was the company in the

16. *Post Office Directory*, 1900–1. Some of these were agents of UK-based companies, probably just with warehouses in Glasgow.
17. *Kelly's Directory of Merchants, Manufacturers and Shippers* (England, Scotland and Wales), 1884, p 185.

industry at this time that it won the highest award at the Edinburgh Exhibition of Industry, Science and Art.[18]

In these early years there were close connections between the cotton and rubber industries and asbestos manufacture. As the qualities and advantages of asbestos became apparent, a number of cotton and rubber manufacturers diversified into asbestos, which was seen as a more effective insulator and packing agent than cotton and rubber variants. The machinery used to manufacture cotton fabrics was readily adapted to card, spin and weave asbestos fibres. J. and W. Tinto Ltd are an example of a cotton manufacturer who diversified into asbestos spinning and weaving. They expanded as demand for their asbestos-based products increased, and after World War One they moved into a larger factory in Govan, located conveniently in a major shipbuilding district of Glasgow.[19] One of Scotland's largest cotton manufacturers, James Findlay and Co. (Deanston Works, near Doune, Stirlingshire) also manufactured asbestos under the name of the Glasgow Asbestos Company until 1913. This was primarily for export to the East.[20]

In some cases, rubber and asbestos were blended together to make highly flexible, durable and flame-retardant packing and drive bands. Hence, one of Glasgow's largest rubber manufacturers, George Mac-Lellan Ltd, produced a range of asbestos-based products – including wide sheets for marine insulation and thin strips for electrical insulation – at its factory in Maryhill, on the Forth & Clyde canal in north-west Glasgow from the 1880s.[21] This company (which employed around 500 in the 1950s) undertook the entire processing of asbestos, from crushing and mixing the mineral and carding the fibres (all extremely dusty processes), to spinning and weaving yarn and cloth, and wet-mixing pulped asbestos into sheets and boards. In 1930, its asbestos product list included millboard, locomotive insulation mattresses, brake linings and high-pressure steam engine and hydraulic packings and jointings. MacLellan's was described in the late 1930s

18. *Glasgow of Today, Businessmen and Mercantile Interests* (Mitchell Library, Glasgow Collection, 1888), p. 112.
19. *Glasgow Chamber of Commerce (GCC), Journal*,. XXI, no. 5, May 1938, p. 122.
20. Letter, K. and G. MacLellan to H. T. Kinloch, 23 March 1949 (Glasgow City Archives, Mitchell Library, TD512/37).
21. Letter, K and G MacLellan to H. T. Kinloch, 23 March 1949 (Glasgow City Archives, Mitchell Library, TD512/).

as 'one of the leading asbestos firms in the country', and was reputed to have been the first in the UK to begin the manufacturing of asbestos millboard. The asbestos side of the company was expanded considerably in 1932 when MacLellan's bought the site and buildings of an adjacent chemical works and converted them into its asbestos factory (see plate section, 1 and 2).[22]

Similarly, the Clyde Rubberworks, established in 1883 in the Port Dundas area of Glasgow, also manufactured asbestos products. These included asbestos hoses and products for the shipyards and the locomotive makers, presumably exploiting the market offered by their neighbours in north Glasgow, the North British Locomotive Company, which used asbestos extensively to insulate locomotive boilers and fireboxes (see plate section, 15). They were amongst the first to develop these products in the West of Scotland industrial area. The company outgrew the capacity of their original premises and moved to extended facilities at a green field site in Renfrew in 1912.[23] Other Scottish companies combined the manufacture of rubber and asbestos products, and a combined asbestos/rubber trade journal was published from the 1880s right up to the 1950s.[24] By 1914, Scottish trade directories reveal that there were more than 60 asbestos manufacturers throughout the country, including seven in Aberdeen and three in Edinburgh. Clearly, however, Glasgow and the West Scotland industrial region remained the centre of asbestos production and consumption throughout the twentieth century.

Turner Brothers, the company that came to dominate the UK asbestos industry (as Turner & Newall), began manufacturing asbestos at their plant in Rochdale in the late 1870s. In 1938 Turner's set up a factory at Dalmuir, Clydebank (on a plot of land previously occupied by the defunct shipyard giant Beardmore's) to manufacture asbestos cement products, to be used largely in the construction industry (see plate section, 3–6).[25] At the plant raw asbestos was opened up, crushed and mixed with Portland cement to create

---

22. *GCC, Journal*, XXII, no. 2, February 1939, p 37. This factory is still operating, though it no longer manufactures asbestos products.

23. See entry for William Ewing Birrell by A. Slaven, in A. Slaven and S. Checkland, *Dictionary of Scottish Business Biography*, Vol. 2 (Aberdeen, 1990), pp. 212–14.

24. *The India Rubber Journal: The Organ of the Rubber, Gutta Percha, Asbestos and Plastics Industries*, 1885–1954.

25. *Clydebank Press*, 25 February 1938.

corrugated roofing sheets, tiles, and non-corrosive pressure pipes for
water mains. Such products were widely used at the Empire Exhibition
in Glasgow in 1938 and in armament and other factories constructed
under the Defence Programme, as well as in post-war prefabricated
houses.[26] Turner's Clydebank asbestos factory expanded to employ
at maximum capacity in the 1950s some 320 workers, of whom 45
were women.[27] They continued production until closure in 1970,
ostensibly as a consequence of 'excessive capacity'. Turner's decision
to close the Clydebank factory may have been influenced by the
passage of new, more stringent safety regulations covering asbestos
workers passed in 1969 and by the belated unionisation of the plant
which resulted in a protracted three-month-long strike for improved
wages.[28] Other multi-national asbestos companies also expanded into
Scotland. Cape Asbestos and Johns Manville, for example, established
Marinite Co. Ltd in Glasgow in 1952 to produce asbestos panelling,
which was widely used in the building industry and on ships as an
insulator and fire retardant.[29] This product was first developed in the
USA in 1937 by Johns Manville and came to replace Cape's crocidolite
'Plutoboard' insulating panels. It was Marinite that was widely used
to insulate the Cunarder *Queen Elizabeth II*, built at John Brown's
shipyard, Clydebank, in the 1960s (see plate section, 14). Marinite
employed around 250 workers at this time.[30] Most of those employed
in the asbestos manufacturing companies such as Marinite and
Turner's in Scotland would have been unskilled labourers and this
would have made collective organisation difficult to sustain, especially
prior to the expansion of union membership in the late 1960s and
1970s. We return to the attitudes and policies of the unions and
employers in more depth in Chapter 5.

26. *Glasgow Chamber of Commerce Journal*, XXII, no. 4, April 1939, p. 96.
27. M. S. Dilke and A. A. Templeton, *Third Statistical Account of Scotland* (Glasgow, 1959), p. 235; Clydebank Burgh Council, *Official Handbook,* 1960, p. 39. The 1966 Handbook reported 275 employed. By rateable value, Turner's asbestos factory was the third largest employer in Clydebank (after Singer's and John Brown's).
28. *Clydebank Press*, 1 May 1970; 29 May 1970; 24 July 1970; 7 August 1970. This was reported as the first strike at the plant in 32 years. For more detail see Chapter 3.
29. *Glasgow Herald*, 27 May 1952. Cape Asbestos, *The Cape Asbestos Story* (1953), p. 73.
30. Interview A 22. This respondent worked in the Marinite factory.

TABLE 1:3. ASBESTOS MANUFACTURERS AND DISTRIBUTORS
IN SCOTLAND IN 1950

Athol Asbestos and Rubber Co.	McGruther and Marshall Ltd
A. Baird and Co.	G. MacLellan and Co. (Glasgow Rubber and Asbestos Works)
Bell's Asbestos and Engineering Co.	P. and W. MacLellan Ltd
R. S. Brown and Co.	W. MacLeod and Co.
Cape Asbestos Co.	Newton, Robertson and Co. Ltd
Clan Asbestos and Rubber Co.	Nu-Style Products Ltd
Clyde Rubberworks Co.	G. and W. Paton
Cochran and Co.	S. Pitt and Co.
T. Corrance and Yuill Ltd	F. B. Price and Co.
Cresswell's Asbestos Co.	J. A. Reid Ltd
Currie and Co.	The Rubber Company of Scotland Ltd
Donald-Bean Insulators and Engineers	The Scottish Asbestos and Rubber Co.
Gardner and Greenshields	J. C. Sinclair and Co.
R. Hamilton and Son	C. Steven and Co.
J. and W. Henderson Ltd	T. Stewart and Co.
W. Hollywood and Co.	J. D. Taylor and Co.
Johnston's and Paton Ltd	J. and W. Tinto Ltd
The Kar Asbestos and Rubber Co.	Turner's Asbestos Cement Co.
Kenneth and Brown Ltd	The Universal Asbestos Manufacturing Co.
J. A. McAra and Co.	J. Walker (Insulators) Ltd

Source: *Glasgow Post Office Directory, 1950–51*

Clearly, the manufacture of asbestos products was well established in Scotland by mid-twentieth century. The massive range of products testified to the versatility of the 'magic mineral'. One account in 1959 noted that apart from its major uses in building construction, thermal, electrical and acoustic insulation, friction materials (especially brake and clutch linings) and asbestos textiles, asbestos was used in abrasives, lubricants, adhesives, for flooring, paint and road building, for protective, fire resistant clothing and hoses, and as filters in gas masks and cigarettes. It was also reputed to have medical applications. One pharmaceutical handbook recommended using asbestos as a foot dusting powder and noted, incredibly, 'for temporary dental fillings and relief of toothache, a paste of zinc oxide and powdered asbestos can be used'.[31]

31. D. V. Rosato, *Asbestos: Its industrial applications* (1959).

However, in Scotland it was the building contractors (and Direct Works Departments of the urban corporations), shipyards and engineering companies that were the major users of the product. Boiler-and pipe-covering companies emerged at the end of the nineteenth century which specialised in thermal insulation. By 1900 there were 26 boiler-covering firms in Glasgow alone. These were relatively small but by the 1920s had combined together in an employers' organisation to represent and protect their collective interests. This organisation expanded to absorb other Scottish firms, becoming the Scottish Thermal Insulation Engineers' Association in the 1940s. One of the largest and most active member companies was Newall's Insulation, a subsidiary of T&N. The biggest shipbuilders, such as John Brown's, Clydebank (see plate section, 12–14) had their own asbestos preparation sheds in the yards. Some also used the shipyards' old air raid shelters for this purpose.

TABLE 1:4. MAJOR THERMAL INSULATING COMPANIES
OPERATING IN GLASGOW, 1945–50

Anderson's Insulation Co.	Kitson's Insulators Ltd
W. Beaton and Sons	McAndrew Wormald and Co.
Bell's Asbestos and Engineering Co.	McEwan Insulators
R. S. Brown and Co.	J. Muir and Son Ltd
Cape Asbestos Co.	Neil's Insulation Co.
Chemical and Insulating Co.	Newall's Insulation Co.
Clyde Insulation Co.	Reid Parker and Co.
Cork Insulation and Asbestos Co.	Scottish Asbestos and Rubber Insulation Co.
Darlington Insulation Co.	J. D. Taylor and Co.
Donald-Bean Insulators and Engineers Ltd	Walker (Insulators) Ltd
Drumoyne Asbestos Covering Co.	

Source: Glasgow Master Boilermakers' and Pipe Coverers' Association, Minutes, 16 April 1946 (Glasgow University Business Records Archive, UGD 339/2/41); *Post Office Directory of Glasgow, 1950–51*

A clear indication of the expansion of the asbestos industry can be gathered from the UK and Clydeside statistics of raw asbestos imports. Asbestos imports into Clydeside docks and harbours increased thirtyfold between 1920 and 1967.[32] Asbestos imports into the UK

---

32. G. H. Roberts, Necropsy Studies of Asbestos Bodies in Glasgow (Doctor of Medicine thesis, University of Wales, 1968), p. 80.

grew at a similar rate from the early years of the twentieth century – Graph 1:1. Asbestos use changed over time as different applications for the product were discovered. A UK survey in the mid-1960s indicated that 39% of raw asbestos went into the manufacture of asbestos cement, 11% into the manufacture of fire-resistant insulation boards and 7% into other insulation, including spraying. A further 11% went into friction materials, such as brake and clutch linings, and 17% into fillers and reinforcement for tiles, roofing, felts, millboard and the like.[33]

GRAPH 1:2: USES OF ASBESTOS IN THE UK IN THE 1960S

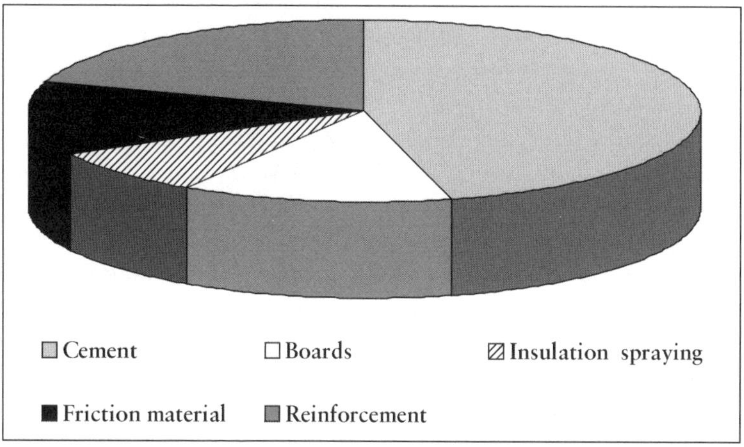

☐ Cement   ☐ Boards   ⊠ Insulation spraying

■ Friction material   ■ Reinforcement

Source: Clydeside Action on Asbestos (Turner & Newall Archive)

What is clear is that there was widespread use of the product in Scotland in construction, in the household, and in shipbuilding and engineering for insulation and fireproofing. Amongst the main exposure points in Scotland were the shipyards, the building sites, the asbestos factories (such as Turner's, Clydebank and Marinite, Springburn) marine engineering, locomotive construction and repair (notably at the North British Loco., Springburn), motor engineering (in the aero engines at Rolls Royce, Hillington), maintenance and repair (friction products such as clutch and brake linings), the oil

33. CAA, Turner & Newall Archive, Memorandum on Asbestos and Asbestosis, December 1965 (Microfilm ref. 0060/0/152/0441).

refineries in Grangemouth, chemical engineering (including I.C.I., Ardeer in Ayrshire), heating engineering (including storage heater construction) and electrical engineering.[34] In the shipyards asbestos was used to insulate boilers and pipes and as a fire retardant to comply with increasingly strict fire prevention regulations. The extent of the exposure can be gauged from the fact that there were 42 shipbuilding and ship-repairing yards in Scotland in 1960. Moreover, although there were dockyards and shipyards in all of the four main Scottish cities in which asbestos was used extensively, shipbuilding was concentrated on Clydeside, where there were 32 shipbuilding and ship-repairing yards between Glasgow and Greenock in 1960 – accounting for around 90% of shipbuilding capacity in Scotland. The *Queen Elizabeth II*, built at John Brown's in Clydebank between 1965 and 1967, provides a prime example of the extensive use of asbestos in ship construction at this time. All the ceiling panels and bulkhead linings of the *QE2* were made of Marinite, a fireproof product consisting of almost one-third asbestos.[35] More than 3,000 workers were employed in the ship's construction and many of these, across a whole range of trades (including laggers, joiners, plumbers, french polishers, plasterers and electricians), were exposed to asbestos dust.

There was also significant exposure at dockyards beyond Clydeside, including Leith, the Royal Naval Dockyard at Rosyth (see Chapter 3), the nuclear submarine base at Faslane, and at the shipyards in Aberdeen and Dundee. Demolition and stripping operations at both Faslane and Rosyth in the mid-1980s revealed the sheer amount of asbestos that had been used in their construction, and caused severe risk for those involved in its removal.[36] Rosyth management were censured by the Health and Safety Executive (HSE) under the Asbestos Regulations on 14 counts in 1985, including inadequate ventilators, non-provision of protective clothing and failure to properly segregate 'clean' and 'dirty' areas.[37] Asbestos panels and 'monkey dung' were

---

34. One Clydebank respondent recalled working with asbestos in Singer's in the late 1960s. It was used to insulate the electric motors.
35. Testimony of Robert Dickie, *QE2* joiner, cited in I. Jack, *The Sea* (1998), p. 208; see also, *Glasgow Herald*, 21 May 1994 for details of a successful case made for compensation for a *QE2* french polisher who died of asbestos-related cancer. See Clydebank Library Press Cuttings files and plate section 7.2. We are indebted to Pat Malcolm of Clydebank Library for these references.
36. *Glasgow Herald*, 25 June 1985; 5 November 1985.
37. *Ibid.* The Rosyth union convenor, George Aitchison, responded with the comment: 'Some of us could be walking dead men'.

also used in oil rig construction, with exposure both in the manufacture of rigs in the yards in North-East Scotland and in repair and maintenance work on site.[38] Similarly, asbestos was used extensively as an insulator in the heavy chemicals industry – notably at the B.P. plant at Grangemouth. Again, demolition and stripping operations at Grangemouth in the late 1970s caused concern and led directly to a series of unofficial strikes to ensure that asbestos dust levels were safe.[39]

From the 1970s onwards the dangers of asbestos became widely realised and it was used less and less. Incombustible substitutes such as fibre glass, mineral and rock wool were used in place of asbestos. The UK Marinite factory in Springburn Glasgow changed its name to Cape Boards and Panels and produced its first non-asbestos insulating boards in 1975. Very quickly, these products proved to be stronger and *superior* thermal insulators than asbestos.[40] Tweedale has shown that 'satisfactory substitutes were available even before asbestos was commercialised in the 1880s'.[41] By 1950, the US navy had converted from asbestos to fibre glass in naval insulation work – 20 years before the UK. Clearly, then, this process of substitution could have been initiated much sooner in the UK.

In the 1970s the main danger point shifted from application to removal. For some time, though, many demolition workers remained dangerously exposed, and it has only been over the last 10–15 years that specialised asbestos removal companies have developed techniques for safely removing asbestos insulation. However, progress has been painfully slow, and although there are around 700 licensed asbestos removal contractors in the UK, it has been estimated that only one in every 10 asbestos removal jobs could be inspected by a government inspector. Moreover, of the 85 contractors who have been prosecuted in the last 10 years, only 13 have lost their licences.[42] This problem with its roots in the past, then, is set to be a long-term problem. In 1998 the government requested that all local authorities perform asbestos audits to try and ascertain just how much asbestos was in place throughout the housing stock. The next phase would be

38. Information from Richard Johnston, former offshore safety officer.
39. *The Sunday Post*, 14 May 1978.
40. *Glasgow Herald*, 12 September 1987, p. 16. On Cape Industrial, Springburn.
41. G. Tweedale, 'Sprayed Limpet Asbestos', in G. A. Peters and B. J. Peters (eds), *Sourcebook on Asbestos Diseases* (vol. 20), p. 104.
42. BBC Radio 4 programme, 'Too little too late', 15 October 1998.

a survey of all premises, and this would be followed by the complete removal of all asbestos from buildings. Some idea of how difficult a task this would be can be gauged from the fact that a city the size of Glasgow has over a million buildings. The legacy of asbestos will be with us for a long time to come.

Asbestos diseases and deaths

It is impossible to gauge the number of people in Scotland who have been exposed to asbestos. However, the above survey of the development of the industry suggests that a considerable number would have been exposed directly through their occupations and many more indirectly. There were four main points of contact: the manufacture of asbestos products; the use of such products in construction, insulation etc; the stripping and demolition of buildings, boilers etc; and environmental exposure, including dust being brought home on work clothes. In Scotland, heavy exposure would have applied particularly to those working in the asbestos manufacturing plants, and those in the insulation trade on ships, and few building construction workers would have failed to come across asbestos in the 1950s and 1960s, with those working on the building of high-rise flats heavily exposed. The origins and nature of workplace exposure and workers' attitudes to working with asbestos in these three occupations from the 1930s onwards are explored in more detail in Chapter 3.

Occupational exposure to asbestos also included dockers, labourers and warehousemen at the point of entry at the wharves and docks along the Clyde. There was also significant contact, especially in the period before dust proof bags were introduced, by carters and other transport workers. The product was also used widely in engineering, especially electrical engineering (as a respondent from the Singer factory in Clydebank testified) and in brake and clutch linings – for cars and a range of machine tools (such as heavy lathes). Exposure was heavy in locomotive construction and railway carriage construction and maintenance, which took place primarily in the giant North British Locomotive works in Springburn, Glasgow. Several asbestos-disease cases have been traced back to these works, where from the turn of the century to the 1950s steam locomotive boilers, fire boxes and pipework under construction in the giant erecting shop were wrapped in asbestos mattresses for heat insulation (see plate section,

15).[43] Technical journals and locomotive specifications indicate the heavy use of 'chemically pure asbestos' mattresses, asbestos yarn, asbestos webbing and J. W. Roberts patented Sprayed Limpet Asbestos in locomotive construction. Locomotive maintenance workers would also have been heavily exposed because the asbestos mattresses were frequently removed (at six-to twelve month intervals) to enable safety checks to the boiler and firebox.[44]

Asbestos was also used in the I. C. I. factory at Ardeer. One of those exposed at I. C. I. in the 1950s as a student summer worker (removing and replacing asbestos lagging on boilers and tanks) recently died of mesothelioma, winning an unusually high damages claim in the courts.[45] He had not been warned of the dangers, nor had he been supplied with a respirator or mask. Workers were also frequently exposed through employment in several workplaces. In one asbestosis compensation case taken to the Court of Session in Scotland, William McMeekan cited exposure to asbestos in two of his previous workplaces, Turner's Asbestos Cement Co., Clydebank (1948–55) and Babcock and Wilcox engineering company (1955–67), Glasgow. At Turner's he worked with asbestos pipes and sheets, whilst at Babcock's, he was exposed to heavy quantities of asbestos dust whilst shot blasting steam chests made up of units lined with asbestos. No ventilating apparatus was provided and the masks were ineffective.[46] Engineering workers were identified as a particularly endangered group in a Glasgow hospital survey in the 1960s which found heavy quantities of asbestos particles in the lungs of 7 out of 15 deceased engineering workers.[47] However, exposure to asbestos at work was widespread. A study of over 400 asbestos-disease victims in the mid-1990s found cases amongst teachers, hospital workers,

---

43. We are grateful to Murdoch Nicolson (Scottish railway historian), Willie Dewar (an ex-North British Locomotive employee), and to Springburn Museum for this information.

44. E. A. Phillipson, *Steam Locomotive Design, Data and Formulae* (London, 1936), pp. 111–12; Government of India (Ministry of Railways), *Standard Specification for Steam Locomotives and Tenders* (Simla, 1949), pp. 21–3.

45. Sir Gordon Beveridge, previously Professor of Chemical Engineering, Strathclyde University. He died aged 65. *Daily Record*, 16 September 2000.

46. Copy Form of Summons, Court of Session, Scotland (William McMeekan, 1969); Letter Robertson, Chalmers and Auld, Solicitors, Glasgow, 23 July 1969 (Chase Manhattan Archive, Manchester).

47. G. H. Roberts, 'Necropsy Studies' (Doctor of Medicine thesis, University of Wales, 1968).

transport workers, a French polisher, cleaners and office workers: in one case a secretary in an asbestos factory contracted mesothelioma; in another a cleaner in a bus garage where the mechanics worked on the asbestos brake linings. There have also been cases in Scotland of women contracting asbestos-related diseases which they trace back to exposure to asbestos in their World War Two jobs in gas mask manufacture and in the Royal Dockyard at Rosyth.

TABLE 1.5. OCCUPATIONAL DISTRIBUTION OF CLYDESIDE
ASBESTOS-DISEASE VICTIMS, 1985–95

Insulation	92
Tradesmen	83
Construction	75
Shipbuilding	53
Engineering	38
Factory workers	19
Electricians	15
Transport	15
Textiles	5
Cleaners	4
Railways	3

Source: J. Lenaghan, *Victims Twice Over* (c. 1994), p. 23

There may well also have been some direct contact through mining the mineral in Scotland. There were asbestos seams in Kincardineshire and Banffshire, though one report in 1938 noted that 'comparatively little has so far been quarried'.[48] Given the origins of asbestos manufacture in Scotland in the 1870s and the high number of companies operating as early as the 1890s, Scottish workers would have been disabled and killed from asbestos-related diseases long before asbestosis was officially recognised with the first government Asbestos Regulations in 1931. Given the symptoms and pathology of the asbestos diseases, such cases would most likely have been misdiagnosed, probably as heart and/or lung failure, tuberculosis/

48. *Glasgow Chamber of Commerce Journal*, XXI, no. 5, May 1938, p. 122. Cape Asbestos was also involved in mining a long-fibre rock wool (termed 'Rocksil') from a pit sunk in Stirling in 1954. Whether this was seen at the time as a less *hazardous* alternative to asbestos is not known.

phthisis or bronchial pneumonia, and recorded thus on death certificates before World War Two.[49]

There are several ways that working with or near asbestos damages workers' health and can kill. The disease asbestosis is a clogging and scarring of the lungs caused through inhaling asbestos fibres. The disease can develop after only a few years of exposure but commonly it can take over 20 years before any symptoms are experienced. It is progressive and incurable, causes pain and disablement, and may eventually lead to heart or lung failure The inhalation of asbestos fibres can also cause thickening of the pleura – the membrane between the lungs and the rib cage – and this also leads to progressive breathlessness. Somewhat less serious are what are known as pleural plaques, which are isolated thickened areas on the pleura.

However, by far the most serious of the asbestos-related diseases is mesothelioma. This is a form of cancer which, until fairly recently, was quite rare and is almost wholly related to asbestos. Mesothelioma can present up to fifty years after the victim's first exposure to asbestos, and is a suffocating tumour which spreads around the lining of the lung. It is very painful, and normally kills the sufferer within a year of diagnosis. Long before he became famous, the film star Steve McQueen worked in the shipyards, in the navy and around car mechanics where he was exposed to asbestos dust. Sadly, at the very height of his fame, this time-bomb from his former life exploded and killed him. Between 1968 and 1991, 1,074 Scots were *officially* recorded (by the Health and Safety Executive) as having died of this condition – 1020 men and 54 women.

Finally, exposure to asbestos can also cause lung cancer, and this is now reckoned to be the most significant work-related cancer in the world. One big difficulty, however, is telling the difference between cancer caused through cigarette smoking, and that caused by asbestos. Both agents are carcinogens and can weaken the lungs and hence raise an individual's susceptibility to developing lung cancer. It has been estimated that cigarette smokers, who have also been exposed to asbestos, could be up to 92-times more likely of contracting lung cancer than non-smokers.[50]

49. The earliest known case of asbestosis in Scotland was reported by the MOH in Glasgow to the Factory Inspectorate in February 1928. See J. C. Bridge, 'Remarks on Occupational Dust', *British Medical Journal*, 21 December 1929, pp. 11–45.

50. H. De Vos Irvine, 'Asbestos and lung cancer'.

In Scotland deaths from mesothelioma rose markedly from the end
of the 1970s as those who had been exposed to the deadly dust some
20 or 30 years earlier began to develop this asbestos-linked cancer.
Indeed, recorded mesothelioma death rates rose *five-fold* between the
late 1960s and the late 1980s. Many of these afflicted workers –
including those in the lagging and construction industries – had not
been protected by the regulations aimed specifically at those who
worked in the so called 'dusty trades'. Relative to imports and the
rising amount of asbestos manufactured in the country, deaths from
asbestosis fell in Scotland as the death toll for mesothelioma began
to rise.

GRAPH 1:3. DEATHS FROM MESOTHELIOMA AND ASBESTOSIS
IN SCOTLAND 1968–97 (1993–97 ARE PROVISIONAL FIGURES) [51]

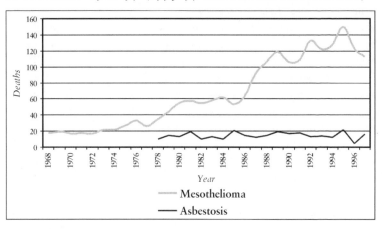

Anyone who has been exposed to asbestos at the workplace has
been exposed to danger, and the recent case of a senior hospital
consultant, diagnosed with mesothelioma, caused through exposure
to asbestos fibres shed from pipes in a hospital corridor, highlights
this. Graph 1:4 and Table 1.6 below shows this breadth of disease
incidence and the most at risk occupations.

51. Figures kindly provided by the HSE Epidemiology and Medical Statistics
Unit, Merseyside.

GRAPH I:4. MALE MESOTHELIOMA DEATHS IN SCOTLAND:
BY EMPLOYMENT CATEGORY, 1968–91

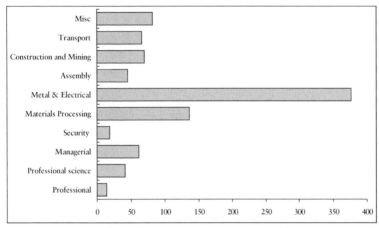

Source: HSE *Decennial Supplement* (1995), p. 134 (note: 1981 figures are omitted
in this series)

TABLE I.6. MALE MESOTHELIOMA DEATHS IN SCOTLAND:
MOST AT-RISK OCCUPATIONS, 1968–91

Carpenters and joiners	92
Metal working production fitters and fitters/machinists	67
Metal plate workers, shipwrights and riveters	54
Machine tool operators	43
Electricians, electrical maintenance fitters	42
Plumbers, heating and ventilation fitters, gas fitters	36
Painters and decorators, french polishers	30
Construction workers	28
Sheet metal workers	23
Welders	22

Source: HSE Statistics Unit

Clearly, it has tended to be those involved in physical jobs who have
had to endure the heaviest death toll, and especially so in shipbuilding,
engineering and construction. As a consequence there are several 'hot
spots' throughout Britain where the work processes used asbestos in
large quantities from the 1930s to the 1970s. Most of these areas are
places where shipbuilding and ship-repairing predominate, such as
Clydeside, Portsmouth, Barrow-in-Furness, and Tyneside. It is here

that the qualities of asbestos as an insulator have been most in demand since the 1940s. However, what is striking about the geographical pattern of asbestos mortality is that Clydebank consistently tops this grisly league table of asbestos deaths in the UK. In 1989 the mesothelioma death rate stood at 69 per million in the industrial region of West Scotland, whereas the corresponding figure for Clydebank was nine times higher at 596 per million.[52] The female mesothelioma death rate was also high in this area.

TABLE 1.7 WEST OF SCOTLAND MESOTHELIOMA DEATH RATES, 1976–91

District	Males		Females	
	Deaths per million	UK rank out of 462	Deaths per million	UK rank out of 462
Clydebank	212	1	17.0	6
Bearsden/Milngavie	49	20	6.1	42
Glasgow City	49	21	5.0	66
Dumbarton	47	22	6.1	39
Renfrew	42	27	2.9	178
UK Average	19	—	3.3	—

Source: R. Howie, 'Asbestos: The Way Forward by Learning from Past Mistakes', in T. Gorman (ed.), *Clydebank Asbestos*, p. 88.

The high concentration of shipbuilding and engineering in the Clydebank area, coupled with the fact that the area had its own asbestos cement factory, pushed the rate of asbestos-related disease there to record levels. Moreover, Clydebank also has the distinction of having one of the highest rates of asbestos disease anywhere in Europe. It is apt and poignant, therefore, that a recent book detailing the asbestos disaster in Clydebank should have had its launch in the epicentre of the European asbestos tragedy: the Clydebank Boilermakers' Social Club.[53]

52. H. De Vos Irvine, D. W. Lamont, D. J. Hole, C. R. Gillies, 'Asbestos Lung Cancer in Glasgow and the West of Scotland', British Medical Journal, 306, 1993, pp. 1503–6; T. Gorman (ed.), *Clydebank: Asbestos, the Unwanted Legacy* (Clydebank, 2000), p. 42.
53. T. Gorman (ed.), *Clydebank: Asbestos, the Unwanted Legacy*.

GRAPH 1:5. MALE MESOTHELIOMA DEATHS IN BRITAIN
1986–95 (EXPRESSED BY STANDARDISED MORTALITY RATE –
SMR) [54]

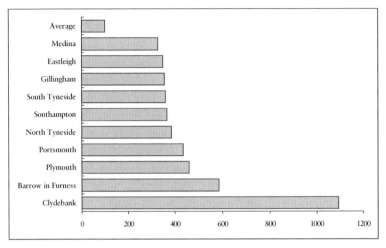

Within Scotland, the asbestos disease map shows up a series of
high mesothelioma mortality clusters – headed by Clydebank – and,
not surprisingly, a close correlation between urban-industrial areas
and high mortality rates. In Edinburgh there were almost 120 recorded
mesothelioma deaths between 1976 and 1995, a reflection of heavy
workplace exposure in industrial areas such as Leith and
Grangemouth. Renfrew, on the Clyde, included many shipyards and
the high mesothelioma death rates in Dunfermline and Kircaldy may
well be accounted for by the location of the Rosyth Naval Dockyard
in that region. Aberdeen also recorded a heavy death toll from
mesothelioma. One Aberdeen-based solicitor reported 30–40
asbestos-disease claims each year in the North-East of Scotland in the
late 1990s. The cases included the tragic premature death of a plumber,
Brian McInnes, of mesothelioma, aged just 47.[55] At the other extreme,
and not surprisingly, asbestos-related cancer deaths remain very low
in rural areas.

54. HSE Mesothelioma Area Statistics, 1986–1995. The SMR compares deaths
    with the prevailing population in the geographical area.
55. *Aberdeen Evening Express*, 17 February 1998.

GRAPH 1:6. MESOTHELIOMA DEATHS IN SCOTLAND BY AREA, 1976–95 [56]

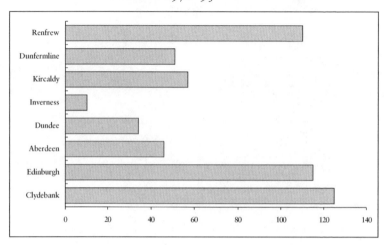

This book is an attempt to get under the skin of these appalling statistics and investigate exposure at work, attitudes and social policy in Scotland on this issue and how asbestos affected individuals and their families. We trace the history of this unfolding tragedy, and try to discover the depth to which asbestos has scarred Scottish society. Throughout, we draw heavily upon the memories and experiences of men and women who were directly affected by the asbestos tragedy. It is really their story. However, we also try to locate the asbestos issue within the wider context of Scottish occupational health. Historically, working conditions in Scotland – particularly in the industrial conurbation of Clydeside – have been poor compared to those in the rest of the UK. The annual Factory Inspectors' Reports record consistently high figures for work-related injuries and deaths for the Scottish area and recent research suggests that this 'Scottish anomaly' persisted into the late twentieth century.[57] Moreover, it has recently been estimated that Scottish workers are 80% more likely to take time off work for bad health than in the rest of the UK, whilst

56. HSE, Mesothelioma Deaths by County, 1976–1995. Figures kindly provided by the HSE, Epidemiology and Medical Statistics Unit, Merseyside.
57. C. Woolfson and M. Beck, 'Fatal and Major Injuries to Employees: The Scottish Anomaly', unpublished paper given at 'Hidden Hazards of Work' conference, Western Infirmary, Glasgow, April 1999 and Scottish Trade Union Research Network Conference, June 1999.

cancer deaths in Scotland are also currently running 10% above the national average.[58] These are statistics that pose serious questions. Would the figures be different had a higher priority been given to occupational health in Scotland? Moreover, if more attention had been paid to occupational health issues by the government, the employers and, perhaps, the trade unions, would asbestos have ruined so many Scottish lives? We also look at the broader issue of state welfare. The asbestos disaster occurred during a time when Britain's welfare state was in place to protect the population, to borrow Beveridge's phrase, 'from the cradle to the grave'. To what extent can the high number of asbestos deaths be seen as a betrayal of this very principle?

58. Ibid.

CHAPTER TWO

Work and Health in Twentieth-Century Scotland

Asbestos-related disease has become something of a *cause célèbre* at the end of the twentieth century. Rightly so, if estimates that somewhere in the region of one million people will die in western Europe because of contact with this mineral over the next 35 years are anything near correct.[1] However, asbestos is only the latest of a long line of toxic substances and dangerous practices that Scottish workers have been exposed to throughout the twentieth century. Therefore, to fully understand the asbestos disaster in Scotland, we have to see it as part of a long tradition of employer indifference, state neglect, and worker stoicism. What we want to do here is locate the asbestos disaster within a wider picture of occupational health in Scotland, and provide an historical overview of the impact that employment in a heavily industrialised economy could have upon workers' health and wellbeing. For most of the twentieth century asbestos was relatively insignificant in contrast to other occupation-related diseases and hazards. For example, a great many more miners died of respiratory diseases than did asbestos victims over the 1914–1970 period. Scottish workers, then, faced many hazards and dangers, commonly experienced fatigue and overstrain, and regularly succumbed to a wide range of occupational diseases and ailments.[2] As Sandy Doig, a Deputy Senior Medical Inspector of Factories (responsible for Scotland) noted in 1968: 'It is pretty safe to say that there are very few factories without some risk to health'.[3]

1. J. Peto, 'The European Mesothelioma Epidemic'.
2. For one of the few British studies of this issue, see P. Weindling (ed.), *A Social History of Occupational Health* (London, 1985). An overview is provided in A. J. McIvor, *A History of Work in Britain, 1880–1950* (2000), chapter 5.
3. *Glasgow Herald*, 31 January 1968. Doig (1906–84), a native Scot, was a specialist in occupational chest diseases, particularly the pneumoconioses. He was a medical inspector for Scotland from 1943 to 1970 and lectured in industrial health at the University of Aberdeen.

Deadly and debilitating toil

To a great extent the late Victorian period was the time when work was most important in Scottish people's lives. Although the Victorian work ethic has been exaggerated to some extent, workers spent most of their lives in paid or unpaid work at home, in factories, or in farms or workshops. In this sense, then, it is reasonable to think of people's existence in this era as work-centred. Standards of living, housing and material possessions depended to a great extent upon the rewards of labour. Thus the health and wellbeing of individuals and families were intimately linked to employment, both through the wages earned and, more directly, because of the dangers and hazards (fatigue; traumatic injury; occupational disease) that characterised almost every job in the late nineteenth century. The meaning and significance of work extended beyond this, however. Work brought its own psychological rewards: it provided an identity and, especially for craft workers, a sense of pride, passion and purpose. Conversely, the loss of work could lead directly to demoralisation and despair, and this was epitomised in the dole queues of the 1930s. Moreover, occupation dictated, to a large extent, a person's standing within a highly stratified and status-conscious community (as Edwin Muir noted in his sharply perceptive *Scottish Journey* in 1935). Looking inward, the workplace provided an arena in which friendships were forged and social relationships developed, as well as a focus for collective activity and solidarity, manifest in the emergence of trade unions, disputes and strike action. The attempts of British employers and managers to obtain and sustain control over their labour was rarely complete and was invariably subject to challenge and conflict (especially so on 'Red' Clydeside). The organisation of work was chiselled out of this uneasy interaction between capital and labour over what one American observer of British industrial relations, Carter Goodrich, called the 'frontier of control'.

Occupational health was one issue subject to the changing power relationships and interactions between capital and labour, and undoubtedly in the late Victorian period it was the industrialists – such as the mineowners, textile millowners, ironmasters, shipbuilders, engineering magnates – who held the upper hand. Some wielded this power with responsibility and treated their workers with respect; and there was a long tradition of employer paternalism and welfarism in

Scottish industry.[4] Nonetheless, the majority of Victorian employers paid scant attention to the health and wellbeing of their employees, and looked upon them as expendable commodities in a relentless pursuit of maximum profit. What really stands out in contemporary accounts of working lives in the period before World War One is that overstrain and exhaustion were endemic features of employment in Scotland. This resulted in an impaired lifestyle and a premature degeneration in workers' mental and physical health. Worker fatigue derived from long working hours, low pay and the intensity of labour, and was exacerbated by the conditions and environment in which people toiled.

This was despite the fact that in comparison with other nations, working hours in Scotland were, *on average*, relatively short. This was confirmed by the socialist Tom Mann, who travelled widely and worked in engineering factories in the USA, Australia and New Zealand. The Saturday half-holiday was introduced in Britain in the 1860s and the average length of the working week by the end of the nineteenth century was 55–60 hours. This commonly entailed a ten-hour day, with perhaps five or six hours' work on a Saturday. However, such averages obscure as much as they illuminate, and in reality working hours varied enormously across the country. To a large extent the work effort depended on the nature of the work, on local custom, on trade union strength, and on the patchy coverage of regulatory legislation. In the 1890s national government employees, building workers and coal miners worked the lowest hours, at 45–55 per week. However, wide variations existed. In Scotland, prior to legalisation in 1909 which brought the eight-hour day, Ayrshire coal hewers worked a 39-hour shift, Lanarkshire hewers 50 hours and those in Fife up to 60 hours.[5] Most workers in large factories were tied to the legal 56-hour week. At the other extreme sweated clothing workers and shop workers commonly toiled for between 70 and 85 hours a week; railway workers endured a work regime constituting a twelve-hour day, six days a week; domestic servants were held in virtual bondage by their employers for six and a half days per week, often working over 80 hours in total, whilst housewives laboured

4. J. Melling, 'Scottish Industrialists', in T. Dickson (ed.), *Capital and Class in Scotland* (Edinburgh, 1982); W. W. Knox, *Industrial Nation: Work, Culture and Society in Scotland, 1800-Present* (Edinburgh, 1999).
5. T. C. Smout, *A Century of the Scottish People* (London, 1987), p. 101.

even longer in homes that had few labour-saving devices. Moreover, the seasonal nature of much casual work, both on the land and within the cities, often led to irregular bouts of inactivity followed by frantic work: the Glasgow carters, for example, worked a 98-hour week in season that involved a 17-hour week day that started at 4.30 a.m., and a 'short stint' of 13 hours on a Saturday. Those particularly affected by large seasonal variations in working hours in Scotland were dressmakers and milliners, shipbuilders, construction workers and sections of the food industry (including the jam makers).

Given the long working hours that large segments of the labour force had to endure, it is hardly surprising that serious problems of overstrain and exhaustion occurred. There simply was no time for proper rest necessary for physical and mental regeneration. However, even amongst those workers privileged enough to have a relatively shorter working week, fatigue invariably existed as a perennial problem because of the intensity of labour and poor working conditions. As foreign competition grew from the 1870s and 1880s, especially from the USA and Germany, employers and managers responded by speeding up work processes in an effort to squeeze more effort out of workers and stay competitive. A central component of this costs reduction drive was a movement across a number of industries to slash labour costs by reorganising traditional work methods: introducing new technology, speeding up machinery, tightening supervision and discipline on the shop floor, extending job specialisation and the division of labour, extending payments-by-results wage systems and introducing novel types of bonus payments in an attempt to cajole, motivate and manipulate workers to increase effort and raise levels of productivity. In the Royal Ordnance Factories and Royal Docks, for example, the introduction of the shorter eight-hour day in the 1890s was combined with the introduction of clocking in and out, a more draconian fining system and greater shopfloor supervision that involved 'workchasers' hounding the workforce. One docker noted: 'The men find that they really have to work all their time in the yard. Much of the idling has been stopped, and it is probable that more work is being turned out per man than ever before'. Similarly, an engineering worker made the point that 'the severity of the labour is increased by it being compressed from nine hours into eight'.[6] In a similar fashion, workloads of railway workers were increased as rail

6. *The Engineer*, 4 May 1894 and 3 August 1894.

traffic grew without an increase in the number of railway staff. Some employers, as in the boot and shoe industry, used the opportunity of successful lock-outs to initiate extensive reorganisation of working methods. Others, as with cotton textiles, speeded up existing technology and purchased cheaper, poorer-quality raw materials which, because of more yarn breakages in the mule, significantly increased workloads. Admittedly, the extent and nature of work intensification varied greatly between and even within industries, and in well-unionised sectors the effects of work intensification could be countered to some extent. Nevertheless the trend was a real one, and such work intensification had detrimental effects on workers' health. Arguably, the process gathered momentum as the Scottish economy faced more serious problems of competitiveness during the deep interwar economic recession and, again, as de-industrialisation proceeded from the 1950s.

The spread of piecework wage payment systems and new techniques of 'bonus' wage payments also exacerbated the problems of fatigue and overstrain. This led to a redefinition of what constituted a fair day's work, with rewards for labour being tied more to effort. Moreover, management could use the simplest of pretexts to cut established piecework or bonus rates, with the result that workers were driven to intensify their labours to maintain the earnings level to which they had become accustomed. This, the Trades Union Congress argued in 1910, resulted in a vicious spiral of speed-up, work, declining product quality, together with worker fatigue and ill-health, and a draining of human capital. In the massive Singer Sewing Machine plant in Clydebank near Glasgow such conditions provoked a major all-out strike in 1911. As one Singer worker commented: 'They were the best organised firm in Britain ... It was all piecework and if you didn't make it, you didn't get it ... If you said a word to a gaffer you just got chucked out ... Singer's had a bad name. I myself thought as a boy that they should blow it up'.[7] The connections between piecework, speed-up and deteriorating health were later reaffirmed by the socialist historian G. D. H. Cole and in several reports of the Industrial Fatigue Research Board and the Industrial Health Research Board in the interwar years. This

---

7. Cited in Glasgow Labour History Workshop, *The Singer Strike, 1911* (Clyde-bank, 1989); See also the testimony of David Burnett, 'Working at Singer, Clydebank', *Scottish Labour History Society Journal*, vol. 25 (1990).

continued to be a significant factor in the post-Second World War period. Workers and their trade unions, under pressure from management, continued to prioritise wage payments – demanding 'danger money', for example – rather than prioritising improvements in basic standards of occupational health.

What is also significant, however, is that the vast majority of employers refused to accept the existence of fatigue and exhaustion amongst their workers, despite the growing evidence that this represented an inefficient use of labourpower and a loss of worker productivity. The old classical economist orthodoxy that output always increased or decreased exactly proportionate to the hours worked, remained prevalent. Workers remained a commodity to be exploited just like any other factor of production. Hence, there was considerable opposition from employers and their organisations to any reduction in work hours before World War Two.

Overstrain induced by long working hours and intensified labour was further exacerbated by the kind of environment in which workers toiled. Poor ventilation and lighting, high temperatures and noise levels and lack of seating provision could rapidly dissipate workers' energy. A classic example would be laundry work, the exploitative conditions of which were exposed in a series of reports by the Clydeside women's rights campaigner Margaret Irwin in the 1900s. The British government (in the Interdepartmental Committee on Physical Deterioration) placed a portion of the blame for the poor physique of recruits during the Boer War on the nature and conditions of work. However, it was undoubtedly amongst the female-dominated sweated trades where low wages combined with long working hours in overcrowded and cramped rooms or workshops that the most serious problems of fatigue and the resultant degeneration of health occurred. Here government regulation was minimal and largely ineffective. Even after the passing of the Trades Boards Act of 1909 the Fabian socialist Sidney Webb argued that the situation in such occupations was still equivalent to that of the cotton textile trades a century before:

> These industries are exacting more energy than their wages and
> other conditions suffice to make good, with the result that,
> after a relatively few years of demoralising toil, the sweated
> workers are flung, prematurely exhausted, on the social rubbish
> heap of charity and the Poor Law. It is indeed unfortunately

true that the sweated trades literally use up the men, women and children who work at them, as omnibus companies use up their horses.[8]

Moreover, the stripping of energy during the work process often had damaging knock-on effects. As one historian noted in his study of Victorian public health: 'Factory labour provided the perfect nexus for aggravating or accelerating ill health'.[9] In particular, fatigue could directly increase the risk of injury or death through an accident, as the evidence from the Scottish railways suggests. Overstrain at work could also lower a worker's resistance to a whole battery of diseases, including those associated directly with the job. The miners' eye disease nystagmus and telegraphists' cramp are two such examples. 'Physical exertion carried to excess', as the late Victorian industrial hygienist J. L. Arlidge noted, 'becomes a cause of disease.'[10] An iron worker spoke similarly from experience: 'something approximating 50 per cent of us die from lung and heart diseases which may be brought on by the exhaustion due to working in vitiated atmospheres'.[11]

Whilst the evidence for worker fatigue and overstrain is subjective and difficult to assess precisely, it is much easier to quantify the high toll on the health and wellbeing of workers arising from accidents at work before World War One. It is difficult to extract the Scottish figures from those of the UK as a whole. The official figures show that some 140,000 people died in industrial accidents between 1880 and 1914 in the UK in factories, shipping, the railways and mining alone.[12] Such figures, however, are only the tip of the iceberg. Deaths are under-represented because the official figures compiled by the Labour Department of the Board of Trade only include fatalities occurring within a year of an accident at work, and exclude whole swathes of the labour market not covered by specific legislation such as the Factories Acts, Mines Acts and the special regulations in shipping, quarries, aviation, railways, explosives, docks and construction. Much of this carnage was preventable. It was reported

8. S. Webb, Introduction, p. xi, in B. Hutchins and A. Harrison, *A History of Factory Legislation* (London, 1911).

9. A. Wohl, *Endangered Lives* (London, 1983).

10. J. L. Arlidge, *Diseases of Occupations* (London, 1892).

11. H. Fyrth and H. Collins, *The Foundry Workers* (London, 1959), p. 130.

12. Department of Employment, British Labour Statistics: Historical Abstract (London, 1971).

in the Royal Commission on Labour in 1893, drawing upon the statistics generated by the Registrar of Births, Death and Marriages, that certain unfortunate clusters of workers had twice the mortality rate of the relatively healthy farmers and clergymen. Such 'unhealthy' workers included quarry workers, painters, plumbers, glaziers, cutlers, brewers and innkeepers (presumably the occupational hazard of cirrhosis of the liver!). However, there was an additional small group of workers whose lives were severely cut short by their occupations, with more than three times the mortality rate of the farmers and clergymen. Such unfortunate souls included many pottery workers, file grinders and metal miners.

In relation to numbers employed, railway work was amongst the most hazardous jobs in Scotland in the late nineteenth century. There were both high fatality and injury rates, deriving especially from broken bones, and crushed hands and fingers. Shunters were singularly the most accident-prone of railway workers. Such workers, especially those working the nightshift and involved in hand coupling and uncoupling of carriages and locomotives, were exposed to great danger from passing railway traffic. Rising coal costs and inter-line competition led to a pervasive speeding-up of work. 'The work has to be got through rapidly', one contemporary health expert noted, 'and accidents are the result.' Over a work span of thirty or so years, he continued, 'the balance of probability is against his [the railway worker] leaving the trade without a violent death or injury'.[13] Railway workers at least up to the turn of the nineteenth century also lacked legislative protection and the kind of formal safety inspection that existed for the factories and mines. There were high accident rates also in dockwork, which a Glasgow Factory Inspector called Wilson put down to fatigue caused by the intensity of work in unloading, loading and turning around ships as quickly as possible.[14] There was a high accident risk in shipping and fishing where severe weather took a heavy toll of lives. Obvious difficulties in ensuring that legal safety procedures were rigidly enforced whilst at sea, combined with negligent medical inspection and provision, even on the larger lines, contributed to the high accident rates in this industry.

Work in the coal mines also exacted a heavy toll of death and

13. H. Cunynghame, in T. Oliver, *Dangerous Trades* (London, 1902).
14. Report of the Departmental Committee on Accidents in Places Under the Factory and Workshop Acts, Cmd 5540, 1911, pp. 471–2.

injury through accidents.[15] Primarily because of extended state
regulation of the mines and better ventilation techniques, accident
rates were declining over the period 1850–1914. Yet still in 1914 a
miner was killed in Scotland every six hours and severely injured
every two hours. Whilst large disasters intermittently devastated local
communities, most deaths in mining actually followed from individual
accidents: small roof collapses; falls down shafts; tram collisions –
what Benson called 'a steady drip-drip of death'. Widely differing
geological conditions meant that some coalfields, such as in the West
of Scotland, were much less accident-prone than others.

Factory workers were most extensively protected by legislation
designed to reduce accidents and worker fatigue before World War
One. However, legislation failed even here to prevent a significant
harvest of injuries, disabilities and deaths through accidents at work,
and, juvenile factory workers proved to be the most accident-prone.
Technology changed rapidly throughout the period, creating new,
unforeseen health hazards, especially as machinery manufacturers
were not forced to fit guards and covers – the onus for this lay with
the factory owner. Indeed, the most important single source of
accidents in factories was unfenced or unguarded steam-driven
machinery, especially gearing, shafting, winches, drive bands and vats.
Eye injuries are particularly well documented in textile factories (flying
shuttles) and ironworks (hot splashes). The hazards of power-driven
machinery and working with hot metal were exacerbated by uneven,
wet and slippery floors and by the inability to cut off power quickly
before the widespread adoption of electricity as a prime mover in
factories in the 1920s and 1930s. The carrying and manipulating of
heavy weights was also particularly hazardous. The cotton-finishing
unions were swamped by claims for superannuation from workers in
the bleaching and dyeing section who had become permanently
disabled due to a hernia or rupture contracted while manipulating
vast quantities of heavy, wet cloth through the vats and kiers.
Moreover, there was a close connection between the pace of work
and accident rates in factories. The Report of the Departmental
Committee on Factory Accidents placed payments-by-results wage
systems, speed-up and bad lighting high on their list of causes of
industrial accidents. Workers also suffered fatalities and disabilities
caused by a multitude of diseases related directly to particular jobs

15. J. Benson, *British Coalminers in the Nineteenth Century* (London, 1980).

and the raw materials handled and manufactured. 'There is scarcely any trade or occupation', commented the UK's foremost occupational health specialist Dr Thomas Oliver in 1902 in his pioneering massive monograph on *The Diseases of Occupations*, 'that is not attended by some risk or other.' [16] Recognition of central government responsibility to regulate the most dangerous trades was slowly spreading in the late Victorian period. In 1893 a government enquiry into the lead and chemical industries was initiated, closely followed by the long-standing Miscellaneous Dangerous Trades Committee (1896–99), which included Oliver amongst its number. In the 1880s and 1890s workers who contracted an industrial disease like lead or phosphorus poisoning rarely obtained any financial compensation from their employers (under the Employers' Liability Act of 1880) because of the long process of litigation necessary to prove employer responsibility for diseases which often had a long gestation period. In 1906 the reforming Liberal government amended the Workmen's Compensation Act of 1897 (which provided for occupational accidents) to include automatic financial compensation for six major industrial diseases: lead, mercury, phosphorus and arsenic poisoning; anthrax and ankylostomiasis. This was the first official recognition that exposure of workers to toxic substances in their everyday work could be life-threatening.

Largely due to the widespread use of different types and forms of lead across a range of industries, lead poisoning was one of the most common in Scotland before World War One. Table 1 gives a sense of the wide distribution of occupations where it occurred. Entry of lead into the body could be via the mouth (inhalation or contaminated food), or, more rarely, through the skin, absorption occurring over a protracted period. Most cases occurred in male workers and over 95% of cases were not fatal. However, the symptoms were ugly, beginning with sickness, headaches, insomnia, constipation, a sense of weakness and debility, and often the appearance of a bluish-grey discolouration of the gums. In chronic cases, convulsions and paralysis of the working limbs often set in, with loss of sight, mental disturbances and brain damage. In pregnant females the disease induced miscarriage.

16. T. Oliver, *Diseases of Occupations* (London, 1902), p. 14.

TABLE 2.1. LEAD POISONING CASES REPORTED IN FACTORIES AND WORKSHOPS IN THE GLASGOW REGION, 1900–14

Industry	male	female	total
White and red lead manufacture, paints, colours and oils	127	8	135
Shipbuilding	58	—	58
Sanitary engineering and enamelling	44	—	44
Mechanical engineering	30	—	30
Painters, plumbers, glaziers (including factory painters)	18	4	22
Yarn dyeing	2	14	16
Pottery and earthenware	5	9	14
Printing	8	—	8
Metal mining, smelting and refining	8	—	8
Others	7	—	7
Totals (fatalities = 9)	307	35	342

Source: Board of Trade, *Register of Industrial Diseases*, PRO/LAB 56/1–15 (Public Record Office, Kew, London).

Poisoning by contact with phosphorus, mercury or arsenic at work was far less common than with lead – indeed fewer than 50 cases were reported in the whole of the UK over the five years 1901–05. Mercury, used in barometer and thermometer manufacture, dyes and felt-hat making, caused sickness, foetid breath, tooth and gum decay, and muscular tremors and spasms, occasionally ending fatally. Arsenic compounds were utilised in a whole range of processes, including glass, chalk, colouring, dyeing, printing, wallpaper and artificial flower manufacture. Absorption of the dust or gas resulted in almost immediate vomiting, stomach pain and cramp, vertigo, fainting, convulsions and general debility, whilst chronic cases developed skin rashes, pustular eruptions, permanent headache, emaciation, and transient paralysis. White phosphorus was used most extensively in the match-making industry and was usually absorbed through skin contact, inhalation of the vapour or contaminated food. The consequences were appalling. Poisoning usually affected the bone structure of the face, starting with ulceration of the gums, pain and loosening of the teeth, erosion (necrosis) of the jawbone, with fissures and open, foetid and septic holes in the cheeks. Fever and delirium, horrendous pain and emaciation completed the symptoms, with death occurring in most cases, usually by sepsis. There was no specific medical treatment. After the exposure of working conditions at the Bryant and May match factory in London by the socialist Annie Besant in *The Link* in 1889, the government certified white phosphorus as a 'dangerous substance' (1892).[17] However, beyond this the government relied on employers to phase out its use voluntarily, an unrealistic strategy because of the unpopularity in the market place of the alternative 'safety match' made with non-toxic red phosphorus. Only in 1910 did the government finally ban the use of white phosphorus in Britain. Here was an early precedent for the concept of completely banning the manufacture of a highly toxic and dangerous substance. The same could have been done far earlier with asbestos.

Anthrax was a disease commonly associated with cattle, especially in Asia. However, the infection could lie dormant in dried animal blood on wool, hair, hides and skins and could infect workers handling, transporting or manufacturing such imported materials through absorption by inhalation, or, more commonly, through an abrasion on the skin. There were 920 reported cases of anthrax in the UK between 1900 and 1914, 167 (or almost 20%) of which ended fatally, usually after only a few days of contracting the infection. There was no cure prior to treatment with antibiotics after 1945. A few cases occurred in Kilmarnock, Ayrshire, in the 1910s, where the affliction was known as 'woolsorter's disease'.

The six diseases included in the 1906 amendment of the Workmen's Compensation Act represented just a fraction of the occupational diseases then in existence. A document produced by the American Bureau of Labor in 1912, for example, listed 54 common industrial poisons being handled by workers. Indeed, the rationale for the inclusion of the six diseases in 1906 was simply that the linkages between occupation and disease in these cases were virtually irrefutable. Workers in most other occupations were susceptible to diseases and disabilities which could seriously impair health. Domestic servants suffered from anaemia and knee-joint inflammation ('housemaid's knee'). Cotton spinners were exposed to carcinogenic mineral oils used on the mule and contracted scrotal cancer (the connection here between oil and cancer was not made until 1922). Weavers passed on all kinds of diseases via the process of 'shuttle kissing' – sucking the yarn through the shuttle eye preparatory to weaving. Rheumatism, sciatica and lumbago also resulted directly from the nature of work in occupations like pottery, coalmining and

17. There was a Bryant & May match factory in the Maryhill/Possil area of Glasgow.

textile bleaching and finishing. Nicotine poisoning afflicted women engaged in biting cigar ends and moistening tobacco leaf with their tongues. Dermatitis, skin damage, tooth and bone rot were also common complaints of those working with various chemicals and gases across a wide range of processes. Referring to the United Turkey Red Company in the Vale of Leven in Dumbartonshire, one commentator noted:

> In many cases the women and girls are working under the most shocking conditions I have ever come across ... I have seen a girl with flesh burned off her hands by working with caustic soda. This girl suffered great agony. But this is only one case. There are others. I have seen girls arms with holes burned in them from chrome.[18]

Conditions in Scottish chemical works were also bad. The Royal Commission on Labour heard that most chemical workers in Scotland worked an 84-hour week and were paid much less than their counterparts south of the border.[19] The witness also said that 'On Saturday, being pay day, you will find that the furnaces are in a great number of cases out, for the simple reason that the men's exhaustion is so great that they generally get drunk immediately after getting their pay'.[20] This evidence is borne out by a report of government inspectors who visited chemical works in Rutherglen, Glasgow and Falkirk in 1893. At all three sites the inspectors found that the labour force was being paid less than workers in England. Moreover, they also found that in all three works the workers' habitual inhalation of noxious fumes had left them with perforated septums – the skin between the nostrils – and that many of the workers had no septums left at all.[21] The works at Rutherglen were owned by Lord Overtoun,

---

18. *Forward*, 9 December 1911.
19. Royal Commission on Labour [c. 6894-XII], George Mitchell's evidence, p. 19, and T. Steele's evidence [c. 6894–IX], p. 3. Mitchell's evidence is refuted to some extent by government statistics for 1890. These show that the average hours worked in Glasgow were 57 – one of the lowest averages for chemical workers in the whole of the UK. Only vitriol workers in St Helens, according to these figures, worked 84 hours a week. Board of Trade Returns of Average Number of Hours Worked 1890 [375], pp. 24–5.
20. Royal Commission on Labour, George Mitchell's evidence [c. 6894-XII], p. 19, and T. Steele's evidence [c. 6894–IX], p. 3.
21. Report on the Conditions of Labour in Chemical Works 1893 [c. 7235], p. 50. According to this evidence no women were employed at any of the works.

and Keir Hardie exposed in the *Labour Leader* just how bad the conditions were:

> In some of the cases the men observed the hard piece of gristle
> when it came away while blowing the nose. The men examined
> hold there is not an employee working inside under roof in
> Messrs Whites' but has a chrome hole in the gristle partition of
> his nose ... the majority of them could pass such an article as
> a common lead pencil right through the hole from one side to
> the other.[22]

Teeth were also often corroded as a consequence of inhaling noxious vapours. R. S. Sherard recalled meeting chemical workers with teeth so damaged from their employment that they paid colleagues five shillings a week to masticate their food for them.[23]

However, it was the inhalation of dust whilst at work that was particularly deadly. Indeed, pulmonary or respiratory diseases caused by inhalation of fine particles of dust within the factory, workshop or mine environment were probably the most prevalent of all occupational health hazards. Industrial processes which generated dust were placed at the top of a 'Classification of Occupations by Health Hazards' drawn up *before* World War One by the industrial hygienist Arlidge. In his autobiography, the Clydeside labour activist Tom Bell recalled conditions in a local foundry in the late nineteenth century thus:

> The conditions under which the moulder worked were vile,
> filthy and insanitary. The approach to the foundry resembled
> that of a rag and bone shop ... The inside was in keeping with
> the outside. Smoke would make the eyes water. The nose and
> throat would clog with dust ... The lavatory was usually
> placed near a drying stove, and consisted of open cans that
> were emptied once a week – a veritable hotbed of disease.[24]

Inhalation of dust resulted in throat irritations, coughing, shortness of breath, chronic catarrh, bronchitis, emphysema, and eventual damage to lung tissue with the spongy texture being replaced by a

22. 'The Overtoun Horror', No. 5 in the 'White Slaves' series of pamphlets, published by the *Labour Leader*, Glasgow, 1899.
23. R. S. Sherard, *White Slaves of England* (London, 1897), p 29.
24. T. Bell, *Pioneering Days* (1941), pp. 64–5.

hard, solid, fibroid tissue. Silicosis, caused by the inhalation of inorganic dusts – stone, flint, clay and metal – afflicted masons and metal miners and was endemic amongst Scottish stone masons and other building workers responsible for constructing and repairing the nation's stone tenements. Byssinosis, contracted by inhaling textile fibres, was especially prevalent in the preparatory departments and the cardroom, whilst pneumoconiosis commonly afflicted coalminers, some 150–200 Scots miners meeting their death by the 'black spit' every year before World War One.[25]

Moreover, the significance of dust inhalation at work goes far beyond this. Fibroid phthisis – or pneumoconiosis – caused by dust inhalation seriously damaged the lung and bronchial tissues and thus reduced resistance to a whole range of other respiratory diseases, not associated with employment, including bronchitis, pneumonia and tuberculosis. This was the prognosis of Arthur Ransome, one of the foremost experts on tuberculosis, as early as 1890, and Arlidge, who commented:

> Experience proves that the dust-produced lung disease may
> coexist with tubercular phthisis; and further that where labour
> is prosecuted in a dirty atmosphere tubercular mischief, in those
> constitutionally predisposed to it, is more likely to arise.[26]

However, because of the difficulty of medically determining the difference between respiratory disease caused by dust or the tubercule bacillus, silicosis was not included in the list of occupational diseases for which compensation was automatic until 1918. Nevertheless, statistics compiled by the Registrar General of Deaths in the 1880s and 1890s indicated clearly an intimate correlation between occupation and mortality from respiratory disease. This issue of the interrelationship between tuberculosis and pneumoconiosis was to resurface as the tragedy of asbestos-related disease and miners' respiratory diseases unfolded in the second half of the twentieth century.

25. T. C. Smout, *A Century of the Scottish People*, pp. 103–4.
26. J. L. Arlidge, *Diseases of Occupation*, p. 246.

TABLE 2.2. COMPARATIVE MORTALITY FROM LUNG AND
RESPIRATORY DISEASE, MALES IN SELECTED OCCUPATIONS,
1880–82

Agriculture, fishing	100
Grocers	130
Coal miners	148
Carpenters, joiners	155
Bakers, confectioners	183
Drapers	197
Masons, builders, bricklayers	208
Wool workers	213
Tailors	217
Cotton workers	250
Quarrymen	268
Printers	288
Cutlers	350
File makers	360
Earthenware workers	514
Cornish miners	528

Source: Evidence of Dr W. Ogle, Royal Commission on Labour,
Digest of Evidence, June 1893, C7063, 1893, pp. 38–4.

The evidence therefore indicates clearly that work was a significant
source of ill health – in the form of fatigue, accidents and employment-
related disease – and remained so well into the twentieth century. Of
fundamental importance in any attempt to explain why this was so
must be the attitudes and strategies of employers towards
the utilisation of their labour power. Such attitudes and strategies
varied enormously – employers were no monolithic group. However,
certain generalisations can be made. Firstly, most employers utilised
labour inefficiently and unscientifically, and despite the propaganda
efforts of a small group of 'welfarist' employers, most industrialists
had a deep-rooted disregard for the biological limitations of workers
and remained unimpressed by the arguments that improving the
welfare and health of workers produced dividends in improved
worker productivity. Workers worth their salt had to be seen to be
grafting. This was partly a result of ignorance and the lack of scientific
training of most managers brought up in the 'rule-of-thumb' school
of management.

However, improving safety standards and workers' health was also seen as a question of resource allocation, and within a wider scenario of a cost-cutting drive in the face of growing foreign competition few employers operating in unprotected markets were willing to spend scarce cash resources to raise health standards at work above the bare minimum required by law. Hence few firms created formal works medical services, or even employed a nurse before World War One, and so the potential for discovering health problems at work at a remedial stage rarely existed. One respondent to the Accidents Committee of 1911 noted how inadequate provision of washing facilities, basic first aid (including antiseptic dressings) and trained workers resulted in many minor abrasions and wounds turning to blood poisoning. Dr Scott, a Glasgow Certifying Surgeon, commented on the high incidence of eye injuries to Clydeside metalworkers and the *ad hoc* treatment administered to victims:

> Hardly an hour passes during the working day in which some dresser does not receive injury through small particles of iron flying from his chisel and lodging in his eyeball. First aid is rendered by his fellow workmen, who are ready to fix the injured party's head against the wall, and, with a pin or pocket knive, extract the offending chip. Should this somewhat heroic treatment be ineffective, the patient is sent to the Eye Infirmary.[27]

Capitalists justified their position by arguing that those furthest down the social scale did not require the same standards, or environmental conditions, or need the degree of regenerative recreation and rest necessary for those in the privileged, upper reaches of society. Each to their place. Moreover, there was a long tradition of blaming the victim – of ascribing responsibility for health at work to the individual concerned. Accidents at work were thus the result of reckless behaviour, stupidity or oversight, and industrial disease was contracted because of hereditary weaknesses, personal habits, manners and lack of cleanliness. Establishment medicine could often be relied on to back up and legitimise such assertions, medical evidence being used in litigation, for example, to prove the victim was to blame for his or her own misfortune, or to suggest that factors outside the employment environment (like diet and housing) had a critical

27. *Clydebank Press*, 13 July 1906.

influence. Furthermore, in the employment contract workers were deemed to have explicitly accepted work under prevailing conditions of risk. Because most employers insured themselves against claims for accident or disease compensation with an annual premium, the incentive to introduce preventive safety standards in the workplace was significantly weakened. Whilst symbolically important, as a preventive measure designed to improve safety standards the Workmen's Compensation Act of 1897 was less successful in practice than might be supposed.[28]

An increasingly interventionist state – stung by humanitarian criticisms of work conditions, influenced by the national efficiency movement, subjected to popular pressure and concerned to retain social stability – was passing legislation which regulated 'dangerous trades'. This reduced working hours, introduced some controls in the factory environment (ventilation, temperature and sanitation standards), enforced the fencing of machinery, and attempted to establish a minimum wage in some of the worst, sweated trades (from 1909, with the Trades Boards Act). Moreover, a growing Mines and Factory Inspectorate policed such legislation, and the inspectors played an important role as social investigators, data collectors, mediators, advisors and teachers, as well as law enforcers.[29] However, industrial legislation developed, in response to particular evils, with many gaps in coverage, cotton textiles and coal mines being well covered, railways less so, and areas like general labouring and domestic service almost completely overlooked. Moreover, many workers and employers remained ignorant of the regulations: it was noted, for example, that the Shops Act of 1886 was virtually unknown and almost totally inoperative for a decade. Anyone examining the Factory Inspectors' Reports cannot fail to be struck by the widespread evasion of the legislation. Breaches of regulations in cotton-relating to mealtime cleaning of machinery, humidity levels (steaming) and time cribbing were commonplace, and the four-week exclusion rule after pregnancy was said to be completely inoperative. This was partly because the fines meted out in the courts for factory crime were paltry and failed to provide a deterrent. On the other hand, the courts failed

28. See P. Bartrip and S. Burman, *Wounded Soldiers of Industry* (Oxford, 1983) P. Bartrip, *Workmen's Compensation in Twentieth Century Britain* (Aldershot, 1987).

29. H. Jones, 'An Inspector Calls', in P. Weindling (ed.), *A Social History of Occupational Health*.

to recompense workers adequately for injuries sustained in the course of their employment. The Inspectorate was also over-stretched and consequently the factories and workshops under their jurisdiction were only rarely and infrequently visited. Family employment remained virtually unregulated, and a wife and children could still be grossly overworked by a husband within the law. Moreover, according to R. H. Tawney, the Trades Board Act of 1909 was a dead letter.[30]

Therefore, whilst legislation provided a significant measure of protection which ameliorated the effects of work on health across some sectors of the economy, its impact should not be exaggerated. Its coverage was patchy, its enforcement often ineffective and its service to the community consequently limited. The connection between work and ill-health remained a very real one: many thousands of Scottish workers continued to be killed or maimed and disabled at work each year. Fatigue and overstrain seriously circumscribed workers' lifestyle, restricted opportunities and diluted the quality of life, leaving little free time for enjoyment of leisure, recreation, education or family life – as Owen bitterly reflected in the socialist novel _The Ragged Trousered Philanthropists_. Moreover, a fatal accident or serious disability meant for many families a spiralling experience of diminished earnings, credit, the pawnshop, immiseration, poverty, malnutrition, deficiency-related illness and the workhouse. As one commentator, Constance Smith, noted in 1905:

> We have only to consider what a loss of an arm, a hand or even a finger, means to a young working man or girl – much more to the breadwinner of a family; how fatally it handicaps such combatants in the hard battle of life; how inevitably it entails upon them descent to a lower place of living, if not to actual penury and dependence upon the community for subsistence.[31]

Continuity and change in war and recession

Whilst the figures for Scotland are difficult to disentangle and interpret, the Home Office figures for occupational injuries and

---

30. See S. Blackburn, 'Working Class Attitudes to Social Reform', _International Review of Social History_, XXXIII (1988), pp. 65–6.
31. C. Smith, 'Dangerous Trades', _Economic Review_, October 1905, vol XV, pp. 435–6.

mortality rates in the UK suggest considerable improvement in industrial health and safety standards in Britain through the first half of the twentieth century. The number of recorded occupation-related deaths fell by more than a half over the period 1900–1950 (from around 5,000 per year to around 2,000 per year). Because of the expansion of the labour force and improved reporting over time this probably meant that workers were something like three times more likely to be killed as a result of an injury sustained at work in 1900 compared to 1950. There is, though, some evidence to suggest that Scotland may have lagged behind the UK, though the pattern is not dissimilar. The slower transition from the more hazardous 'basic' heavy sectors of the economy (such as shipbuilding, coal, textile manufacture and metal working) to the obviously less dangerous service/clerical industries and 'new' high tech light engineering and consumer goods is the main reason for this discrepancy. Scotland hardly had a consumer goods manufacturing sector between the wars – the Hillington estate in Glasgow stood out as the exception. Moreover, the inter-war depression led to a degeneration of occupational health and safety standards, for a number of reasons. Trade unions in Scotland were critically weakened by mass unemployment, and their ability to protect their members was severely undermined (this pattern recurred in the recession of the 1980s and 1990s). The overstocked labour market changed workers' attitudes to their employment, in a period when people were sacked indiscriminately and victimisation was rife. For most it was a case of accepting hazardous working conditions and keeping quiet in order to stay in a job. Unscrupulous employers and managers cut corners to maintain profits, and sometimes just to keep their ailing companies above water. The Second World War brought further intense pressure to maximise output and moral pressure to ignore safety procedures, as well as a massive surge in exposure to hazardous materials – not least asbestos.

The experience of war had important implications for occupational health in Scotland. The demands of war necessitated maximising productivity, and this had to be achieved amidst massive upheaval in the labour market as workers (predominantly male) left their jobs and flooded into the armed forces, to be replaced by what were often new, inexperienced, largely female 'dilutees', drafted into munitions and war-related work. In the First World War little thought was given to work organisation, partly because of the widespread belief that hostilities would be over in a few months. Within a year, the war effort was being undermined by declining productivity. This was the consequence of mismanagement, inexperience and, especially, the common engagement of workers for 70–80 hour working weeks, with few breaks, resulting in accumulated and in many cases chronic fatigue. This emerging crisis led the UK government to establish the Health of Munitions Workers' Committee (HMWC) with a remit to investigate and report on the conditions most conducive to both industrial health and efficiency.

The HMWC carried out a series of pioneering works studies over the period 1915–17, commissioning psychologists, physiologists, statisticians, medical researchers and industrial hygiene specialists to undertake a series of investigations of industrial medicine, health, efficiency and fatigue. In its findings, published in a series of interim memoranda and a comprehensive Final Report in 1918, the Committee pinpointed a clear relationship between excessive working hours and a workers' fatigue threshold and declining productivity levels. It went on to elaborate the correlation between environmental conditions of work – such as illumination, ventilation, seating, washing, sanitary and safety arrangements – and efficiency and to develop awareness of the influence of other factors external to the workplace (such as diet and housing). A number of the HMWC recommendations were incorporated into state wartime labour policy, including the reduction of working hours, rest breaks, the abolition of Sunday working and the provision of works canteens. The primary motive behind such activity remained, however, the maximisation of productivity for the war effort. The agenda of the HMWC was not occupational health *per se*, but was narrowly confined to the munitions sector and represented the continuation of the pre-war concerns of a patriarchal state, exemplified, for example, in the Factory Code. Little attention was paid to the most injury-prone male-dominated occupations, such as mining, the railways, metal working and construction. Therefore, the intense pace of production during the war kept occupational injury and mortality levels high. Indeed, the average rate of industrial deaths over the war years (1915–18) slightly exceeded that of the average death rate over the pre-war decade. There is also some evidence to suggest that such official figures may well have underestimated actual deaths in production during wartime to maintain morale on the 'home front'. The dangers of working with TNT, for example, which led to a number of fatal industrial injuries during the First World War, were kept closely under wraps by the government.[32]

The history of occupational health in the first half of the twentieth century might best be summarised as a combination of ameliorative tendencies and degenerative, retrogressive practices. On the positive side a number of ameliorative influences were at play. In part, this reflects the changing nature of the Scottish labour force, however belatedly. There was a transition from working in more dangerous workplaces in extraction and manufacturing towards safer employment in offices and shops by 1950. This trend accelerated rapidly after World War Two. Moreover, the application of science and technology to the labour process and the workplace could raise health and safety standards, making work less physically demanding (for example mechanisation in agriculture; cranes and conveyors in the docks) and removing specific hazards (such as improved illumination with the transition from gas to electric lighting or the reduction in drive-band injuries due to the replacement of steam motive power by the machine-specific electric motor). This was not, however, a one-way process, and new materials and processes invariably created new hazards (including the risks from electricity). More extensive state regulation of the workplace also helped to protect workers from the worst excesses of competitive, free-market capitalism. In this respect the Workmen's Compensation legislation, rationalised by the Industrial Injuries Act of 1948, played an important role, as did the extension of the Factory and Mines legislation and the passage of an increasing number of multifarious 'special regulations' by the Home Office designed to regulate specific, dangerous working practices, such as the use of carcinogenic mineral-based lubricating oils or the inhalation of insidious airborne fibres within the workplace. The latter represented an attempt to control what was perhaps the most serious of occupational diseases – the pneumoconioses. The establishment of statutory medical inspection in the most dangerous trades and the extension of this practice in the 1937 Factory Act to any workplace where the Secretary of State deemed illness might be due to the nature of work was also a massive stride forward, though many workers were suspicious,

32. On the HMWC, see A. J. McIvor, 'Employers, the Government and Industrial Fatigue in Britain, 1890–1918', *British Journal of Industrial Medicine*, vol. 44, 1987; A. Ineson and D. Thom, 'TNT Poisoning', in P. Weindling, ed., *A Social History of Occupational Health*.

sceptical and evasive, fearing loss of employment and the use of such mechanisms to victimise labour activists (as occurred in shipping and coal mining in the 1940s). Furthermore, given the interconnections between general standards of health and occupational problems, the general improvement in real wages and living standards (housing quality; diet; reduced working hours; increased leisure time) undoubtedly had an ameliorative impact. In this respect, the extension of a state National Insurance system from 1911, the passage of the Holidays With Pay Act (1937: not enforced until after World War Two) and the creation of the post-war 'Welfare State' were vital contributory factors.

What is also evident is that workers, managers and employers became more aware of the interrelationship between occupation and health, and from such consciousness evolved self-help and collective strategies to address the issue. The revival of Scottish trade unionism proved important in this respect, at two levels. The unions operated as effective parliamentary pressure groups, campaigning for extension of legislative protection, as, for example, with the Factory Act of 1937 and the Injuries Act of 1948. More importantly, perhaps, the growth of workplace representation and the power of the shop stewards, especially in manufacturing and mining, added another tier to the protective matrix offered by collective organisation. By the 1940s many stewards were operating as unofficial health and safety officers, acting as a conduit through which information was passed on to the Mines and Factories Inspectorate. The Inspectorate policed the legislation, and research has shown how important their educative role was, not least in facilitating the formation of joint committees between employers and unions to promote health and safety (particularly successful, for example, in the inter-war cotton textile manufacturing sector). Many of the wartime Joint Production Committees also embraced health and safety functions. This reflected both the ethos of wartime co-operation and the enhanced power that war conferred on workers, their representatives and their collective organisations.

The development of occupational medicine and state-sponsored research also played key roles in changing attitudes and influencing policy, though the gap between identification of a specific hazard and effective action to address it remained a wide one.[33] The influence of

33. For a fuller discussion, see A. J. McIvor, 'Manual Work, Technology and Industrial Health, 1918–1939', *Medical History*, no. 31, 1987.

individual doctors and industrial hygiene pioneers like Sir Thomas Legge – a specialist on lead poisoning – continued to be important. Periodically, the *British Medical Journal* publicised occupational health problems, as, for example, the discovery by two Manchester physicians of the link between cotton spinners' cancer and the oil used to lubricate the spinning mule machine.[34] More important, however, was the work of several organisations created during the interwar period specifically to promote industrial health, including the Industrial Welfare Society, the National Institute of Industrial Psychology (founded 1921) and the Industrial Fatigue (1918–29) and Industrial Health (1929–48) Research Boards. The latter organisations significantly extended the theoretical knowledge of the 'human factor' in industry, broadening out the work initiated by the HMWC during World War One. The IFRB and the IHRB alone produced 84 special research monographs and numerous articles in the academic and medical press, publicising their findings on methods of work, job design, the work environment, vocational psychology, occupational disease and monotony at work. These were amongst the first British-initiated systematic work studies. Such ideas filtered through to industry – albeit slowly in Scotland where there was much resistance to 'novel' and untested new ideas and little capital to support experimentation. Legislation tended to lag behind much of the 'best practice' of the most progressive employers and to provide a basic minimum standard for the majority of employers. The long-delayed Factory Act of 1937 included the legalisation of the 48-hour week as a maximum, regulated permissible overtime to a maximum of six hours per week, introduced rest pauses and guidelines on weight carrying, extended medical inspection and made the provision of washing, seating and cloakroom facilities compulsory in all factories. This significantly extended the 1901 Factory Act and extended somewhat the role of preventative medicine in industry. Basic, minimum standards across industry rose as a result of such prescriptive legislation.

The point needs to be made, however, that it was predominantly the expanding, relatively prosperous, modern sector of the Scottish economy that registered the greatest gains in improving occupational health and safety standards. The new factories embodied the latest

---

34. See T. Wyke, 'Mule Spinners' Cancer', in A. Fowler and T. Wyke (eds), *The Barefooted Aristocrats* (Littleborough, 1987).

innovations in design and construction and were generally much better illuminated (larger windows and the use of the sodium discharge lamp), heated and ventilated, and had the most modern sanitary arrangements, as the interwar Factory Inspectors' Reports testified. In a comment on the advantages of migrating south for employment the Chief Factory Inspector, D. R. Wilson, noted in 1937:

> Another advantage gained by such transfers is that light and airy modern single-storey factories, scientifically planned to economise labour, and situated in open and healthy surroundings, take the place of the old, many storeyed buildings, with their restricted supply of fresh air and daylight. Work is consequently carried on under far more advantageous conditions both as regards the health of the worker and economy of labour and overhead charges.[35]

Electric power replaced steam and gas and facilitated a cleaner, brighter and less accident-prone work environment. In the most progressive plants medical and welfare departments were established.

It was in the older, depressed, staple sectors of the economy that industrial health standards stagnated. The Factory Inspectorate identified mining, textile manufacture, iron working, heavy engineering, seafaring and shipbuilding as providing the least healthy working environment in the 1950s. This was the result partly of older factory architecture, design, space utilisation, technology, habits and entrenched attitudes. Workers' health was further undermined by the mental strain and anxiety of recurrent short-time working, underemployment and unemployment, and by the intensification of workload ('speeding-up') and increased monitoring and direct discipline that characterised the interwar period. Moreover, improving health and welfare was an expensive proposition that most of the hard-pressed companies in the 'basic' heavy industries could ill afford. In a cut-throat market place such employers were wary of adding to their costs, and so the employment of works doctors, nurses and welfare officers was rare, and technological renewal and electrification relatively slow. Shipbuilding provides a good example. Working conditions stagnated and were notoriously poor in the 1950s and 1960s, exemplified in the evocative novel of working-class life in Clydebank, *The Holy City*, by Meg Henderson.

35. Factory Inspector's Report, 1937, p. 13.

Such constraints and negative attitudes spilled over into the early phase of World War Two, when similar errors occurred in labour utilisation: massive extension of working hours; intensification of labour and dislocation in labour markets, resulting in accumulating fatigue, growing absenteeism and a declining capacity to perform normal work tasks adequately. Nevertheless, the pressures of wartime were again to prove ultimately ameliorative in their impact upon occupational health and safety standards. Improvement in occupational health and safety standards was more widespread and less patchy across the labour force during the 1940s. This was the consequence of rising bargaining power within the older 'staple' sectors of the economy as wartime pressures raised demand and unionisation increased from around 30% of the labour force in 1938 to 45% by 1949. Key factors, however, were the political domination of the Labour Party and especially the more pro-active wartime and post-war state. Ernest Bevin, as Minister of Labour, used coercion and the threat of removal of employers' privileges under Order 1305 to force Scottish companies to radically extend company welfare facilities and improve sanitary and safety provisions. Managerial and employer attitudes towards occupational health and safety continued to vary widely, though it is possible to detect improvement through the course of the first half of the twentieth century, and especially in the 1940s. In part, this represented the absorption, albeit in a slow and uneven way, of the lessons learned in the First World War and the drip-feed diffusion of the ideas of the occupational physiologists and psychologists. More of those in authority – employers and managers – came to realise the validity of the welfarist maxim that maintaining the morale and looking after the health and welfare of their labour force reaped rewards in terms of increased productivity and loyalty. Such developments produced a marked fall in occupational mortality in the post-war years when the UK average fell below 2,000 persons killed per year for the first time since official records began. One significant factor in this was the reduction of exposure time as working lives shrank due to the raising of the school leaving age (12 pre-World War One; 14 after 1918 and 15 by 1950), reduced work hours, more holidays (with payment) and the tendency to retire from work at age 60 (females) or 65 (males).

The continuing saga of occupational disease

This, however, does not tell the full story. The record for reducing deaths through traumatic injury, which continued to improve through the post-war decades until c. 1980, was far better than that of industrial diseases. On the latter issue the balance sheet suggests that as dangerous substances – such as lead and phosphorus –were regulated and controlled, links between ill-health and other materials used in the production process were discovered. New hazards replaced old ones as the economy developed. Between 1900 and 1950 the numbers of recorded cases of industrial disease (itself a significant under-estimation of this problem) hardly changed, but industrial cancers and chemical poisoning took over from lead poisoning as the worst problems.

The failure to control industrial disease caused by the inhalation of dust at work was to be clearly indicated later with the discovery of dust-related disease of epidemic proportions, especially in relation to miners' emphysema, pneumoconiosis, asbestosis and industry-related cancers (such as mesothelioma). This was the product of several related factors. Because of the insidious, longer-term nature of many industrial diseases (where gestation periods of decades are not uncommon, as with asbestosis) the effects were not as apparent as traumatic injuries sustained at work. Secondly, policy-making tended to emphasise safety issues over health, and financial compensation over really effective preventative measures. The state bowed to industrialists' views (for example, in delaying the passage of a new Factory Act from 1922 to 1937), invariably regulating the use of dangerous substances (for example, carcinogenic mineral oils; asbestos) rather than banning them altogether. Particularly disastrous – especially for Clyde shipbuilding and construction workers – was the decision to regulate and control only the workplaces of those directly manufacturing asbestos until the 1960s. The orientation of the trade unions and their failure to prioritise occupational health issues also played a part in this unfolding tragedy. We return to such issues later (Chapters 4 and 5).

Finally, the failure of the state to introduce an occupational health service as part of the NHS has also been cited as a reason for the marginalisation of health at work.[36] Some important occupational health experiments in Scotland have illustrated the utility of a more

36. For a full discussion, see R. Johnston and A. McIvor, 'Whatever Happened

interventionist approach. Glasgow Corporation had its own occupational health department in the early 1950s and demonstrated that it could effectively conduct occupational health research and act upon its findings. At the time there was high absenteeism amongst Glasgow's 42 sewer workers, and a close examination of the nature of their work resulted in improved ventilation, the provision of washing and changing facilities, the initiation of annual medical inspections, and a stipulation that service down the sewers be limited to a maximum of 20 years. As a consequence, the general health of the workers improved, and absentee rates fell. A similar approach was adopted by the Corporation during an investigation of Glasgow's fish market porters when it was found that a high incidence of Weil's Disease – a bacterial infection passed on by rats – amongst the workers was caused by handling fish boxes soiled by rats.[37] Once again, determined intervention at the workplace vastly improved the overall health of the workers involved.

Glasgow's Public Health Department was also innovative in this field. In the late 1940s an investigation into high accident and absentee rate amongst workers employed at a weaving mill in the east end of the city found that poor air quality, bad lighting and a lack of seats were to blame. When these defects were rectified, the accident and sickness rate was reduced dramatically. The Public Health Department adopted a similar approach when it addressed the issue of poor health amongst the city's 2,400 Cleansing Department employees. Significantly, the success of these ventures convinced Glasgow's Medical Officer of Health in 1951 that there was a need for an occupational health service: 'If occupational health services were put into full operation throughout industry and succeeded in preventing widespread sickness, there might come a time when many of the hospitals could be closed down'.[38] The results of Glasgow's pioneering occupational health ventures were presented as evidence to the Dale Committee in 1951, and one of the Committee's recommendations was that large local authorities should conduct occupational health experiments along the lines of those undertaken in Glasgow. Sadly, and rather ironically, the only public health

to the Occupational Health Service?', in C. Nottingham (ed.), *The National Health Service in Scotland* (Aldershot, 2000).

37. *Transactions of the Association of Industrial Medical Officers*, 2 January 1953, p. 141.

38. *Glasgow Herald*, 15 April 1952, p. 3.

authority to take up this challenge was Glasgow itself. Subsequently, in 1953, 10,000 workers in Govan became the guinea pigs in the first large-scale occupational health experiment in the UK. This investigation found poor hygiene in the food factories; a lack of shower facilities in engineering shops; cellulose paint being sprayed in poor ventilation; inadequate dust control in the saw mills; and a desperate need for washing facilities for shop staff. One engineering firm in Govan was found to be referring 300 of its workers every year to the Glasgow Eye Infirmary – an excellent example of the NHS patching up the work-wounded and sending them back to the battlefield, rather than addressing the root of the problem.[39]

One of the main findings of the Govan experiment was that health risks were especially severe in small work units, and this was the case throughout the period. In 1976 a survey found that only the largest firms had anything like an Occupational Health Service, and that the only medical service offered by 85% of companies was a first aid box.[40] It was primarily to address this need that the Nuffield Foundation sponsored the setting up of several group occupational health schemes throughout the UK – the first one being in Slough. The scheme set up in Dundee in 1964 was the only Nuffield initiative of its kind in Scotland, and Alex Mair, Professor of Public Health and Social Medicine at the University of Dundee, was appointed as its Director. It soon had two medical officers, and its fleet of mini-vans took eight travelling nurses around 63 companies that subscribed to the scheme. The Dundee Occupational Health Service also had its own travelling laboratory that was capable of quickly analysing air samples and determining to what extent working environments were dangerous to workers – and we see in Chapter 3 that this was called into the notorious Red Road flats site in 1967.

Other European countries, such as France and Spain, decided to mesh general health much more closely with occupational health. However, in the UK the strategic failure to prioritise occupational health contributed to delays in addressing the problem of dust-related disease and in effective diagnosis and treatment of victims.

The present system of occupational health and safety in Scotland dates from 1974, supplemented by European regulations dating from

39. *Glasgow Herald*, 14 January 1954, p. 6.
40. Health and Safety Commission, *Occupational Health and Safety, the Way Ahead* (1977), p. 7.

1992 onwards. In 1974 the Health and Safety at Work Act delegated a shared responsibility for workplace health and safety between employers and their employees. This act saw the initiation of the main institutions currently responsible for British health and safety at work: the Health and Safety Commission and the Health and Safety Executive (HSE). Three years later – as part of the Labour Government's Social Chapter – regulations were also passed that permitted *unionised* workers to set up safety committees with their employers. However, the decline of trade union membership across Scotland from the 1980s meant that fewer and fewer British employees were covered by this enabling legislation.[41] In 1986 the Reporting of Injuries, Diseases and Dangerous Occurrences Regulations (RIDDOR) came into force, and this compelled employers to report any injuries resulting in absences from work of more than three days. However, the statistics collected under RIDDOR suggest that there is substantial *under*-reporting of non-fatal injuries. Moreover, the stipulation that employers should investigate reported accidents – if company safety representatives make such a request – has not been taken up by the majority of employers, as many workplaces do not have trade union coverage. In response to EEC directives, some of the shortcomings of the 'shared responsibility' principle of the 1974 act were addressed with the introduction of the Management of Health and Safety at Work Regulations in 1992. This compelled employers and self-employed to carry out 'risk assessments' of potential workplace hazards – and to determine what measures should be taken to comply with the employer's or self-employed person's duties under the 1974 HSWA. However, despite this new measure the principle of shared responsibility for workplace health and safety established in 1974 still stands.

The shortcomings of workplace health and safety coverage in Scotland have been highlighted from several perspectives. The HSE itself has admitted that it has placed too much emphasis on workers' safety instead of workers' health, and has recently stated that it 'does not have a complete picture of current practice in accident and disease investigation in all industry sectors'.[42] There is also a growing literature highlighting the inadequacies of the current occupational health and safety system, and some commentators have suggested that

41. See, for example, D. Walters, 'Health and safety and trade union workplace organisation – a case study in the printing industry', *Industrial Relations Journal*, 18, 1, 1987, pp. 40–51.
42. HSE, Consultation Document, 1998, p. 4.

a new crime of 'corporate killing' should be introduced which would compel employers to direct more attention to workers' safety.[43]

The working landscape of Scotland has changed over the years and the old staple industries are no longer with us on the same scale as they used to be. In the 1950s the car industry came to Linwood and the light truck division of British Leyland to Bathgate, and these were to represent the way forward for Scottish industry at the time. However, they too have now gone, and in the late 1980s and early 1990s around a million manufacturing jobs were lost in the country.[44] The work landscape is now dominated by service industries, the microchip industry, and the semiconductor industry – notably at IBM in Greenock. All jobs, though, bring their own hazards, and intense speculation relating to the safety of the Scottish semiconductor industry continues. Some work has also been done on the hazards of working within an office environment, and this is particularly timely with Scotland destined to become the call-centre capital of Europe.[45]

Conclusion

In Scotland, the type of job a person did continued to have a significant bearing upon health, wellbeing and life expectancy well into the second half of the twentieth century. As late as the 1960s, engineering, construction, transport and foundry workers suffered twice the incidence of bronchitis of professional employees; labourers more than three times; and miners and quarrymen almost four times.[46] The Piper Alpha oilrig tragedy in 1989 brought home the recurring possibility of death and serious injury in industrial employment. Moreover, recent research has demonstrated how occupational health and safety standards in Scotland deteriorated during the economic recession of

43. A. J. P. Dalton, Memorandum to Select Committee on Environment, Transport, and Regional Affairs (1999); See also A. Dalton, *Safety, Health and Environmental Hazards in the Workplace* (London, 1998); N. Adnett, 'The economic analysis of industrial accidents: a re-assessment', *International Review of Applied Economics*, 12, 2 (1998), pp. 241–55; B. M. Hutter, 'Regulating employers and employees: health and safety in the workplace', *Journal of Law and Society*, 20, 4, 1993, pp. 452–70; C. Woolfson, and M. Beck, 'Deregulation: the contemporary politics of health and safety', in A. McClogan (ed.), *The Future of Labour Law* (1996), pp. 171–205.

44. Lords' Hansard, Lord Ewing of Kirkwood, December 1998, col. 441.

45. C. Baldry *et al.*, 'Sick and tired? Working in the Modern Office', in *Work, Employment and Society*, 11, 3.

46. P. Kinnersley, *The Hazards of Work* (London, 1973), pp. 8–11.

the1980s and 1990s. Scotland now has a significantly higher rate of work-related mortality than the rest of the UK.[47] In this sense the uniquely high level of social deprivation in Scotland compared to the rest of the UK is mirrored by poorer conditions inside Scottish workplaces. This had a cumulative effect, seriously undermining Scottish workers' health standards.

Privatisation and deregulation have had a serious deleterious effect. In what is left of the Scottish coalmining industry pneumoconiosis has recently revived (mirroring the recent revival of tuberculosis – the classic disease of poverty). In a periodic screening of miners at Longannet colliery in 2000, 19 new cases of pneumoconiosis were diagnosed, 16 of which were amongst sub-contracting workers – one as young as 38 years. The main cause has been identified as extended exposure to dust underground, resulting from the return to Victorian-length working hours for such contractors in the 1990s, typically more than 70 hours per week, in 9–12 hour shifts.[48]

Moreover, because of slow and relatively negligible change in patriarchal attitudes – Clydeside in particular retained many aspects of a particularly chauvinist, 'machismo' culture well into the second half of the twentieth century – female workers continued to face the debilitating dual burden of paid work and sole responsibility for what were still very labour-intensive tasks within the home. The comment made by Sybil Horner, one of the female Factory Inspectors, in 1933, was still valid in the 1970s: 'women's work often begins where it nominally ends. The house and dependents make their claims upon the woman worker. Her work is never done'.[49] There was also a growing awareness of the adverse impact of deskilling and monotony upon the worker's psyche, as well as work-related stress, which cut across the manual/non-manual work divide.

So, for Scottish workers, a major injury at work, incurring one of many serious occupational diseases and/or death caused by an accident or industrial disease were important causes of economic deprivation,

47. Woolfson and Beck, *Deregulation*; On Piper Alpha, see J. Foster, C. Woolfson and M. Beck, *Paying for the Piper: The Piper Alpha Disaster* (New York, 1996).
48. Information from Nicky Wilson, General Secretary, Scottish Union of Mineworkers, 8 June 2000.
49. Factory Inspector's Report 1933, pp 50–1. For a discussion of women and gender relations at work, see A. J. McIvor, 'Women and Work in Twentieth Century Scotland', in A. Dickson and J. H. Treble (eds), *People and Society in Scotland*, vol. 3 (Edinburgh, 1992).

relative poverty and, invariably, a slide into what would now be termed 'social exclusion'. Moreover, this often meant severe physical incapacity and deep psychological shockwaves, as crippled and blighted workers came to terms with their dependence upon others, their impaired capacity to work, to provide and to socialise. Everyone reacted differently to such trauma, and the oral testimony of Clydeside asbestos victims examined throughout this book demonstrates a variety of emotions and attitudes, ranging from anger and bitterness, to stoic, fatalistic, sometimes even good-humoured acceptance and deep resignation and depression in the face of inevitable death. In a society still deeply imbued with the Calvinist work ethic, occupational disability triggered a loss of identity, morale and self-esteem. These issues are explored in more depth in Chapter 6, through the oral testimony of asbestos-related disease victims.

Asbestos, then, although by far the worst single occupational disaster to hit Scotland since the dawn of industrialisation, fits in to a long British and Scottish tradition in which workers' health consistently ran a poor second to workers' output. Much of the blame, therefore, for the high asbestos death toll in Scotland can be attributed to a long acceptance of this tradition and the tendency of employers, management and the state and its policy makers to place profit before health. Sadly (though understandably, given the context) the trade unions and many workers themselves also contributed, for a long time, by fatalistically accepting the status quo and failing to prioritise occupational health. For many born into an economic environment dominated by the profit motive, the working environment was one in which bad working conditions were all part of the game. A sense of this acculturated disregard for personal health comes through quite poignantly in the testimony of a 71-year-old retired sheet metal worker from Glasgow reflecting on his working life:

> The filth that we worked in right fae 14 years of age. And being a man with no education, the only thing you had was the muscle in your arm and what experience you got with metal, and a very willingness to work. I would go in and say to people, 'Yes I'll do that in that time'. And whatever it took to do that [job] I would do it. Silly now, looking back through the years, you know.[50]

50. Interview A. 9.

CHAPTER THREE

'It Fell Like Snow':
Working with Asbestos

I used tae say tae him 'Was Peter there today at his work?'
And he used to say 'I couldnae tell you, I couldae see him'.
He couldnae see him for a' the dust. And then I used tae
take his overalls and take them out tae the stairs and brush
them before I could wash them. [Joiner's wife] [1]

The aim of this chapter is to take the reader deep into the workplaces
where Scottish employees were exposed, sometimes fatally, to asbestos
dust. In Chapter 1 we noted just how widespread such exposure was
across a diverse range of workplaces, affecting both male and female
labour in Scotland. Here we discuss working conditions from the
1930s, narrowing the focus and paying particular attention to three
areas: asbestos manufacturing, shipbuilding, and the construction and
demolition industries where contact with asbestos was most widely
experienced. The surviving documentary evidence is analysed and we
draw upon oral testimony from workers employed in the Turner's
asbestos manufacturing plant in Clydebank, laggers, boilermakers,
riggers, heating engineers, asbestos sprayers, and labourers and joiners
in the shipyards and building sites. Some of the more graphic
descriptions note how the deadly asbestos dust 'fell like snow' (an
often repeated phrase) and how the density of dust made it difficult
to see fellow workers close by.

Recently, Patrick Joyce, a prominent social historian of work,
lamented the dire lack of research on the inner world of the British
workplace. We still know very little about work culture, workers'
attitudes and the changing work environment. However, recent
research on the issue of skill has gone some way to develop debates
about the nature and extent of work *degradation* in twentieth-century

---

1. Interview A6.

Scotland, and the relationship between work and politics.[2] Where the literature remains especially sparse is in relation to the interaction between work and health. Whilst there are, as previously noted, a number of pioneering American studies of the social history of occupational health, this topic has been curiously neglected in Britain, and even more so in Scotland.

This chapter has two main aims. Firstly, to examine in some detail the nature of work and the working environment of those working with asbestos. The oral testimonies shed a great many insights into how workers were exposed to this toxic substance, either *directly* through their manufacture or working of the material, or *indirectly* by working in close proximity to those who were. Secondly, we analyse the attitudes of workers towards their contact with this highly toxic and dangerous substance. The lack of awareness about the dangers of working with asbestos before the 1970s comes through the testimony, as well as a mixture of stoical acceptance, fatalism, bitterness and anger, and the sense of humour that Scottish workers brought to this tragic scenario. The evidence strongly suggests there was negligence from the top (employers and management), through the state officials (Factory Inspectors; Health and Safety Executive) and doctors, to the bottom (organised labour and, on some occasions, the workers themselves).

'Dante's inferno': asbestos manufacturing in Scotland

As we noted in Chapter 1, the manufacturing of asbestos in Scotland has a long history with quite a number of specialist factories in existence from the 1870s. Unfortunately, little documentation has survived from before World War Two to illuminate what it was like to work in these early asbestos manufacturing plants. However, if they were anything like the factories in England where asbestos was processed in its raw, dry form, then Scottish workers in these plants would have been exposed to extremely dangerous, life-threatening levels of dust inhalation.

From the late 1930s, the dominant UK-based asbestos manufacturing multi-national Turner's established a factory in Clydebank to produce asbestos cement products. A case study of work and working

2. See especially W. W. Knox, *Industrial Nation: Work, Culture and Society in Scotland, 1800–Present* (1999).

conditions in this particular factory which operated for almost 32 years from 1938 until its closure in 1970, employing at peak some 320 workers, tells us much about how employees in asbestos manufacturing were exposed to the deadly fibres on the factory floor (see plate section, 3–6).[3]

After delivery, the raw asbestos was stored in a warehouse on the site. Jack Walsh remembered how up to 3,000 tons of raw blue and white asbestos fibre was stacked in hessian sacks piled up to 30 feet high.[4] Warehousing, bag handling and fibre treatment prior to the 'wet' cement manufacturing processes were identified by Turner & Newell's (T&N) own Medical Adviser – Dr H. C. Lewinsohn – as being amongst the most dangerous jobs in the factory. Lewinsohn was commissioned by T&N to produce a report on working conditions and medical facilities in all the group's six asbestos cement factories (including Dalmuir) in the late 1960s. The reports were a damning indictment of grossly unhealthy work conditions in asbestos cement. The stacking and storing of the raw asbestos was identified as a major problem area because invariably palletisation was not practised: 'In sheds with non-palletised stacks burst bags are still visible far too often, and spillage constitutes a problem'. This 'problem' was compounded by crude cleaning methods – often by brush and shovel – which threw up an enormous volume of dust in the warehouse and treatment areas. Even where more modern vacuum cleaning equipment was provided, Lewinsohn noted that 'insufficient use is made' of them and 'insufficient care is often exercised in these areas and old-fashioned … methods prevail'.[5]

Thereafter, the bags of asbestos were transported to the upper level of the factory and deposited in a mixing hopper. Here somebody worked attaching a sack over the outlet chute, constantly filling bags of the blended fibre to the required capacity. Another operator then took several of the sacks and loaded them into the 'beater', together with the required proportion of water and Portland cement. This

---

3. M. S. Dilke and A. A. Templeton, *Third Statistical Account of Scotland* (Glasgow, 1959), p. 235; Clydebank Burgh Council, *Official Handbook, 1960*, p. 39. The 1966 Handbook reported 275 employed.

4. *Evening Times*, 26 October 1987. One of our respondents also testified to the use of the more dangerous blue asbestos in the works. Interview A 19.

5. H. C. Lewinsohn, T&N Medical Adviser, *Reports on Visits to Turner's Asbestos Cement (TAC) Factories*, to J. K. Shepherd, TAC, Trafford Park, Manchester, 17 June 1970.

machine created the asbestos cement which flowed downwards to the factory floor to be moulded into boards, panels, tiles and pipes. After this the products were dried in ovens before dry boards and pipes were trimmed to size in giant cutting machines, with final preparation undertaken by hand. Some of the finished products were then sunk in seven large water-filled vats to allow them to 'mature'.

The factory was organised on 'flow' principles, with the raw materials being processed stage by stage and moved from machine to machine by banks of rollers, not dissimilar to a steel mill. The majority of the Turner's Asbestos Cement (TAC) Dalmuir workforce could be classified as unskilled and semi-skilled machine operators, and a respondent from Donegal noted how a substantial proportion of Irish and Irish descendants were employed. Those to whom we spoke differed, as one might expect, in their attitudes to their work. However, all our respondents noted that the work was very physical, dusty, dirty, noisy and dangerous.

The preparatory processes with the dry asbestos fibres on the upper level of the factory were amongst the most dusty, and hence dangerous, jobs in the factory. One respondent was directed as a wartime 'dilutee' into employment at Turner's by the Labour Exchange in 1940 when a male machine operator left for the Navy. She took on the heavy and dangerous job of loading and operating the 'beater' which created the asbestos cement. She described her work:

> The job itself was quite interesting; I quite enjoyed it. I would never have left if the Blitz hadn't have come. I was in what was called the beaters. I was upstairs putting the fibres in and there was a man downstairs another floor below me. So many revolutions of water I put into the beater tank y'know. And then I went upstairs and I put in, if I remember right it was six bags of fibre, all different types of fibre in. He put on his light to say he was putting the asbestos in so we both did it at the one time, y'know. I used to flick the light and I was ready too. And that was all you did. You just put your six bags of fibre into the tank, the beaters beat it up and then it came out through and on to the machines and the men cut it off into sheets y'know. It was quite interesting. It was a hard job, because they were heavy bags, about 20–30 pounds in each bag of fibre and they said I could never do it because I was a slight 18 year old, y'know but you get there ... It was quite a good

job. I quite enjoyed it anyway. But that was really all there was
to it. So many revolutions of water, so many bags of fibres, so
much cement and it all went into this beater and it all mixed
up into cement and then it came out through the machine and
the men at the machine cut it off into sheets.

She could also remember having to open the sacks of asbestos:

It was like, you had a platform and then it was like a tunnel.
This was where you put the ... When you were on the
platform you had so many bags ... You opened them up and
put them into this tunnel and your head was in the tunnel as
well.[6]

Another Turner employee commented on the dusty atmosphere and
confirmed that dust levels were most dense on the upper level:

The machines in it, they were flying up and down by you and
they were blowing up the dust off the floor You got that used
to it you didn't care about it, y'know what I mean ... It was
mixed up in the loft where there was a big mixer y' know ...
Dust was flying around all over the place. He cut the bag and
threw it into the machine. Anything that was left, he gave the
bag a shake. You look up and you wouldn't even see the man
who was working in it. Like everything else if you don't do it
somebody else will. The firm didn't care if you jacked [left] or
not. Oh no, no.[7]

By the time TAC started operations in Clydebank in 1938, the
British government had introduced measures aimed at regulating the
asbestos hazard. The Asbestos Regulations of 1931 were a response
to growing medical evidence from 1924 of confirmed deaths from
asbestosis. Britain was the first country to pass such pioneering
legislation, which looked impressive, at least on paper. Provisions
included the wearing of respirators; dust checks and suppression of
dust through localised exhaust ventilation; medical checks and
monitoring. Asbestosis was also made a prescribed occupational
disease, which enabled workers to claim compensation. However,
researchers have shown that in practice these regulations were

6. Interview A22. This respondent suffers from the asbestos-related disease
   pleural thickening.
7. Interview A23.

relatively ineffective. Only a small proportion of workers in Britain exposed to asbestos were covered; the Medical Panels were too conservative and compensation was far too meagre; whilst the asbestos manufacturers, insulation companies and their employers' associations continued to deny the extent of the problem and to lobby to minimise their liability.[8] Critically, the asbestos industry succeeded in getting only a core group of workers in so-called 'scheduled areas' included in the 1931 scheme. These were the primary *textile* manufacturing processes of crushing, carding, spinning, weaving and mattress-making. Laggers (including sprayers) and those working with asbestos brake linings were not included, nor were most asbestos cement workers. Turner & Newall's internal documents indicate that the risks were not deemed to be as high for such workers.

This is borne out in relation to the cement workers by the evidence of asbestosis compensation claims in the 1930s, which were much higher in the 'dry' processes in the scheduled areas than in Turner's Asbestos Cement. Indeed, the risk in the asbestos cement section of Turner & Newall's UK business (which employed about 30% of the total Turner & Newall workforce) was regarded as so small that TAC were informed in 1939 by the parent company that they could stop the contributions they had been making to the corporation's internal asbestosis insurance scheme.[9] This is very significant. At just the point when TAC Clydebank started production, Turner's regarded asbestos cement manufacture as safe, with the risk of asbestos exposure causing health problems as negligible. Hence no special measures to minimise workers' contact with dust were deemed necessary.

Apart from the specific Asbestos Regulations, there also existed a

8. G. Tweedale and P. Hansen, 'Protecting the Workers: The Medical Board and the Asbestos Industry, 1930s–1960s', *Medical History*, no. 42, 1998; D. Jeremy, 'Corporate Responses to the Emergent Recognition of a Health Hazard in the UK Asbestos Industry: the Case of Turner and Newall', 1920–1960', *Business and Economic History*, no. 24, 1995; M. Greenberg, 'Knowledge of the Health Hazard of Asbestos Prior to the Merewether and Price report of 1930', *Social History of Medicine*, no. 7, 1994; R. Johnston and A. J. McIvor, 'Incubating Death'. For a less critical perspective, see P. Bartrip, 'Too Little, too Late? The Home Office and the Asbestos Industry Regulations, 1931', *Medical History*, no. 42, 1998.
9. N. Wikeley, 'Turner and Newall: Early Organizational Responses to Litigation Risk', *Journal of Law and Society*, 24, 1997, pp. 258–9. See also N. Wikeley, 'The Asbestos Regulations, 1931: A Licence to Kill?', *Journal of Law and Society*, 19, 1992.

general legal obligation upon employers under the 1937 Factory Act to provide a dust-free work environment. However, the evidence for TAC Dalmuir suggests that this was very poorly policed and enforced. This, combined with the exclusions under the 1931 Asbestos Regulations, meant that many workers in TAC Dalmuir were exposed to disabling and life-threatening quantities of dust. As the Turner & Newall historians Tweedale and Hansen note: 'At the periphery of the Turner & Newall business the medical surveillance in the satellite firms grew even weaker or even non-existent'.[10] They conclude their analysis by arguing that whilst the asbestos companies bear the brunt of responsibility for the escalating deaths, government agencies (including the Medical Panels) and policymakers also bear some of the blame. Moreover, the major asbestos companies vigorously contested compensation claims whilst continuing to reap massive profits. Using Turner & Newall's own internal company papers as evidence, Tweedale and Jeremy have argued:

> The company's health and safety policy was directed at minimisation and denial. This meant, *inter alia*, failing to treat many legitimate asbestosis claims sympathetically; misleading the government regulators about asbestos-related disease in shipyard insulation workers; attempting in the 1950s to suppress research about the carcinogenic potential of asbestos; and in the 1990s doggedly contesting 'bystander' mesothelioma claims from environmental exposure.[11]

The oral evidence of former TAC Dalmuir workers shows that the Asbestos Regulations and factory legislation were largely ineffective, and this is backed up by the report on conditions in the asbestos factories produced by T&N's own Medical Adviser. Localised exhaust ventilation reduced but did not eliminate dust emissions and there is little evidence of workers at TAC wearing proper respirators or even basic face masks to protect themselves, even when sweeping the dust from the factory floor. In legal evidence in the late 1960s it was reported that the wall-and roof-mounted general exhaust extractors

10. G. Tweedale and P. Hansen, 'Protecting the Workers', p. 444.
11. G. Tweedale and D. J. Jeremy, 'Compensating the Workers: Industrial Injury and Compensation in the British Asbestos Industry, 1930s–60s', *Business History*, vol. 41, April 1999. See also G. Tweedale, *Magic Mineral to Deadly Dust: Turner and Newall and the Asbestos Health Hazard* (Oxford University Press, 2000).

in the factory 'were frequently clogged up and did not satisfactorily succeed in drawing out the dust from the premises'.[12] Those we spoke to indicated that masks were either not provided, or were available, but the necessity of workers wearing the masks was not impressed upon those working on the factory floor. A female moulder, whose health was badly affected by asbestos, recalled how fellow women workers and herself used aprons, tied sacks around them and used scarves around their faces and heads to try to protect themselves from the insidious dust.[13] Another woman worker also testified to an absolute lack of safety provision. Speaking of the 1940–41 period she said:

> I don't remember a mask or anything. No. First time I ever remember wearing a mask was when I went back into Singer's after the war was finished and I became a – trust me to get all the dangerous jobs – a paint sprayer and it wasn't paint it was laquer for the sewing machines you know. But no I don't remember any safety precautions at all ... You never thought of danger. I mean asbestos was nothing. Just never gave asbestos a thought, you know. [14]

A machine operator employed at Turner's between about 1958 and 1966 also commented on the lack of masks or protection:

> Well I never had a mask and I'll be honest with you I never seen anyone ... I never even knew where they were, never mind not wearing one. I'm not saying that they actually wasn't there, but if they were there nobody offered them to you. Know what I mean. You did get gloves. Your hands got that bad your skin got all worn off. The sheets was that sharp y'know.[15]

One man found himself walking the streets of Clydebank searching for work in 1964. When he arrived at Turner's he was immediately taken on and started work the very next day. He described very graphically conditions in the plant in the mid-1960s:

12. Letter, Ross, Harper and Murphy, Solicitors, representing Thomas Williamson, to J. Chapman and Co, Turner's Asbestos Cement, 21 March 1969 (Turner & Newall Archive, Manchester).
13. *Evening Times*, 16 June 1993.
14. Interview A22.
15. Interview A22.

I'll never forget till the day I die the first impression of that place. It was like walking into Dante's inferno without the fire. It was just hell. The noise was unbelievable. The size of the machinery was awe-inspiring you know, awe-inspiring. Three big machines took up the whole width of the factory. They were a sheet machine, and a pipe machine, and then another sheet machine. Dust was flying through the air everywhere, clouds of dust. And there were wee men walking about – I ended up daen it for the first two or three days I was there – sweeping the floor. Nae masks, just overalls. Clouds of stoor everywhere it just filled the air, and it was settling just as fast as they were sweeping it. And then it was then dumped. Shovelled intae wheel barras, taking out tae the side of the Clyde and dumped down at the grounds of what's the hospital down there now ... Tae be heard. I know it sounds crazy but you had tae shout in a whisper. That was the strange thing, you had tae get in between the pitch of the machines and you could be heard.[16]

Interestingly, other commentators noted how you could smell and taste the dust. As in the cotton industry, the major problem was the accumulation of muck and dust on the machinery:

The worst of the whole thing was the clean-downs. You had to clean the machine once a shift. You had big steel tools like scrapers, and they were for all the world like a big broad blade 6 or 7 inches long eh wide, with a handle maybe 4 or 5 feet long, that was made out of steel. And eh, you scraped off all the hardened asbestos cement fae round the sides of the machine with high pressure hoses and these scrapers. And every weekend the machines all closed down throughout the factory and they did what they called 'the clean down.' It was the big job when they did all the repairs tae the felts; washed out tubs and vats, and stripped everything back tae the bare metal and it was all washed away. And because you were working with high pressure hoses you got an awful lot of splash-backs and you were covered in wet asbestos cement.[17]

Lack of knowledge and information on the hazards of asbestos left

16. Interview A19.
17. Interview A19.

many in ignorance of the danger they were in. Either people were not told, or they were informed that the risk was minimal, associated only with one type of asbestos and with the 'dry' preparatory processes. Referring to the mid-1960s at Turner's, one worker noted:

> When you went in the door of Turner's asbestos there was a Factory Act with all the stuff. The only problem was that you couldnae see through it with the layer of asbestos cement on the glass you know. We were offered masks and told tae use them if we were upstairs at the beaters with blue asbestos, the dry form which if you breathed it in it was bad for you. They didnae tell you that once it came down it was wet then it dried out it could make you just as ill. You never got any warnings of that kind. You never got any warnings about brown asbestos; you never got any warnings about white asbestos. Ah, you weren't told that when you took it home in your clothes your wife was going to breathe it in as well. As far as we were concerned the only dangerous stuff was the stuff that came out the bag and went intae the beater. That was the only time that was dangerous.[18]

Another Turner machine operator demonstrated an acute awareness of the potential of his cutting machine to take fingers off if you weren't careful but, significantly, when asked when he first realised that asbestos was dangerous replied: 'Oh, I was ignorant of the fact, ignorant of the fact, aye. I, I don't really know. I cannae answer that question'.[19] This is indicative of a tendency for workers at this time to be more aware of the immediate threats to their safety at work, and less aware of occupational health problems which incubated over long periods of time. The provision of gloves but not respirators mentioned before is also significant in this context. Clearly, the wearing of masks was not being enforced and workers were not being adequately informed of the long-term effects the inhalation of asbestos dust could have upon their health.

Nor have we come across any evidence that there was systematic medical surveillance and monitoring of TAC employees. None of the respondents we spoke to could recall any such medical scheme. This was a major point of criticism in the Lewinsohn reports on the

18. Interview A19.
19. Interview A24.

asbestos cement factories in the late 1960s. The system that prevailed was that TAC Dalmuir engaged a local GP who examined new employees and 'problem cases' referred by management. However, his presence at the factory was rare, attending only once a week between 9 and 10 am 'if he is required'. Moreover, the company made no provision for routine X-ray monitoring of its asbestos cement workforce. Lewinsohn regarded this as a major flaw, demonstrating the lack of commitment within T&N to modern methods of industrial medicine. Of the part-time medical officers he noted: 'None of these gentlemen are particularly interested in factory hygiene and I do not believe that they are expected to contribute greatly to the running of the factories'. Furthermore: 'I believe that the Medical Officers at present employed by the company provide a very superficial service and do not in fact practice industrial medicine in the true sense of the word'.[20] This certainly appears to apply to the Clydebank GP who acted as the Company Medical Officer. In the mid-1980s an asbestotic lagger reported to the same GP for examination and was treated with neither sensitivity or sympathy. Incredibly, the doctor commented that he could do with a spell 'in Belsen' to lose weight and informed our respondent that he did 'not believe in asbestosis'.[21] Comments such as this testify to the bone-headedness of some of the medical profession regarding their attitudes towards asbestos at this time.

Lewinsohn was also shocked to find that the medical records of the asbestos cement workers were not confidential but 'freely available to the Personnel Department'.[22] The knowledge that this was so, he concluded, inevitably 'led to some concealment of facts'. In other words workers hid the extent of their illness because they feared transfer or even dismissal. Thus it was only the fibre-treaters and beater operators covered by the 1931 Asbestos Regulations who were likely to be diagnosed in the initial and periodic medical examinations through the Pneumoconiosis Medical Panels. However, the Lewinsohn reports show clearly that the dust problem was much more widespread in the asbestos cement factories than these operations and that T&N had ignored the numbers at risk: 'This company has been lulled into

20. Lewinsohn Report, 17 June 1970; see also Lewinsohn to Shepherd, 18 May 1970 (Turner & Newall Archive, Manchester).
21. Interview A14.
22. Lewinsohn Report, 17 June 1970; see also Lewinsohn to Shepherd, 18 May 1970.

a false sense of security and has not appreciated in the past the number of employees who are being exposed to asbestos dust'.[23] Lewinsohn went on to propose a major overhaul in the company's industrial medicine services, including the appointment of a full-time medical officer specifically for the asbestos cement group, confidentiality with medical records and the standardisation and modernisation of procedures for periodic extensive medical examination of employees at least bi-annually to provide epidemiological surveys and a 'biological monitoring device'.[24] He also proposed the use of the National Coal Board X-ray facilities for periodic examination of Turner's workers. To Lewinsohn, these were minimum requirements necessary to satisfy the new more stringent 1969 Asbestos Regulations, and he reminded the company that 'where a health hazard exists such as that associated with exposure to asbestos, there is both a moral and a practical responsibility involved'. Significantly, T&N never established such a comprehensive medical service and Lewinsohn eventually resigned in disgust in 1976.[25]

More research is necessary to determine the reactions of asbestos companies in Scotland such as Turner's, MacLellan's and Cape (Marinite) to the discovery over 1955–60 that asbestos causes cancer. One report on working conditions at an asbestos cement factory in Livingston indicates that only certain workers were given protection. A quantity surveyor who died of mesothelioma was employed at the factory during the building of an extension there, and remembered working near the assembly line. Clearly, according to this account the work processes were quite similar to those of Dalmuir:

> They would empty the raw asbestos into a hopper which is just like a filter funnel upside down. It would then be mixed with cement and hot water to form a matrix. This mix would then be rolled out onto templates to form sheets and the templates would be set aside and the asbestos cement was then allowed to harden. Once it was hard it was moved to a curing shed where it was then left to dry out ... There was also a massive area outside the factory which they used for storing the asbestos sheets ... It wasn't enclosed but was out in the open

23. Lewinsohn Report to J. K. Shepherd, TAC, 18 February 1969.
24. Lewinsohn Report, 17 June 1970; see also Lewinsohn to Shepherd, 18 May 1970.
25. We are grateful to Geoffrey Tweedale for this information.

air. By the time the boards came from the curing sheds to this outside area they were hard ... The only people that I can recall wearing masks were the people who worked at the de-bagging areas. This is where the asbestos and cement bags were opened. I recall that these areas had dust extractor fans in place. However, the asbestos dust was throughout the whole factory and not just confined to the de-bagging area ...[26]

As was the case in Dalmuir, those who lived near the Livingston asbestos factory complained that white dust constantly blew into their homes from the factory, and it was also said that most of the workers in the factory were not issued with any protective clothing.[27] This was largely true of Dalmuir too. It would appear that *some* workers in the most dusty processes were issued with masks. However, as in the shipyards, those who happened to work in the immediate vicinity were not deemed to be at risk and so no effort was made to protect them. There was still an assumption in this period that very large quantities of dust needed to be inhaled to get cancer, indicated in the fact that compensation was initially only allowed where lung cancer was diagnosed in *conjunction* with asbestosis. As asbestosis was not deemed by the manufacturers to be a problem in asbestos cement production, the risk of cancers amongst such workers was probably also deemed to be negligible in the 1960s.

At Turner's, Dalmuir, the other major exposure points were in waste disposal and the 'dry-end processes' where the finished product was cut, trimmed and prepared at lathes, sawing machines and sanders. None of these workers were covered by the 1931 Regulations. Much of the asbestos waste was ground up and either recycled or dumped down on the adjacent land between the factory and the River Clyde. The breaking up, grinding and transport of dry waste were extremely dusty processes and in some cases resulted in contaminating 'clean' areas when waste was being transported back to the beater and mixer floors for re-blending back into the cement.[28] Some oral testimony indicates that by the 1960s some (if not all) of the heavy cutting machinery at Dalmuir was fitted with exhaust air extractors to draw away the dust. However, the Lewinsohn Reports indicate

---

26. Interview A 20.
27. Unidentified newspaper clipping, John Todd Papers, Clydeside Action on Asbestos (CAA) Archive.
28. Lewinsohn Report, 17 June 1970.

serious problems with ventilation systems in the asbestos cement factories. Much of the machinery was old-fashioned and difficult to ventilate effectively with strategically placed exhaust hoods, so 'most attempts at ventilation of saws of various kinds appear to have met with very little success' and (referring to lathes) 'operatives appear to need more determined instruction in the use of these systems and more rigorous enforcement by line supervision of instructions designed to improve the dust extraction on these machines'. Much hand cleaning and fettling was also still being done without either respirators or any exhaust ventilation.[29] One Dalmuir machine operator whose job involved cutting 10-foot-long pipes into six–inch 'pots', described such an exhaust dust extractor, though he also noted that his had a tendency to get blocked and needed to be relieved by a heavy bang with a brush. He did not use a mask or a respirator at his work, described conditions as 'terrible' and 'crap' and only stuck the job for a year.[30]

This experience ties in with others and suggests a growing recruitment problem and a considerable turnover of workers at Turner's Dalmuir plant by the 1960s. Lewinsohn also noted that labour turnover was particularly high at the Dalmuir factory. Few, it appears, tolerated such conditions for any length of time. One Irish machine operator described bitterly how he left the plant after several years in the late 1950s/early 1960s only to be forced to return because he was desperate for work and had a young family to provide for: 'They were always going and coming. Always people going out and new ones coming in. A good man wouldn't have stayed in it. Any man that has any sense'.[31]

Making matters worse was the fact that the plant does not appear to have been unionised before the 1960s. One respondent described how wages were relatively poor in the 1960s and how management deducted the cost of any damages to sheeting from these already meagre earnings.[32] Whether the factory regime at Turner's was any more or less draconian than other Clydeside employers at this time is not known. The evidence suggests, however, that there was very little, if any, organised protest against conditions at TAC Dalmuir until the late 1960s. Significantly, the three-month 1970 strike for

29. Lewinsohn Report, 17 June 1970.
30. Interview A24.
31. Interview A23.
32. Interview A23.

higher wages was reported to be the first in the history of the plant.[33] Instead workers voted with their feet, leaving Turner's for more congenial employment elsewhere. This was probably facilitated by the expansion in job opportunities in the 1960s. For some, however, this was not an option. The wife of a machine operator who worked in the plant for around eight years commented:

> He was frightened to walk out of the job because he was married with a family and he just could not afford to do it, and that was the ins and outs of it. It was a job, the money was coming in ... What could we do, we were trying to bring up two kids We were trying to bring them up as decent as possible and do our very best ... Folk don't really understand when you actually say to them. I was trying to do the best for my husband, my family and my children.[34]

In response to the question, 'Were you aware that asbestos was dangerous?' her husband replied:

> I knew it was dangerous before I went in there cause there was people complaining but when you have two of a family to bring up it was better than walking the streets. I never was idle in my life.[35]

Moreover, like the Singer Corporation in Clydebank, Turner's developed something of a reputation as a welfarist employer, with extensive sports and welfare facilities, including a gym and works football, badminton, golf and bowls teams.[36] The TAC Amateur Boxing Club was very successful, with Scottish titles won by three of their members in the 1950s.[37] Such diversions perhaps went some way to sweeten the pill, helping some workers to tolerate what were by all accounts very grim working conditions in the 1960s.

The legacy of all this was a high incidence of asbestos-related diseases amongst those formerly employed by TAC. Precise figures are not known, but the weight of evidence appears irrefutable. Significantly, the first common law asbestosis claim against Turner & Newall was from a worker of TAC, Dalmuir, in 1949/50. Unfortu-

---

33. *Clydebank Press*, 1 May 1970; 29 May 1970; 7 August 1970.
34. Interview A21.
35. Interview A22.
36. *Clydebank Press*, 7 August 1970.
37. J. Hood, *The History of Clydebank* (1980), pp. 201–2.

nately little is known about this case after the claimant dropped it when T&N repudiated liability in January 1950.[38] There are also several other documented cases of asbestosis of Dalmuir workers recorded in the main Turner & Newall archive in Manchester and at least one fatality from mesothelioma recorded prior to the works closing down in 1970. This was Thomas Williamson who died aged just 50 in February 1950. Significantly, Williamson was not a scheduled area worker but a plumber who had worked throughout the factory on repair and maintenance work. Cases multiplied as time went on. An ex-Turner employee noted in 1987 that he could cite the names of a dozen former colleagues who had died as a consequence of asbestos exposure, whilst Clydebank Asbestos Group have recently identified five confirmed deaths of ex-Turner workers from mesothelioma over the past seven years.[39] Three out of four of the ex-Turner workers we interviewed suffered from some asbestos-related respiratory disorder, and in 1993, 12 workers in a Turner's works photograph taken 40 years previously in 1953 were discovered to have subsequently died of breathing-related problems (see plate section, 7–8).[40] Whilst not definitively traced back to asbestos in all cases, the prevalence of lung disorders of this magnitude indicates dust inhalation as the primary cause. Misdiagnosis by doctors in the 1950s and 1960s was also not uncommon, so the full extent of this particular tragedy will probably never be known. In one of these cases, Nancy Ferguson was told by her doctors that she suffered from emphysema due to her smoking. However, a *post mortem* found a substantial amount of asbestos fibre in her lungs. Tragically, Owen and Margaret Lilly have both been diagnosed as asbestotic – he as a result of working at Turner's and she from washing his asbestos-impregnated work clothes. Turner's thus contributed to a somewhat unusual pattern of asbestos-related disability and mortality in Clydebank. Male mesothelioma deaths were high; but so were female mesothelioma deaths in Clydebank, which exceeded the expected incidence by more than ten times.[41] Ironically, Turner's policy of job rotation of workers out of the

38. John Collins, Report on the T&N Asbestosis Fund for year to 30 September 1950, 23 November 1950 (T&N Board Papers; Chase Manhattan Archive, Manchester). We are grateful to Geoffrey Tweedale for this reference.
39. Information provided by the Clydebank Asbestos Group Chairperson, Locky Cameron; *Evening Times*, 26 October 1987.
40. *Evening Times*, 16 June 1993.
41. Figures provided by the Health and Safety Executive, Epidemiology and

scheduled 'dry' areas after a maximum of five years – designed to minimise the asbestosis risk – actually worked to spread the cancer risk across a wider segment of the workforce. Lewinsohn warned the company of this in 1970:

> The company has a policy of only employing such persons for five years in a scheduled area and then moving them to another part of the works. I cannot see the logic in this arrangement as to me it appears that a large number of people are being exposed for a reasonable period of time to asbestos dust and that this is increasing the risk of producing diseases related to asbestos exposure in your population over a prolonged period of time. If mesothelioma can occur after minimal exposure then I think that the ideal situation is brewing-up here for such an event.[42]

Employment in Turner's cast a dark shadow, long after the whirring beaters, thudding rollers and shrieking cutters fell silent in Clydebank when the factory closed in 1970.

The 'monkey dung' men: asbestos exposure in the shipyards

Many of our interviewees were first exposed to asbestos in the shipyards of the Clyde where asbestos was used extensively, mostly as an insulator for pipes and boilers. The use of asbestos for such purposes dates back to around 1880. From the late 1930s to the mid-1960s asbestos (largely blue crocidolite) was sprayed on to bulkheads and deckheads. Moulded sections of 15–90% amosite asbestos was used to insulate pipes and machinery (see plate section), often covered by a layer of white chrysotile asbestos cloth. Heavy asbestos dust exposure occurred in both the insulation process on new ships and the refitting and maintenance processes when the old lagging would be ripped out and replaced.[43] Undoubtedly (and ironically), the insulating properties of asbestos made boilers and heating systems safer and hence saved lives on board ships. Indeed right up to the 1970s stringent fire regulations *dictated* the use of

Medical Statistics Unit, Bootle, Merseyside. A UK mesothelioma death register has been kept since 1968 from which standardised mortality rates have been calculated.

42. Lewinsohn Report, 18 May 1970.
43. P. G. Harries, 'Asbestos Dust Concentrations in Ship Repairing', *Annals of Occupational Hygiene*, Vol. 14, 1971, p. 241.

asbestos in ships' boilers.[44] Robert Murray, the TUC Medical Adviser, was amongst those who reminded the Clydeside shipbuilding workers of this. But those who made the ships paid a very high price for this.

Working conditions in the Clyde shipyards were notoriously hard. One insulation engineer could remember the primitive on-site accommodation that the laggers had to endure:

> You went for your dinner and you went into a hut, and there were rolls of asbestos cloth. All kinds of asbestos ... They made mats, asbestos mats in the hut for round flanges and valves. That was all lying about and the asbestos filling for in these mats probably lying all over the floor where they'd been pulling handfuls of it out and stuffing the mats before they stitched up the ends ... You took your dinner in amongst asbestos as well. And if you didnae have a hut in the place what you used to do was eh, eh ... The sections came in three foot square cases – they were three foot long the sections – so they came in these three ... So, they put these cases up at the side and opened it, took the lid off, put a couple of planks across the top and made a howff as they called it. Threw a tarpaulin over that. So, you went in there and took your dinner. Normally a fire outside with all the smoke blowing in as well.[45]

The workforce was divided into three main groups: those who constructed the hull and shell of the ship – the 'black squad'; those in the finishing trades – such as the joiners – who fitted the ship out; and the office staff. Asbestos exposure was most intense amongst the middle group where the material was used extensively to insulate pipes and boilers, as well as to fireproof walls and ceilings throughout the ship. These shipyard workers had a tradition of craft independence and often worked under minimal supervision. This was one of the last bastions of the skilled craft worker in the heavy industries that once dominated the Clyde.

Early Clyde-built ship specifications from the late nineteenth century show asbestos being used as an insulant and fire retardant. The *Kiev*, constructed by J. and G. Thomson, Clydebank, for example, specified boilers to be coated with 'asbestos non-conducting

---

44. See Box file SLA–3, letter dated 23 June 1970, in CAA Archive, Glasgow.
45. Interview A 14.

cement' then 'lagged with asbestos' two layers thick, with all steam pipes 'covered in asbestos and sewed up in canvas'.[46] Even before the First World War, the Clyde shipyard boiler coverers' union claimed in their rules additional payments of time and a half for 'stripping old marine work', an early recognition of the health hazards associated with such dusty and dirty work. During World War One, Scotts of Greenock and the Elderslie Graving Dock, Scotstoun were amongst those using asbestos-based panels called 'asbestocel' and 'asbestoslab', 'for lining living spaces on board torpedo boat destroyers'.[47] The shipyard joiners who cut this material negotiated an extra ¾d. per hour allowance for doing this job in July 1915.[48] However, whether this indicated a clear awareness at this stage of the health hazard of asbestos dust, or solely represented an allowance for tool damage in cutting hard materials is not recorded.

From the 1920s depression, shipbuilders faced intense international competition and a contracting market and developed a reputation for being unwilling to reinvest and re-equip, so that antiquated machinery and the fossilisation of working methods and attitudes came to characterise the industry on the Clyde. Few shipyards invested much of their scarce capital in medical and health facilities, whilst little thought was put into preventative measures to improve safety standards. The Home Office complained to the shipbuilders in 1928 and threatened an extension of safety legislation to address poor standards. In response, the Shipbuilding Federation gave an undertaking that 'energetic steps would be taken in the industry to improve the position regarding accident prevention', including creating shipyard safety committees. Over 20 years later a Clydeside survey found that only 15 of 28 firms had such committees; in only 8 were the workpeople represented and in just 3 did the workpeople or shop stewards have a say in who was nominated to the safety committees.[49] An independent, deeply entrenched *machismo* work culture in the yards meant that workers accepted very high levels of risk on the job, which was invariably dirty and dangerous. A riveter

46. Ship Specification, no 279, 1895 (John Brown's Records, UCS1/91; Glasgow University Archives and Business Records Centre).
47. Clyde Shipbuilders' Association (CSA), Correspondence Files, 3 August 1915 and 26 August 1915 (Ref. TD 241/12/392; Mitchell Library Archives).
48. CSA, Minutes, 1 August 1958 (Ref. TD 241/12/392; Mitchell Library Archives).
49. CSA, Minutes, 12 April 1950 (Ref. TD 241/1; Mitchell Library Archives).

employed in John Brown's Clydebank shipyard recalled of the 1930s: 'You couldnae get a dirtier job ... you were black from head to foot; grime and sweat. Every riveter's shirt was torn – we walked about the shipyard like ratbags'.[50] Another noted: 'Riveting in winter was really cruel ... conditions were pathetic in the shipyard'.[51]

Asbestos use in ship construction spread from the boiler and engine rooms to the living quarters and public areas to such an extent that one commentator noted in 1968 that 'it is difficult to find a compartment in which there is no asbestos'.[52] From 1931 it was also sprayed directly on to pipes, boilers, bulkheads and many other surfaces (including railway carriages) after a chemical engineer Norman Dolbey invented the Sprayed Limpet Asbestos (SLA) process.[53] Inevitably other trades became involved in the work, including joiners, shipwrights, plumbers, electricians, smiths, sailmakers and boilermakers, as well as labourers (not least in cleaning up). By 1943 the Clyde branch of the joiners' union was claiming additional payments for such work noting asbestos panels were 'unpleasant to work with and in certain cases owing to their composition were dangerous'.[54] Whilst initially rebuffed by the CSA, the industry could do little given the wartime situation to prevent shipyard after shipyard on the Clyde conceding such extra payments to joiners 'in view of the unpleasant conditions created by the dust'.[55] The shipbuilders continued, however, to frustrate attempts by the government's Medical Research Council to investigate work conditions and introduce widespread medical examinations on the grounds that this would 'be likely to have a disturbing influence on the workpeople, and to aggravate labour difficulties'.[56] Sadly, the state failed to press the issue despite being aware of the hazards of asbestos use in lagging in the early 1930s and the 'murderous' nature of spraying – to use the expression of a prominent occupational health

50. A. McKinlay, *Making Ships, Making Men: Working in John Brown's, Clyde-bank Between the Wars* (1989), p. 28.
51. A. McKinlay, p. 29.
52. P. G. Harries, 'Asbestos Hazards in Naval Dockyards', *Annals of Occupational Hygiene*, vol. 11, 1968, p. 136.
53. On the development of sprayed asbestos see G. Tweedale, 'Sprayed 'Limpet' Asbestos', in G. A. Peters and B. J. Peters, *Sourcebook on Asbestos Diseases*, vol. 20 (Charlottesville, V. A, 1999).
54. CSA, Minutes, 20 April 1943.
55. Ibid., 16 March 1944; 10 May 1944.
56. Ibid., 30 March 1944; 16 June 1944.

specialist in 1934.[57] These concerns were communicated directly to the shipyards near the end of World War Two (see appendix 1). This was a pattern that would repeat itself until well into the late 1950s, with disastrous results in relation to workplace exposure to asbestos.

The shipyard work environment changed little in the immediate post-Second World War years, though circumstances could differ significantly from yard to yard. As a marine engineer who worked in Ailsa shipyard in Troon in the mid-1960s remembered:

> In the shipyards there was no health facilities there when I was there. There was nothing. If it was raining you worked out in it or did your best, you know. There wisnae even any toilets aboard the boats that you could use. But eh, oh, it was something awful. You just didnae think oh it. You just worked on.[58]

Shipyard work on the Clyde was also unpredictable in nature and employment insecure. A ships' plumber recalled:

> I can remember when I went tae try and get a loan they classed you as a ... You were like a nomad, you were like an Arab. They didnae want to know you. 'Oh no your job's not steady enough.' A boy driving a bus would get a loan quicker than you. It was more steadier employment. Oh then they would come up in a Friday at 3.00 and say 'You're going tonight'. That's the way it was. It was kind of hazardous. You know when I say hazardous, your employment, you werenae guaranteed a job. Much like the way it is the now. But there was plenty of work. When one shipyard was going down a bit the other one was maybe getting orders in, so you just moved about, and then your face got known to people. Oh aye 'You worked here' and then 'Oh aye start the morrow'.[59]

Hard, physical graft in all weathers characterised shipyard work for generations, and it is important to understand this when considering the asbestos issue. The asbestos problem should be firmly located within what was already an unhealthy working environment, located in a relatively unhealthy region. The effects on workers' health and

57. The expert was Donald Hunter. See G. Tweedale, 'Sprayed Limpet Asbestos', p. 88.
58. Interview A 15.
59. Interview A 2.

well-being were cumulative, and will be explored in more detail in Chapter 6.

It was the insulation engineers – the laggers – generally employed by outside contractors (including Newall's Insulators – see Chapter 1, table 1.4 for a full list), who were most closely involved in the use of asbestos. These men cut and fitted the asbestos mattresses to shape around the ships' water pipes and boilers. The fact that most of this work was done by relatively small sub-contractors exacerbated the problem because they were brought in by the shipbuilders, but were not directly governed by shipyard rules and regulations. These small companies – sometimes sub-licensees of Newall's – were also more difficult to monitor by the Factory Inspectors and tended to pay relatively high wages to compensate for the hazardous work. As one Clyde shipyard worker noted: 'Because they worked for contractors and the contractors only object in life was to finish the job. And the guys that worked in the lagging and so on always got more money than anybody else so they werenae too interested in the dangers of the material they were working with'.[60] One lagger recalled the nature of the work in this way:

> What you done was, you got the flange which was 10 inches. Well we used to just multiply it by three and add an inch ... Now they dae it pi squared cause the boys have got all these calculators now. So that's what we done anyway to get the circumference. You opened the mat up and left enough so you could stitch it up. You filled it with asbestos, fold your cloth. Then you patted it all to try and make sure – just an inch and a half or two inches – so it was all the same. And some times it was hard stuff so you got big lumps of wood and battered it. So you could just picture ... You worked in a fog making this up. And you done flanges and valves and that, especially on the ships. In later years they used metal boxes, but on the ships it was always asbestos mat.[61]

In the 1940s and 1950s some of the insulation companies used by the major shipyards were allowed to construct a work shop within the shipyard environs. Exposure to asbestos amongst the laggers was severe both working on ships and within these huts. It was in such

60. John Ower. See CAA Video, 'Hidden Hazard, Forgotten Victims' (1995).
61. Interview A21.

a hut located in John Brown's shipyard in Clydebank that Joseph Meanen – a boiler/pipe coverer employed by Newall's – worked for 31 years, mainly filling, beating (to evenly distribute the insulation filling), levelling and sewing asbestos-filled insulating mattresses. He died in September 1951, leaving a wife and two children, aged 7 and 9. The Pneumoconiosis Medical Panel awarded his 44-year-old wife a pension, recognising that his prolonged exposure had resulted in the chronic asbestosis that killed him. In the subsequent civil action to attain compensation from the company, one of the first in Scotland, Joseph Meanen's working conditions were described in graphic, and tragic, detail:

> The processes in which the deceased was chiefly engaged were (1) the making of insulation slabs or sections, composed wholly or partly of asbestos, and processes incidental thereto; (2) the covering of pipes and boilers with the said insulation slabs; and (3) the making or repairing of insulating mattresses, composed wholly or partly of asbestos, and processes incidental thereto. The said processes (1) and (2) were usually carried on by the Defenders on board ships under construction and being repaired in Clydeside shipyards and especially in the shipyard of John Brown and Company Limited, Clydebank ... The said process (3) was carried on in a hut belonging to the Defenders in the said shipyard of John Brown and Company Ltd aforesaid. In all the said processes the deceased had to handle asbestos, and during the whole period of his employment with the Defenders he was constantly working in an atmosphere laden with asbestos dust.[62]

It was further claimed that Joseph Meanen was not supplied with any 'suitable breathing apparatus' by the company as protection, nor was there 'adequate exhaust and inlet ventilation' either in the work hut, or on board ship. In the ensuing litigation the company contested the claim and denied such negligence – a pattern that was often to repeat itself. In this case Newall's used the death certificate – which did not actually specify death by asbestos exposure but 'phthisis pulmonalis' – to undermine the compensation claim. Newall's also

---

62. Lanarkshire Sheriff's Court Papers, Letter from J. Chapman, Solicitors, to Newall's Insulation Ltd, 15 March 1954 (Chase Manhattan Case Files, 0009/1476), in Clyde Action on Asbestos Archive, Glasgow.

filed an appeal against the widow's application for legal aid (something which could be done in Scots law, but not in England). Eventually, after two and a half years of legal wrangling the case was settled out of court, the widow accepting an *ex gratia* payment of £1,000 (£7,000 had originally been claimed), with the company denying responsibility.

Many more workers were exposed *indirectly* to asbestos during the course of their employment in the shipyards. Because of the nature of their work the laggers were frequently required to work alongside other finishing trades and those involved in routine maintenance and repair work on board ship. As one Clyde shipyard worker put it:

> We always knew we were working in asbestos environments,
> but nobody, absolutely nobody told us about the dangers
> behind the use and misuse of asbestos in yards, especially in
> shipyards because of the type of setting you're in. You're in
> wide open spaces inside a hull of a ship so it could be eight,
> ten twelve different trades working together in the same space.[63]

During and after the war many warships were sprayed with 'Limpet' asbestos, and in the early 1940s worried Factory Inspectors in Hull recommended to the insulation companies that masks be issued to sprayers and to their assistants. On the Clyde, workers at John Brown's shipyard demanded extra money for working alongside those operating spray guns in the 1940s – causing the management to reply that 'the fuss made about dust is largely unjustified'. However, some employers were also unhappy about the dangers of the process and Fairfield's decided to change from using sprayed insulation to fitting asbestos sheets in 1943 – what was not realised, of course, was that cutting the sheets was just as dangerous.[64] An ex-lagger remembers working in the yards during the war when the main priority was insulating destroyers and sloops bound for the Atlantic convoys:

> We had sprayers there. They sprayed on the blue – the blue
> was fireproofing – and white asbestos. But what happened
> then ... When they sprayed that on we were in there, and we
> finished it in cement ... They sprayed on the, the, 'Limpet'
> asbestos, flattened it down with big floats, and eh, expanded
> metal on top of that, and we come at the back and put cement

63. John Ower, 'Hidden Hazards' Video.
64. G. Tweedale, *Magic Mineral*, p. 46.

on. But you couldnae see the place for dust ... I mean the
asbestos came in bags. It was teased up, you know, it was just
loose.[65]

Another ex-lagger has similar recollections of these wartime days:

After the spraying was a' done we would go in and cement it,
but that was the same. If you went in to this place days and
days after the sprayers had finished, and you'd see maybe a
streak of sunlight coming through – you've seen maybe years
ago in the old picture houses when all the smoke went through
– well this was just fibres you saw. It never ever left. It amazes
me that anybody that worked in the shipyards in these days ...
I'm no just talking about insulation engineers, any trades ...

Denmark banned asbestos spraying in 1972, and Holland followed in
1978. In 1983 it was banned in Britain too – although the naval
dockyards had stopped using the process 20 years earlier.[66] It was a
Factory Inspector at Hull Dry Dock in 1944 who first drew attention
to the risk to other trades working near Newall's Insulation asbestos
sprayers. Thereafter the wartime Ministry of Labour advised that
workers in the vicinity of asbestos sprayers should wear masks, and
new regulations enforcing the use of respirators were planned. This
prompted opposition from the industry itself, co-ordinated by one of
the most powerful employers' organisations in Britain, the Engineering
Employers' Federation, working with the Scottish Insulating Engineers
Employers' Association.[67] Just what impact these pressure groups had
is not known, though the overhaul and revision of asbestos regulations
in the 1960s and our Clydeside oral testimony suggest that this
wartime initiative affected workplace practice very little (see Chapter
4). One interviewee – now with pleural plaques – remembers his first
days as an apprentice insulation engineer in Harland and Wolff's
shipyard in 1970. One of his tasks was to mix asbestos paste known
as 'monkey dung':

Sometimes they'd spray that on the bulkhead of a boat. And
the sprayer would have a wee drum. So you'd just mix it up
and stick it in the drum. Eh, you got a half pint o milk for

65. Interview A14.
66. *Asbestos Bulletin*, 23, 2, March–April 1982, p. 99; *Financial Times*, 18 May
    1977.

that. It was a good bonus you know. A half pint of milk ...
That's what you were allowed, because they said that you
would ... Well, you would be a bit thirsty. So you were
allowed a half pint of milk. I'll always mind o that. It was a
half pint o milk and you got a paper mask. You know one o
these wee paper masks. Eh, everybody's working alongside ...
You know, you've got a burner, you've got a welder, but *you*
were fortunate cos you've got a wee paper mask on.[68]

Another lagger also recalled how his job put other tradesmen in
danger:

We used tae insulate the boilers actually on the boat, and the
place was covered in asbestos when we were dain that. And the
same in the engine room ... There were pipes everywhere ...
You used to saw the stuff. Well the, the, teased up stuff and
the dust just a' floated. It floated round and everybody got
their share.[69]

The insidious nature of the asbestos dust, hanging virtually in
suspension in the air, made it difficult to control. A ships' plumber,
now suffering from pleural thickening, remembered how he was
exposed to asbestos every day in his work:

I was working in amongst it. Engine rooms, boiler rooms. And
when they – you called them stagers then, it would be like
scaffolders now – when they were erecting the scaffolding
inside the ship, they would turn the batons. The batons would
be full of it, and they would reverse them for, you know, for
safety, anyone walking on them, and it used to come down like
snow.[70]

This image of asbestos cuttings, dust, and dried-out 'monkey dung',
coming 'down like snow', was a recurrent one amongst the
interviewees who worked in the yards. For example, a boilermaker
described his experiences thus:

I'm no exaggerating when I say this: it was like snow coming

67. Letter Newall's Insulation Co. to Ministry of Labour, Box file SLA–1, CAA
    Archive Glasgow.
68. Interview A16. Speaker's own emphasis.
69. Interview A5.
70. Interview A2.

down, and there were nobody there to supervise them, and
nobody there tae say it, and that used to come right down like
snow all the time And they were on staging the whole way up
there ... Now as you put the pipes up the insulators were
following you. And the staging, there was asbestos all over that
an all, and it was all coming down on top of you.[71]

And a sheet iron worker told a similar tale:

The monkey dung guys, they were working away all the time:
laggers. They were working away a' round about you. This
stuff just fell like snow you know.[72]

And a rigger who worked in Fairfield's remembered clouds of asbestos
dust when cranes lifted asbestos-coated pipes:

Now they were all covered in this 'monkey dung' as they called
it. It was just asbestos. And when you were taking them
down ... I mean they were heavy big, big pipes and you had to
put wire strops on them to sling them, to move. When you put
the wire strops on them, and the weight came on the wire
strop, it bit into the 'monkey dung' and it all just crumbled,
and it was like snow flying all over the place.[73]

Inevitably, in this work environment in the 1940s, 1950s and 1960s
a wide range of shipyard workers inhaled the debilitating and
potentially deadly asbestos fibres. The laggers and sprayers were paid
well for their work: 'It was good money we were getting' noted one
Clydeside asbestos sprayer, continuing, 'but good money what to
die'.[74] The joiners also succeeded in getting some limited financial
recompense for their exposure when in 1954 the shipbuilding
employers agreed at Central Conference to provide an additional
allowance of 2d. per hour for working with asbestos-based panels
called Marinite. In the meeting with employers the union pressed their
claim on the grounds that cutting Marinite was 'damaging to tools,
and when being cut created clouds of fine dust, containing about 40%
silica. That caused discomfort to the workmen and was injurious to
their health'. Clearly, the joiners were well aware at this time of the

71. Interview A3.
72. Interview A17.
73. Interview A9.
74. Jimmy Kerr, Clydeside asbestos sprayer, in CAA Video, 'Hidden Hazards'.

damaging effects that asbestos dust inhalation could have on their lungs and, significantly, that 'the proper course was for the employers to provide adequate ventilation and dust extraction'. It was noted at the time that one objective of the union in negotiating the 1954 Marinite Agreement (see appendix 4 for full draft) was 'to penalise those employers who failed to provide such facilities'. Where 'normal atmospheric conditions' were preserved by dust extraction equipment the additional allowance was not payable.[75] Later an ASW official, H. Wilkinson, reiterated that 'the cure is more important than money ... If we could cure this so that people would not suffer as a result of inhaling this dust and getting it into the body five shillings an hour would not compensate them'.[76]

However, relatively minor punitive penalties in the form of extra wage payments proved to be an extremely blunt and ineffective preventative mechanism to control the asbestos dust hazard in the shipyards. Shipyard joiners and other trades working on what was to be the *Queen Elizabeth II* at John Browns in Clydebank found themselves heavily exposed in the 1960s. The joiners cut up and fixed massive asbestos sheets for the bulkheads as well as Marinite panels. The latter were explicitly specified in the Cunard ship order for fire protection throughout the ship in ceiling and wall linings in place of plywood. A doctor employed by Turner & Newall was sent to Brown's to talk to the men and assured them that the sheets in question were not of *blue* asbestos – at this time it was erroneously thought that white asbestos was harmless and that only the blue variety was dangerous to health.[77] As a company (Brown's) official noted: 'it is true to say that there is no constituent of Marinite that has any cancer producing agent in it'.[78] At the same time representatives of 500 insulation engineers expressed their concern at the increasing death-toll amongst their colleagues. This led to some improvements in working methods, including the modification of extraction equipment in John Brown's Marinite shop where most of the cutting took place and the provision of portable industrial vacuums to minimise dust

75. Shipbuilding Employers' Federation, Report of Central Conference with the Amalgamated Society of Woodworkers, 1 October 1954, in CSA, Circular Letters, 10 November 1954 (see also appendix 4).
76. CSA, Central Conference, 15 October 1966 (TD 241/12/1158).
77. *Glasgow Herald*, 24 February 1967. Asbestosis cases among joiners are first mentioned in the T&N archives in 1962.
78. CSA, Minutes, 20 December 1967 (TD 241/12/1136).

accumulation around the ship. On ship, Marinite cutting was isolated as far as possible in two compartments and some replacement of asbestos materials for 'filling in' on the ship was also agreed, together with isolation and removal of asbestos dust in polythene bags. The TUC Medical Adviser, Robert Murray, approved such develop-ments and suggested further precautions, including improved exhaust ventilation, dust sampling, PVC overalls and medical examin-ations.[79] Despite these extra precautions the Clyde delegate of the ASW continued to express concern, noting six months later 'our members are so concerned about the cutting of any form of asbestos that they are prepared to stop work and not even cut it for 3*d*.'. 'Asbestos', he prophetically commented in December 1967, 'is just as bad as lung cancer'.[80]

The problem, however, extended far beyond the joiners cutting the Marinite. Other shipyard workers were exposed as the dust spread around the ship, including the electricians and engineering workers. Despite John Brown's improvements in work practices, the ETU district delegate complained in December 1967 that:

> It was practically impossible to eliminate dust from the atmosphere when Marinite was being cut ... If there is complete elimination of the hazards everyone would be happy, but in the shipbuilding it is much more difficult to do this ... What we find is that despite the fact that certain statutory regulations are laid down and certain safeguards are laid down, these things are ignored by both the firm and the men.[81]

Both the AEU and the ETU claimed that masks should be provided for all those working in the vicinity of Marinite cutting and such workers should also be paid the additional wage allowance as the work was 'a serious hazard to health'. The claims were fuelled by a case of asbestosis amongst a John Brown's worker aged only 26 and an electrician from Stephen's shipyard diagnosed with asbestosis who had a lung removed. Concerns were also raised about female cleaners sweeping up the Marinite dust. Unfavourable comparisons were drawn with more extensive Ministry of Defence precautions at the naval dockyards, especially relating to the systematic provision and

79. CSA, Minutes, 11 May 1967 (TD 241/12/392); J. Brown's archive UCS1/91/144 (Specifications), UCS1/91/145 (Glasgow University).
80. J. O'Neill (ASW), CSA, Minutes, 20 December 1967 (TD 241/12/1136).
81. CSA, Minutes, 20 December 1967 (TD 241/12/1136).

regular maintenance and cleaning of respirators. Brown's agreed to improve the supply of masks, noting 'never at any time do we deny masks to men who feel they need these or want them to protect themselves'. After a joint inspection of the ship it was also agreed that the 3*d*. allowance be also paid to all 'adult male workpeople when working alongside joiners while the joiners are actually engaged on the cutting of Marinite'.[82] This was as clear a recognition as any that exposure to asbestos dust could not be effectively contained and controlled in ship construction.

The same was true of ship repairing and refitting, evident in the prevailing work conditions at the Rosyth naval dockyard, near Dunfermline on the east coast of Scotland. Asbestos hazards in the dockyards was the subject of a detailed investigation by the Devonport Royal Dockyard Surgeon-General, P. G. Harries in the late 1960s. Commenting on pre-1967 conditions in the Royal Dockyards Harries noted:

> Variable amounts of asbestos debris were left scattered about the ships for most of the refit periods (sometimes up to 3 years), because there was no defined procedure for clearing it away. As a result very large numbers of men have been exposed to asbestos dust by working with or near other men who were applying or removing asbestos materials, or because they were themselves disturbing asbestos debris and creating their own local dust clouds ... High concentrations of asbestos dust have spread to parts of the ship in which unsuspecting men would have worked without respiratory protection[83]

Harries' research showed that dust densities in the naval dockyards in *all* asbestos work were over the 1969 Regulations 2 fibre limit and that 'many processes have dust concentrations of 50 fibres per square cm or more'. That is 25 times over the 'safe' limit. Few workers were adequately protected – only one in every nine workers classed as asbestos workers in the Royal Dockyards were subject to the Asbestos Industry Regulations (1931). Moreover, the extent of dust exposure was higher in the stripping and removal of asbestos lagging than it was in the application of new lagging. Exposure was at its height between *c*. 1950 and the late 1960s because demands for more efficient

82. Ibid., 26 February 1968.
83. Harries, 'Asbestos Dust Concentrations', pp. 241–2; p. 252–3.

insulation by the Admiralty led the industry into replacing the mattresses which contained around 15% amosite asbestos with sections consisting almost entirely of amosite asbestos. These facts, 'help to explain the prevalence of asbestos disease in Dockyard workers'.[84] In a confidential letter to Turner & Newall's company medical adviser, Dr William Knox, in September 1967 Harries revealed that 49 Devonport dockyard workers has been diagnosed with asbestosis over the previous year and that the yard had '10 proven cases of mesothelioma'.[85] The Devonport welders refused to work with asbestos cloth in 1967 when they became aware that five welders had or were dying of asbestos-related diseases. The Admiralty at this time was facing some 50 writs at Common Law alleging negligence. Nonetheless, work continued at the yard because of what Harries described as 'good relations' with 'the men and their Trade Unions'. The men were also reported to have been paid a 'discomfort allowance' of 4d. an hour 'to encourage them to wear their respirators'. Harries 'good relations' with the unions and with the local coroner were adduced as the reasons why not a single case report had been leaked to the press by November 1967.[86]

Harries' path-breaking epidemiological studies and meticulous dust-counting exercises at Devonport were replicated over 1968–69 by investigations at the other yards. Surgeon-Commander T. P. Oliver's study of Rosyth indicated that whilst laggers were provided with respirators and monitored with annual chest-X-rays and medical inspections, 'it was not previously recognised that other people in the same working compartments were also at risk'.[87] Oliver's 1 in 10 survey of the Rosyth workforce in 1968–69 produced evidence of pulmonary fibrosis and pleural change in 13 cases, leading him to

---

84. Ibid., p. 253. See also P. G. Harries, 'Asbestos Hazards in Naval Dockyards', *Annals of Occupational Hygiene*, vol. 11, 1968, p. 135.
85. Harries' letter to Knox, 6 September 1967 (T&N Archive, Manchester).
86. Letter H. C. Lewinsohn to D. W. Hills, 23 November 1967 (T&N Archive).
87. H. C. Lewinsohn, paraphrasing Oliver in a report on Oliver's talk on exposure to asbestos at Rosyth to the Society of Occupational Medicine conference, 1 July 1969 at Aviemore, Scotland. See letter Lewinsohn to D. W. Hills, 9 July 1969 (T&N Archive). This meeting gave the T&N medical adviser an opportunity to talk informally, to gauge changing attitudes and find out more about ongoing research by Factory Inspectors, Medical Officers and the like. He reported thereafter to his superiors the likelihood of 'strict watch' by the Deputy Senior Medical Inspector of Factories (responsible for Scotland, 1943–1970), Dr A. T. Doig.

estimate that around 130 cases could be expected across the entire Rosyth workforce.[88] These figures were considerably lower (proportionately) than Harries found at Devonport and did not include those who would have already left through ill-health. Consequently, they significantly under-estimated the problem.

Spraying was discontinued in the naval dockyards in 1963, primarily because of reasons of weight rather than safety. However, largely as a consequence of Harries' research findings, a whole range of stringent preventative measures to control dust exposure were introduced in the naval dockyards over 1967–68, pre-dating the new Asbestos Regulations. Increasingly thereafter the naval dockyards replaced asbestos with substitute materials, including rocksil fibre, mineral fibre marine board and glass fibre and cloth.

Mirroring the Harries and Oliver evidence for ship repairing and refitting, oral testimony indicates the persistence of very dangerous work practices in relation to asbestos in the Scottish shipbuilding yards in the 1940s, 1950s and 1960s. Some respondents remembered asbestos cuttings falling like snow from above, and some could recall an asbestos fog. For example, the retired marine engineer who once threw asbestos at his foreman as a prank remarked:

> You did all the engine room work. And then the asbestos men would be lagging them up above you. And you could see it in the summer time. If you looked up before they put the engine room skylights in you could see this haze. And this was asbestos dust.[89]

A 74-year-old retired fitter – whose asbestos-damaged lungs only became apparent in 1997 – described asbestos dust in his workplace in the 1950s in this way:

> I've seen times when you couldnae see the other side of the boat. That's only what? 40 or 50 feet away. You couldnae see it for the dust. The dust in the air. It was just like dust ... Anyway, we had planks ... We had planks all round the engine room ... And they'd be covered in it too.[90]

88. Ibid. On Rosyth see A. Law, 'Neither Colonial or Historic: Workers' Organisation at Rosyth Dockyard, 1945–95', in K. Lunn and A. Day (eds), *History of Work and Labour Relations in the Royal Dockyards* (London, 1999).
89. Interview A14.
90. Interview A5.

Another marine engineer recounted how he became aware of the danger of the dusty surroundings when working at Upper Clyde Shipbuilders (UCS) in the late 1960s:

> This one particular day sticks in my mind. I was working in a machinery compartment with this mate of mine. A shaft of sunlight came into the compartment, and we were working beside these laggers. And I remember seeing the air literally foggy. Thick with this asbestos dust. And it passed through my mind then, I thought 'this *cannot* be good for us'.[91]

In this period there was a widespread lack of understanding amongst the workforce regarding the extreme health risks inherent in the material they were handling. Certainly in the 1930s through to the 1960s information on the hazards of contact with asbestos was witheld from the shipyard workforce. 'Nobody at any time told me it was a dangerous substance to work with' noted a shipyard electrician later diagnosed with asbestosis. Similarly John Ower, a Clyde shipyard workers commented:

> Nobody told us about the dangers ... There was absolutely no offers of protection or anything else and the dangers were never really highlighted ... When it was raised in the Safety Committee meetings we were always told there was no real danger, that they worked within the safe limits.[92]

Consequently, it was a common sight in the shipyards to see young workers playing with asbestos cuttings. One man, who was a labourer in the yards for several years in the mid to late 1960s, recalled this quite clearly:

> They were throwing this 'monkey dung' about and that, and hitting folk in the passing just for a game you know. Nobody knew how dangerous it was. These blokes were laggered in it head-tae-foot and they made sure that everybody else was as well.[93]

The ships' plumber also remembered playing with asbestos as an apprentice in the yards; and the marine engineer who worked at Ailsa shipyard – now suffering from pleural plaques – told this story:

91. Interview A8.
92. John Ower, in CAA, 'Hidden Hazards' Video.
93. Interview A18.

They cut it above you, and the bit that they cut off sometimes
it would drop. We used to throw that at each other. There was
an old charge hand there, and he could hardly see. His eyes
were nearly shut and his mouth was always open. And
everybody called him skipper, that was his nickname. And we
used to shout as boys 'ho skipper it's snowing' and belt him
with this stuff. Well he never bothered. He was the most docile
old character. As long as you were working he didnae mind a
bit of fun.[94]

Tommy Nelson, a Clydeside shipyard electrician noted in a similar
vein referring to the 'monkey-dung' men:

They used to make this stuff up by hand and throw it about
the place like snowballs and everybody was covered, that is the
electricians, engineers, cleaners sweeping it up, the place was
just literally covered in it.[95]

In January 1968 the *Scottish Sunday Mail* published an article by
Professor Alexander Mair, the head of a privately funded initiative
called the Scottish Occupational Health Service. Mair was appealing
to workers to pass on to him any information they had on dust
hazards at work. The Scottish Occupational Health Service (SOHS)
had been set up with private funding in 1966 and was part of Dundee
University's Department of Occupational Health. Mair also had his
own mobile laboratory that could investigate work hazards, and he
stated in his article:

We have the only service of its kind in Scotland, a non-profit
making concern backed financially by industry but, alas, not by
many workers. We don't need their money but we would like
them to take an interest in our work. Through the *Sunday Mail*
we appeal to them to let us know of any dust, noise, skin or
other hazards they may have at work in the shipyards of
Clydeside, the factory or the warehouse. Then we can act
quickly.[96]

However, despite the fact that the shipyard laggers of 7/162 (Glasgow)
branch acted quickly by responding to this appeal, they were told

94. Interview A14.
95. Tommy Nelson, in CAA Video, 'Hidden Hazards'.
96. *Scottish Sunday Mail*, 28 January 1968.

that Mair's investigations could only take place if he had the full consent of the employers – who had to pay Mair for the inspections. He and his team, though, had already written to all registered asbestos users asking for permission to inspect their working environments. Almost all of them had refused.[97] If there was a chance, then, that the extent of the Scottish asbestos tragedy could have been made less severe, it had just been missed. This was precisely the kind of hands-on occupational health service that was missing from the state system, and as we shall see below the small pilot service played a role at Glasgow's Red Road Flats. The accelerating asbestos death toll, then, could at least have been contained if such a workplace-centred health service had been given more backing by business and by the state at this time.

'White mice': construction and demolition

As was the case in shipbuilding, working conditions were also hard in the building sites around Scotland, which had a reputation for high injury and death rates. In 1968 the Glasgow District Trades Council expressed its concern at the health hazards posed by asbestos in the building industry, as many employees who had been using the material were developing chest complaints.[98] Once again, though, asbestos was only one problem within a dangerous working environment that was characterised by fumes, mud, dust, and numerous accidents.

Asbestos was extensively used in the building trade, and especially so from the 1950s. Once again the nature of the product meant it could be used for various purposes, for example in refrigeration or as a heat retardant. One heating engineer remembers working on the 'uptakes' at Braehead Power Station near Renfrew, cutting and fitting asbestos slabs that measured three feet by three feet by two inches thick.[99] Another man was involved in spraying asbestos onto ceilings in numerous locations across Scotland before the process was banned. He could still remember his job in some detail:

> I was feeding the machines. It came in bags. I think it was 28-pound bags, but they were big bags. And eh, there was damping drums. You put them in a drum ... You just fed it

97. This information from A. Dalton, *Asbestos Killer Dust* (1979), pp. 98–9.
98. *71st Annual Report of the STUC* (Glasgow, 1968), p. 112.
99. Interview A1.

roughly into a drum, and this rotated. And there was a kind of
holder you put water in, and it sprayed inside the drum. And it
soaked the drum. It was always supposed to be damp. You put
it into your wee machine ... and you had a steel tank like a
compressor with tubes going in and it's giving out a jet of
water with the man holding the hose. The fibres come through
the three-inch nozzle and there's wee jets all round the gun ...
I remember dain a job ... used to be the *Evening Times*. They
had a place in Buchanan Street [in Glasgow]. It was a ceiling
that was getting ... The joiners actually were walking off the
job. So we were ... We had to do nightshift. I don't blame the
people. Obviously they knew what it was all about. I mean, I
didnae walk in with my eyes shut. You know, I knew what I
was doing.[100]

He could also remember that safety procedures were occasionally set
aside for the sake of speed. Although the spray machinery incorporated
two dampening operations to cut down asbestos dust (first by immer-
sion in a tub, and secondly by soaking at the spray nozzle itself, to
save time on bonus work the first operation was normally missed
out).[101]

A quantity surveyor recalled how he was exposed to dust from
sprayers while working on supermarket contracts throughout
Scotland. In particular he remembered a site at Bridge of Dee in
Aberdeen:

There was a pump which pumped the asbestos out and it was
sprayed on with a hose that looked like a fireman's hose ... I
seemed to recall that the men who sprayed this asbestos had
face masks like a surgeon's mask. There were a great deal of
other workers on this site including joiners, plasterers, tilers,
plumbers, electricians, etc. But I do not believe that they had
any face masks or other protective clothing. This asbestos was
sprayed onto ceilings and beams on the underside of a
basement floor to help bring up the fire protection from two
hours to three hours to meet with the then fire regulations. As
well as this asbestos which was sprayed, asbestos suspended
ceilings were also used in this job. These were called

100. Interview A10.
101. Interview A11.

asbestolux. These asbestolux boards were about two feet by two feet and were cream in colour. The workmen would have to cut these boards to fit the ceilings … The place was dusty. The building sites were always dusty and there was always someone sweeping up. Ventilation would not be in operation until the stores opened.

These boards were manufactured at the Marinite Factory in Glasgow, were better finished than normal asbestos sheeting, and were used in a variety of domestic and industrial locations. One insulation engineer remembers a demarcation struggle between laggers and joiners over who should be allowed to work with the material:

They wanted our work. When we started using cleaner looking stuff, they said 'Well, we've been doing this and doing that'. So they were starting to use Maranite. It was nice. It was formica on the outside, but inside it was solid asbestos. So when they were sawing that with … What dae you call it? Rip saws and that. You couldnae see them for dust. So I know for a fact that a lot of the joiners … I worked with quite a lot of them. They kept encroaching and encroaching and they wanted intae this asbestos as it looked a bit clean. But the unfortunate thing is that it done a lot of them in.[102]

The asbestolux boards were used in large quantities during the building of high-rise flats in the 1960s, including those at Red Road in the Balornock area of Glasgow. As was the case with shipbuilding, we have to remind ourselves that the main reason for the increased use of asbestos in the building trade was to protect life. The designers of the Red Road Flats decided to use asbestos extensively throughout the eight concrete blocks of flats.[103] The building of the 32-storey flats – which won a prize for being tallest in Europe at that time – began in 1962 and almost 1000 men were employed on the site during the seven year construction period.[104] The joiners who cut and fitted the four foot square asbestos panels onto the girders, ceilings and walls were organised in five squads of 20 men in each, and were nicknamed the 'white mice', because of the amount of dust on their work clothes

102. Interview A5.
103. See T. Gorman, 'The continuing use of asbestos in buildings', *17th Proceedings of the BISS* (Glasgow, 1995), p. 33; *Morning Star*, 27 March 1984.
104. See M. Glendinning and S. Muthesius, *Tower Block: Modern Public Housing in England, Scotland, Wales and Northern Ireland* (London, 1982).

at the end of the day. Steel erectors were also involved in fitting the panels to steel beams. Bobby MacDonald from Ayrshire came home every night white from head to foot, and his wife had to frequently wash his asbestos-covered overalls. It was the same with Bill Spiers from Glasgow who worked as a labourer at Red Road. According to his widow, 'Bill used to dust himself down before he came into the house each night. He was always covered in dust'.[105] The joiners did not know the full dangers of working with asbestos, and it was not until 1967 after working with the material for around a year that they began to realise the seriousness of the situation. At this time news of the dangers of asbestos was spreading. The impact of the TV documentary 'Alice: a fight for life', and the concern expressed at the dangers of working with asbestos by the laggers and joiners in John Brown's and other shipyards on the Clyde, helped spread the message around the building sites too. A joiner from Glasgow called Roderick Irvine remembered this:

> There was a change in attitude in 1967. Some of the men had been reading about it. The *QE2* had started then and there were certain precautions being taken there against asbestos. The word from the shipyards was that asbestos might be dangerous and it was taken up by some of the men.[106]

A lagger who was involved with the Insulation Branch of the TGWU at the time remember how he was told one day that there were dangerous working practices going on at Red Road:

> I got a complaint from my members who were up there [at Red Road] working for an insulation company, and when I went up there they were complaining about the dust they [the joiners] were making with the rip saws and the boards. Now, the climax is at the finish of this. Now they says to me – well they used abusive language, which we a' can use if we want – they used abusive language and told me to get to f, in a nice abusive manner: 'You're always moaning and groaning about something'. We were complaining about the dust but they wouldnae listen to us. So I went away and phoned up a Factory Inspector, and he created and made them polythene it off. Do you know these ten joiners I warned? Every one of

105. *Daily Record*, 28 March 1984.
106. *Glasgow Herald*, 27 June 1984, p. 4.

them's dead. There's the climax. Now they got a warning and wouldnae take it. Now ten of them's dead.[107]

However, it soon became clear that warnings such as these could not be ignored, and several of the men began to insist that something be done. One of the joiners on the site who took up the issue was Jimmy Fullarton from Linwood in Renfrewshire. He became a ringleader of a group of men who eventually refused point blank to handle the asbestos until they were assured of their safety. The trade union was called in, and at a meeting with Glasgow Corporation the union officials were told that asbestos was the only fire retardant available to the builders, and that the Corporation had already stockpiled £11000-worth of asbestos for use on the contract. So that this supply be used up, a deal was struck in which the men were to be offered an extra 2*d.* an hour as 'dirty money' if they would continue to work with the asbestos. The *quid pro quo* for continuing to risk their health was that the Corporation would endeavour to find a substitute material, and would order an immediate investigation of the working conditions on the Red Road site. This investigation was carried out by the Scottish Occupational Health Service.

Previously barred through employer reluctance from examining the working environment of the insulation engineers, Professor Alex Mair's travelling laboratory from Dundee pulled into Red Road, and the most up-to-date dust-sampling equipment was unloaded. The three-man team from the SOHS spent two days on the site, evaluating, as they put it, 'the health risk to operatives handling asbestos products during the construction of multi-storey flats'.[108] The SOHS's report on conditions at Red Road was absolutely damning. During their inspection they found that levels of asbestos dust were on average four-times above the recognised safety limit – which was a higher limit than used today. In one process – sweeping up the dry waste material in an area of poor natural ventilation – the dust level was 18 times higher than the 'safe' datum line. 'In the vast majority of cases the acceptable level is grossly exceeded' the Report noted, and, 'even when the natural ventilation is described as very good, the

107. Interview A22.
108. A. Mair, J. T. Sanderson and T. D. Guthrie, Report no. 14/7/67 on the Asbestos Dust Survey carried Out at the Red Road Building Site, Glasgow, for the Corporation of Glasgow, May 1967 (in T&N Archive, attached to letter A. B. Boath to Dr H. C. Lewinsohn, 5 September 1967). See appendix 5 for a copy of the full report.

asbestos dust concentrations are higher than they should be and involve some degree of risk to the operatives'.[109] The Report urged the Corporation to take on board the various safety measures relating to asbestos that were going through Parliament at that time – which were destined to become the 1969 Asbestos Regulations. However, over and above this, the team also recommended that asbestos boards be dampened before being cut and shaped; that portable dust extraction equipment be put in place immediately; that the men be given regular medical inspections and X-rays; and that protective clothing without turn-ups and pockets – which could trap dust – be issued to the squads at once. The team also noted with some dismay that respirators were already available on site, but that none of the workers were using them.

Following the SOHS's visit to Red Road, Glasgow Corporation issued protective suits and masks to all the men who were involved with asbestos. However, Roderick Irvine remembered that the masks were so uncomfortable to wear, and the PVC suits so unbearably hot, that most of the men didn't bother to wear them. A safety officer on the site called James Anderson could also recall that he was 'never off the men's backs' to try and get them to wear the masks.[110] Moreover, Roderick Irvine could also remember that after the SOHS investigation the joiners were told that they had to take the asbestolux boards down to the ground floor and cut them there using a special extractor saw – despite the fact that the Corporation had been urged to install *portable* dust extraction machinery. It is interesting to speculate whether the Corporation's freedom of movement was constrained by the escalating costs of the Red Road scheme and the desire to get the flats completed as quickly as possible. Sam Bunton, the Red Road architect noted when the scheme was mooted: 'The whole conception of the structure and planning as presented for this development has been based on endeavours to obtain extremely high building speeds and an early completion of the dwellings'.[111] By 1967, though, the project was massively over budget (around £2–3m) and almost two years behind schedule. The complaints from the men about work safety, then, could not have come at a worse time.

109. Ibid., p. 6
110. *Daily Record*, 27 June 1984, p. 27.
111. Letter Sam Bunton Associates to Glasgow Corporation Housing and Works Department, 16 August 1962, in Red Road Enquiry papers, 1967–68, Glasgow Corporation Minutes (Mitchell Library, ref. DTC 8/20 R75).

Unfortunately, despite a thorough search, no Corporation papers have been located which record the response to the SOHS report. It is possible that the report was suppressed and the whole thing hushed up. Whilst some improvements were made on the site, the completion of the contract and higher wages continued to take precedence over safety. Even the use of the special extraction saw on the ground level was frequently ignored as, according to Roderick Irvine, 'Greed got the better of us as our bonuses dropped because we had to go up and down the building'.[112]

It was not until 1983 that the consequences of the bad working conditions at Red Road became known. That year a joiner from Glasgow who had worked at Red Road called Ron Hill died of mesothelioma. His son recalled his father 'coming home covered in a white dust as if he worked in a bakery'.[113] More ex-workers began to complain of asbestos-related symptoms, and it was out of this concern that several of them helped form Clydeside Action on Asbestos to look into the issue in more depth.[114] With the help of the Labour MP for Springburn – where the flats are located – the DHSS, the Channel 4 TV programme '4 What It's Worth', and a campaign by the *Daily Record*, the action group managed to trace 180 former Red Road workers. Sixty of the men were already dead, and most of these (87 per cent) had died from asbestos-related cancer. The average age was just 51.[115] The extent to which the asbestos dust from the cutting and planing of the asbestolux boards had permeated the Red Road site was revealed in the occupations of the dead men: there were 17 joiners, 3 joiners' labourers, 2 electricians, a storeman, 9 steel erectors, a cleaner, 7 plasterers, and a lift engineer.[116] However, nothing is ever clear-cut, and a Senior Registrar at Glasgow's Western Infirmary cautioned at the time that because of the limited number of men traced, and the fact that many of them could also have worked in the shipyards, there was no clear link between Red Road and their

---

112. *Daily Record*, 28 March 1984, pp. 24–5, also front page.
113. Clydeside Action on Asbestos, 'Asbestos Cancer Hazard' (leaflet, n.d., c. 1984–85).
114. T. Gorman, *Hidden Hazard, Forgotten Victims: Some Aspects of Asbestos Abuse in Britain* (B. A. Hons Dissertation, Glasgow Caledonian University, May 1997), p. 37.
115. T. Gorman, 'The continuing use', p. 33.
116. Clydeside Action on Asbestos Archive, unpublished list of traced Red Road workers.

untimely deaths.[117] This was also the opinion of the Sheriff who conducted a two-day fatal accident inquiry into Ron Hill's death in June 1984. His judgement was that Hill had been exposed to dangerous levels of asbestos dust, but, because he had previously worked in the shipyards, it could not be positively concluded that it was the Red Road dust that had killed him. For many building workers, exposure to asbestos would undoubtedly have been occurring in their daily work on a frequent basis on other contracts, both before and after Red Road. The Glasgow Corporation Housing Department lists a total of 327 multi-storey flats built between 1960 and 1975 in the city.[118] The Assistant Director of Housing for Glasgow told the Red Road inquiry that sprayed asbestos would be removed from the flats, and that other areas where asbestos was present would be sealed off from the tenants – who were to be instructed not to do any home maintenance. The Sheriff had this final word: 'If I were a tenant in the flats I would want to be sure that there was constant monitoring'.[119]

The work process on construction jobs such as Red Road was one in which a diverse range of trades people worked in close proximity to each other. This was commented upon by a foreman electrician from Lanarkshire when taking about the building trade in general:

> They drill and they clatter and they saw. They don't have any thought of the other trades. The main contractor certainly doesnae have any thought of the other trades, as he's got as many folk as he can get bloody working in there, you know ... Every building you went tae was always the same. They always got held back getting out the ground, and then they tried tae recover their programme by squeezing all the finishing trades. And that goes on tae this day, and it'll always go on.[120]

Interestingly, he could also remember a certain amount of horseplay where asbestos was used in the sites:

> The heating engineers were using it. They were fighting with it.

117. *The Times*, 21 April 1984, p. 3.
118. Glasgow Housing Department Multi-Storey Buildings List (Planning Dept, Bell St, Glasgow). We are grateful to Mick Haughey for allowing access to this source.
119. *Daily Record*, 17 August 1984, p. 4.
120. Interview A19.

'Monkey dung.' They used to fight with it, and they were bloody white.[121]

Under such working conditions, then, the asbestos dust created by one worker would quickly cover anyone else in the vicinity. This is what happened to a plumber who worked at Aberdeen University in the 1960s. His job involved installing pipes at the new Central Refectory building in Elphinstone Road. However, at the same time asbestos was being sprayed in the building near to where he was working. 'Some days', he said, 'it was like a blizzard. The stuff was flying about all over the place ... I was just 17 when I was working in rooms where the asbestos was falling like snowflakes – we used to brush it off our shoulders like dandruff.'[122]

Demolition and de-lagging jobs were every bit as dangerous as construction. However, it was not until August 1984 that new regulations came into force stipulating that those who removed asbestos had to be licensed. These regulations were criticised as being inadequate as they did not cover such things as insulating wallboards, ceiling tiles containing asbestos, and asbestos cement products – which as we noted contain about 10% asbestos.[123] More importantly, like all regulations the new protective measures could only work if they were enacted. A lorry driver/labourer who worked in demolition for some time remembers that on some occasions his employer would get a specialist removal company to make it look as though he was complying with the regulations. However, the regular workers were still removing asbestos from sites with little protection:

What was I getting? About 4 quid a day was it? Something like that I think. Aye 4 quid a day we were getting. And the company had got a, you know, a registered asbestos guy in tae take another bit down. These cunts were getting fucking £4 an hour, and we were getting £4 pound for a shift. You know that's just tae keep their books right. They were just trying to keep it under the carpet sort of thing. We didnae know anything about it, you know. We just carried on ... Nobody would dae it now bar they've got the masks.[124]

121. Interview A19.
122. *Evening Express*, 25 March 1997; also *Aberdeen Press and Journal*, 26 March 1997.
123. *87th Annual Report of STUC* (Glasgow, 1984), p. 660.
124. Interview A4.

In 1976 the then owners of Glasgow's Central Station Hotel knowingly exposed workers to asbestos in the hotel's boiler house. The company had decided not to use a professional asbestos removal company because their estimate for the job was too high, and had not bothered to inform the two men who stripped the insulation from the boiler that they were handling asbestos. The company was subsequently fined £100.[125] The same year a Fort William company was fined for failing to take adequate precautions to protect their workmen while they were removing an asbestos-covered boiler from the Royal Northern Infirmary in Inverness.[126] These two cases were amongst the first trials in Scotland under the 1974 Health and Safety at Work Act relating to the handling of asbestos. The Inverness Court heard that the contractor had failed to take any samples to determine whether asbestos was present; had not separated the boiler from the rest of the boiler house to contain the dust; had not dampened the asbestos before removal; and had not provided any protective clothing or breathing apparatus to the men. The Factory Inspector estimated that the extent of asbestos dust (in this case the more dangerous blue crocidolite fibres) in the atmosphere on the job would have been in the region of 100 times the safe level.[127]

A heating engineer from Glasgow could also remembers slipshod procedures. Recalling his experience in the early 1980s he said:

> If we went down tae strip a boiler we just took it [the asbestos] off with a hammer and chisel, you know. There was nae masks or anything at that time, you know. If you came out for a breather they were asking you what you were daen sitting outside, you know. You were spitting up black for maybe a week, you know, when you came out.[128]

There was a lot of stripping work in power stations that were riddled with asbestos insulation. A foreman in several power station contracts in the late 1970s remarked:

> Well the power stations every year had a shut down period, maybe about six weeks during the summer when they get essential repairs done. We had to go in and strip off the old

125. Letter from HM Factory Inspectorate to J. Todd, dated, 1 April 1976. Also, *Daily Record* cutting (No date. In John Todd Papers, CAA Archive).
126. *Aberdeen Press and Journal*, 29 October 1976.
127. *Aberdeen Press and Journal* 28 October 1976.
128. Interview A 6.

asbestos. And nine times out of ten we stuck new asbestos and
some of the old stuff back on again ... So you were covered in
dust fae morning tae night. You coulnae see each other for
dust. I was in charge of the job down in Auchinleck, the
Barony Power Station in Auchinleck. It was stripping jobs, so
we were stripping asbestos, and re-covering it with non-asbestos
material – well *supposed* to be. But what happened was
that ... all the old asbestos got slung back in with some new
stuff.

He went on:

We were continually told that, if you complained about
working in a dusty atmosphere, that it didnae dae you any
harm. That it contained magnesia which was good for the
stomach. Well, we're only talking about foremen on jobs. They
were usually thickoes.[129]

With the passage of the 1974 HSWA, insulation firms had a duty
to ensure the safety of their workers and those who were working
near them. A senior engineer employed at the commissioning stage
of several power stations recalled how steps were taken to ensure
workers' safety in the early 1970s:

Being the shift engineers we had to deal with permits to work
and, you know, safety etc. And when we started demolishing
the E station we'd to be very careful. And it took 28 days to
issue a permit if there was asbestos involved, or suspected even.
Ah, and the 28 days took time for samples etc. to get analysed,
and various things. And then they sealed the places and you
had to go in with masks and everything like that. [130]

However, despite this concern, many of the safety procedures were
quite impossible to put into practice. For example, one night an
asbestos alert alarm sounded:

And of course you're running a power station and you can't
control a power station. Oh, [we're] supposed to all leave, but
they wouldn't have it. They wanted to leave and the engineer
said 'No you can't leave this etc. etc.' They consulted various

129. Interview A5.
130. Interview A10.

people and eventually they operated for a little while with
breathing apparatus. But, as I say, it was a hit-and-a-miss thing.
Although the engineers ... We did try and make it as safe as
possible and take every precaution you could. It was more or
less the lagging contractors that were responsible for the sealing
of areas, and monitoring and safety aspect. [131]

Another lagger was in charge of a job at a power station in Wales
in the late 1970s, and he also recalled how safety had to be sacrificed
at times. During a weekend shut-down all the asbestos in a particular
location had to be stripped before the station personnel returned on
Monday morning. To this end his employer – Cape Asbestos –
guaranteed him and his squad a £100 bonus, and promised that around
a dozen extra men would be sent to help out on the contract.
Eventually, though, only three turned up, and the squad worked a
24-hour shift to clear the asbestos from the site. To meet this deadline,
though, corners had to be cut, and instead of wetting the asbestos to
nullify the danger of dust, bagging it, and using chutes to send the
stripped sections down to disposal skips, they 'just chopped it with
axes and papped the bags over the side into the skip'.

Not surprisingly, therefore, when jobs had to be done under-staffed
and in double time, lives were put in danger. The same respondent
who had been compelled to break the rules at the Welsh power station
also remembered stripping asbestos from a mine shaft in a Fife
colliery. In this case the asbestos was too far down the shaft to render
it less dangerous by soaking, and the men were asked to dry-strip it.
However, they were also told not to let the miners know what they
were doing:

> That was one thing we kept quiet. Obviously you couldnae
> have what you would call a wet strip ... We didnae have eh,
> strips of hoses tae run as far as that. So we were told 'Just take
> it aff, just stick it'. You were supposed tae put it in a black
> bag; then another bag; then a red bag with asbestos on it. But
> obviously we were told 'Just miss out the red asbestos bag'. We
> would wait till they [the miners] were away down the shaft. [132]

He went on to recount a conversation he had at this pit with an old
miner regarding the relative dangers of their jobs:

131. Interview A10.
132. Interview A16.

By this time they'd introduced the regalia, you know you put the red suit and the mask and that on. But we werenae letting the miners know what we were dain. And I'll always mind a comment that an old guy made tae me. He says tae me 'You must be hard up for a job son'. I said 'how do you make that out Pop?' He says, 'I see you with a' that stuff on.' ... They had a tonnage thing, and that was the bonus for that week. And eh, I says 'what does that represent?' And he says 'we've earned a good bonus.' And I says, 'How much will you get out o' that?' And I think he says it was about 75 quid. I didnae have the heart tae say, 'By the way, I get that in expenses.' I was just comparing it, you know? That he was down there in the shit that he was, and he thought that *I* had a dangerous job.

He also noted that by this time the dangers of stripping asbestos were fully realised, and this was reflected in the safety procedures that the licensed companies had to implement:

You were given underpants, you were given eh, slippers, you were given socks. And you went through a process. You had changing cabins, cabin units. Before you went up site you would just go, in take your normal gear that you wore, slippers, go through, have a shower. And then go into another unit, get a white suit, eh, slippers, and then go out. You would have your red suit in a bag, and you would go up to the job, wherever the job was, whatever you were doing. And then you would go through the same process again. You would go through another unit, although it may have been made of plastic, you know. Your mask ... You also had a mask. You would wash the mask out every time you came off the job. Go and do your work, then come back out. Put the suit that you were working with in a bag. Go through the showers, change into the white suit, change into your slippers, come down off the job, and then go back to the cabin. And then have another shower, and then put your ordinary gear on.[133]

Prior to this his only protection had been a small paper mask.

Up to the late 1970s then, exposure to asbestos in the workplace in Scotland was widespread, though clearly in some occupations the density of asbestos dust – often described in personal testimony as

133. Interview A16.

'falling like snow' – was much greater than in others. The shipyard insulation laggers, asbestos factory workers in the 'dry' fibre processes and the joiners and other building craftsmen who cut and fitted asbestos board in buildings such as the Red Road flats, were amongst those groups of workers who were most at risk. J. Lenaghan has shown in her analysis of the files of over 400 Clydeside asbestos-disease victims that the largest group – 34% – had worked in the shipbuilding industry.[134] Many were not laggers but had worked in the vicinity of asbestos insulators and inhaled the dust in the confined working spaces fitting out the ships. The type of fibre used in ship insulation – large quantities of blue and brown asbestos – and the density of fibre – concentrated up to 85% fibre in pipe and boiler lagging, and 55–95% in limpet asbestos spraying – contributed to the especially high incidence of asbestos disease in shipbuilding.[135] What also needs to be stressed, however, is the widespread use of asbestos in the buildings in which they worked. Hence deaths from asbestos-related diseases in Scotland have occurred amongst a wide range of occupations beyond the blackspots of the asbestos factories, shipbuilding and construction: including cleaners, teachers, hospital workers, engineering workers, friction material (e.g. brake linings) workers, dockers, railway workers and office workers.

For such workers, contact with the 'magic mineral' had debilitating and deadly effects. With the exception of the few – probably less than 100 in total – asbestos factory workers who were employed in the 'scheduled areas' under the 1931 Asbestos Regulations, the evidence shows quite clearly that virtually no precautions were taken to reduce exposure before the mid-to late 1960s or to protect workers effectively from this danger.[136] This was despite widespread knowledge of the hazards, circulated within the shipbuilding and thermal insulation industry from at least 1945. Workers were let down by almost everyone in authority within the system – doctors, employers, management, the state and even, to some extent, their own trade unions. We examine in more detail the policies and attitudes of the 'gatekeepers' in subsequent chapters.

134. J. Lenaghan, *Victims*, p. 23.
135. M. Hamilton, *Working with Asbestos* (1987), p. 21.
136. In the first phase of the Asbestos Regulations in the year or so after 1931 some 80 asbestos workers in Scotland were given the statutory medical examination under the Asbestosis Medical Arrangements Scheme. This resulted in just 2 certificates of total disablement or suspension. *The Lancet*, 2 November 1932.

The personal testimonies indicate that the attitudes of workers themselves to the asbestos hazard varied widely. Many were ignorant of the hazards to health that asbestos posed prior to the 1960s. Before the danger was realised asbestos 'fell like snow' from above, hung like a fog in shafts of sunlight, and was something to be fooled around with. Industrial workers experienced very harsh, insecure working conditions, and were socialised into a high acceptance of risk in their employment, especially on Clydeside. Moreover, economic circumstances could draw people into dangerous work, not least if they had several mouths to feed. Choices, in other words, were severely constrained, making it difficult for many to vote with their feet and extract themselves from such clearly dangerous work. The characteristic volatility of the Clydeside economy encouraged folk to take the work when it was there, to work long hours if possible and maximise earnings, even if this meant cutting a few corners, which, in the event, might jeopardise health. Work culture in the shipyards and building sites, moreover, was, to a great extent, dominated by custom and a *machismo* creed where complaints were frowned upon as a sign of weakness. Workers' attitudes towards taking precautions could thus be ambivalent and they invariably accepted danger with a fatalistic resignation. Safety measures got priority where the hazards were clearly evident on the job, whereas the dust risk was a long-term one – a distant possibility.

However, it was the responsibility of management to enforce rules, break through customary practice and promote a health-conscious work culture. Invariably, the evidence indicates this was not the case. The oral testimony shows unequivocally that life-threatening practices continued within the workplaces in Scotland long after the dangers of asbestos were known and safety regulations had been introduced. Within the asbestos factories, shipyards and building sites in Scotland up to the 1970s, the imperatives of production and the maximisation of profit were invariably placed over and above workers' health and well being. Our evidence casts serious doubt on the effectiveness of voluntary industry regulation and state intervention to control exposure to asbestos in the workplace. The *extent* of the tragic consequences of such callous negligence from the 1930s to the 1960s, however, no-one could have foreseen.

CHAPTER FOUR

Recognition, Regulation and Compensation

Many industries vital to the community are also specially dangerous. It is essential that men should enter them and desirable, therefore, that they should be able to do so with the assurance of special provision against risks ... A man disabled during the course of his employment has been disabled while working under orders.[1]

So said William Beveridge in the report that would bring about Britain's welfare state in 1946. The guiding principle of state welfare was that individuals should be shielded by state protection 'from the cradle to the grave'. The extent of the asbestos tragedy across Britain, though, suggests that for many this hope was not fulfilled. In this chapter we chart the accumulation of medical knowledge on asbestos related-diseases and investigate how effectively the state responded when the hazards surrounding asbestos began to be realised. The following chapter looks specifically at the employers, trade unions and the emergence of asbestos pressures groups.

Medical knowledge

The dangers of asbestos to public health have been known by the medical profession and the government for over 100 years. A Factory Inspector, Lucy Deane, first drew attention to the risks in 1898, and two years later a *post mortem* carried out on a 33-year-old asbestos factory worker in London found that his lungs had been scarred by asbestos fibres. The man had been one of a group of ten employed in a textile factory's carding room, and his nine workmates had

---

1. Quoted by N. Wikely in A. I. Ogus (ed.), *The Law and Social Security* (London, 1995), p. 297.

already died of respiratory diseases. Six years later a weaving mill worker was also diagnosed as having lung disease caused through exposure to asbestos dust. The industrial world was waking up to the fact that something was seriously wrong. The United States Department of Labor began calling for extensive investigations of the health risks of using asbestos in 1918, towards the end of World War One – the same year that American and Canadian insurance companies stopped selling life insurance to asbestos workers.

The word 'asbestosis' only appeared in British medical literature in 1927, but within the space of another two years 25 medical articles dealing with the subject of asbestos had been published. In 1928 researchers began subjecting guinea-pigs to various types of asbestos dust, and this clearly showed that exposure caused severe fibrosis of the animals' lungs. From 1940 onwards more experiments were conducted on rats, rabbits, and monkeys, and these revealed that although brown and blue asbestos seemed to cause the most severe damage, white asbestos was detrimental to the animals' health too.[2] The results of the animal experiments, were not published until the early 1950s. More importantly, in the 1940s it was shown that asbestos could cause lung cancer, *without* any evidence of scarring. However, as Castleman has illustrated, the asbestos industry made sure that this research was not published.

Back in the 1930s, though, asbestos was being used in increasing quantities throughout industrial Scotland. However, perhaps because workers here were not involved to as great an extent as in England in actually *manufacturing* the product, the medical profession was not all that concerned. Glasgow's Medical Officer of Health informed the Factory Department in 1928 that an asbestos worker was receiving

2. J. C. Wagner, 'Asbestos in Experimental Animals', *British Journal of Industrial Medicine*, 1963, 20, 1, pp. 1–12; D. M. Hiett, 'Experimental asbestosis: an investigation of functional and pathological disturbances. Control animals and exposure conditions', *British Journal of Industrial Medicine*, 2, 1973, pp. 129–35.

3. J. C. Bridge, 'Remarks on Occupational Dust', *The British Medical Journal*, 21, 1929, p. 1145. The importance of this Glasgow case is that it was the first reported case of asbestosis in the UK where there were no signs of tuberculosis also present. There is strong evidence, however, that the authorities were aware of the link between asbestos and chest disease long before this. See M. Greenberg, 'Knowledge of the Health Hazards of Asbestos Prior to the Merrywether and Price Report of 1930', *Social History of Medicine*, 7 (1994), pp. 493–516.

treatment in one of the city's hospitals; but even as this information
was being passed on, at the national level an inquiry was underway
– initiated by Merewether and Price – that would end with the link
between lung damage and asbestos being fully accepted by doctors.[3]
However, even after this report was published the Scottish medical
profession still took little interest and the *Glasgow Medical Journal*
made no mention of asbestosis until 1949 – and even then this was
just a passing reference.[4]

As a response to the Merewether and Price Report the government
brought in the Asbestos Regulations of 1931. Asbestosis became a
compensatory disease under the Workmen's Compensation Act with
sufferers obtaining the right to disability benefit from their employers,
and their dependants a lump-sum payment in the event of death.
Regulations were also laid down to control the levels of asbestos dust
in the work environment, and a medical monitoring scheme was
created to check new workers and periodically monitor the health of
employed asbestos workers. The underlying notion behind the
regulations was that it was the workers processing asbestos fibres in
their 'dry' form in asbestos factories who were the ones at risk, and
that the less asbestos dust they breathed in, the less chance they would
have of contracting asbestosis. However, although Merewether and
Price recommended that dust levels be reduced, dust sampling was in
a primitive state and their subsequent 'dust datum' measurement
continued to expose workers to risk – most asbestos dust being
invisible to the naked eye and to the optical microscope. What was
not realised at the time of course, was that lung cancer and
mesothelioma were caused by relatively short exposure levels.

The first case of lung cancer caused by exposure to asbestos was
reported in the USA just four years after the 1931 Regulations came
into force in Britain. Merewether, who had first drawn medical
attention to asbestosis, also speculated that there could be a causal
link and he repeated this claim in 1947.[5] However, it was not until
1955 that the first mortality studies of asbestos workers were
published, and it was only then that the connection was acknowledged
to be a direct one.[6] The situation was complex, though, and a two

4. *Glasgow Medical Journal*, 30, July 1949, 7, pp. 235–6.
5. *Chief Inspector of Factories Annual Report for 1947* (1949), pp. 79–81.
6. R. Doll, 'Mortality from lung cancer in asbestos workers', *British Journal of Industrial Medicine*, 1955, 12, pp. 81–6.

tier system of knowledge operated. On the one hand, the employers and their medical advisors – along with the Factory Inspectors – were the ones who were most aware of the link between asbestos and lung cancer. However, throughout Britain most doctors and pathologists – and of course the workers themselves – remained in the dark for some time to come. Therefore, a significant amount of time passed – and a large number of workers remained at risk – before lung cancer in asbestos workers was made a prescribed disease. However, even then compensation was paid only if lung cancer was accompanied by asbestosis.[7] Unfortunately, though, asbestosis was a difficult condition to diagnose, and the fact that many asbestos workers also smoked made diagnosis and subsequent compensation even more complicated.[8] However, the number of people being diagnosed with asbestos-related tumours increased dramatically from the 1960s, and by 1964 over half of those seeking compensation for asbestosis were found to have a tumour of the lung too.[9]

Sadly, though, as the medical profession was digesting the fact that working with asbestos could bring about lung cancer, an even more startling discovery was being made that would sound 'the death knell of the asbestos industry'.[10] In 1960 doctors in South Africa discovered that a significant number of people living in the crocidolite mining areas had contracted a normally rare tumour of the lining of the lung called mesothelioma. What was even more alarming was that several victims had not actually worked in the asbestos mines, but had only lived near them. The extent of the malignancy, moreover, was not determined by the amount of dust inhaled. Further, mesothelioma was found to occur whether asbestosis was present or not. In 1964, mesothelioma was confirmed amongst American insulation engineers, and the following year a study of 83 patients in London – some of whom were insulation engineers – found that only 10 of them had been working in areas that had been scheduled under the 1931 Asbestos Regulations. This evidence also verified that living near an asbestos factory, or living with someone who worked with asbestos,

7. *British Journal of Industrial Medicine*, 1986, 42, p. 145.
8. D. Gloag, 'Asbestos – can it be used safely?' *British Medical Journal*, 282, 14, February 1981, p. 551.
9. J. C. Wagner, 'Asbestosis carcinogenisis', *British Journal of Cancer*, 32, 258 (1975); K. Constantinidis, 'Asbestos Exposure – its Related Disorders', *The British Journal of Clinical Practice*, 7 (1977), p. 95.
10. J. Tweedale, *Magic Mineral*, p. 157.

were significant causal factors.[11] The findings were reported in the *Sunday Times*, and this prompted a strike by London dockers who immediately refused to handle the mineral.

Back in Scotland, though, the *Glasgow Medical Journal* was still ignoring the asbestos issue, and as late as 1964 an article entitled 'Industrial Diseases in Scotland' made no mention of asbestos whatsoever – although byssinosis (lung scarring by inhalation of textile fibres such as cotton and jute) and coal miners' pneumoconiosis were given some attention.[12] Again it is quite probable that the main reason for this neglect was that relatively few Scottish workers were thought to be at risk from manufacturing processes, and the penny had not yet dropped within the medical fraternity that those who handled asbestos were in danger too. However, the time-bomb was already ticking and, due to the long latency period of asbestos-induced cancer and mesothelioma, it was just about to explode.

In 1964 five cases of mesothelioma were reported at the Royal Naval Dockyard in Devonport – none of whom were workers covered by the 1931 regulations – and from the mid-1960s mesothelioma began to appear on Clydeside too. In 1967, two Glasgow doctors based at Glasgow's Victoria Infirmary reported that in their chest clinic area (covering 200,000 – about a quarter of the population of Glasgow) there had been 21 'proven' cases of mesothelioma over the previous two years.[13] One of the patients was a 41-year-old door-to-door brush salesman who had worked in the shipyards beside laggers for five years after leaving school 20 years earlier. It was a similar picture with the other cases: a foreman fitter had also worked with laggers for three months, 17 years earlier; a 60-year-old porter had worked at the lagging for a year in his late teens; and a 56-year-old joiner and a 61-year-old plumber had also both worked alongside laggers. What was most alarming was that four workers had contracted asbestosis after only a short period of exposure to asbestos – despite the fact that the 1931 Regulations were geared towards preventing high exposure. This is how one case was reported:

11. L. Muriel *et al.*, 'Mesothelioma of Pleura and Peritoneaum Following Exposure to Asbestos in the London Area', *British Journal of Industrial Medicine*, 1965, 22, pp. 261–9.
12. The journal had by this time changed its name: *Scottish Medical Journal*, January 1964, 9, 30, pp. 30–3.
13. *The Newsletter*, 24 June 1967 (John Todd Papers, CAA Archive). The cases were all confirmed by lung biopsy, a process later regarded as dangerous and liable to facilitate the more rapid advance of the tumour.

D.H. (53 years) was working as a Post Office cable engineer for a period of nine years. Thirty years previously, from the ages of 15–23, he had worked as a shipyard plumber next to laggers. He was a classical case of asbestosis proven by lung biopsy. He presented at the clinic with a history of cough and exertional dysponoea [shortage of breath under exertion] of ten years' duration and a recent wheeze ... The X-ray appearances showed bilateral pleural calcification and basal fibrosis.[14]

The doctor's concluding remarks were prophetic:

In view of the grave hazards to health which even very short periods of exposure to asbestos can eventually cause, the increased uses of asbestos must be viewed with disquiet. We feel that the time has come to take a hard look at the possible alternative materials to asbestos before an epidemic of serious and irremediable respiratory diseases ensues.[15]

In 1966 the government added mesothelioma to list of prescribed diseases. From this time on the knowledge of the dangers spread rapidly, backed up by the growing number of death certificates mentioning mesothelioma as a prime cause of death – over 500 across Britain between 1968 and 1970. The news of the Victoria Infirmary study broke, and the realisation that 21 cases of mesothelioma had been found on the Clyde alone – most of which were caused by working as a lagger or alongside laggers – caused 600 Scottish insulation engineers to come out on strike. One of the strikers remarked, 'Soon it will be impossible to cremate insulation engineers who die of mesothelioma, they will be too full of asbestos to burn'.[16] After the laggers had been out for four and a half weeks the employers reluctantly granted them two-yearly medical examinations – although they reneged on this after only one examination had taken place. The laggers were determined to improve their working environment and they next contacted their local MP and the General Secretary of the STUC. Again, though, nothing was done (the policies of unions and employers are explored in more depth in Chapter 5).

Another important investigation took place in the late 1960s at

14. C. Gold and J. Cuthbert, 'Asbestos – A Hazard to the Community', *Public Health*, Vol. 80, No 6 (1966).
15. Ibid.
16. *The Newsletter*, 24 June 1967 (CAA Archive).

the Southern General Hospital in Glasgow where Dr G. H. Roberts carried out random necropsies on the lungs of 400 dead patients to determine the presence of asbestos bodies in the lung tissue. Of the 400, 123, or almost one-third of the total, were contaminated with asbestos.[17] The study showed that men were much more likely to be exposed to asbestos dust than women, with 47% of the 222 male necropsies showing asbestos in the lungs, and 10% of the women (18 out of 178). Whilst the latter evidence suggested to Dr Roberts the existence of secondary or indirect exposure within the urban community, he concluded that contact with asbestos through work was of primary importance: 'In Glasgow, occupational exposure rather than urban contamination explains the asbestos bodies found'.[18] The hospital was located in the shipbuilding area of Upper Clydeside and the study confirmed the high incidence of asbestos inhalation within the industry. Of 27 deceased shipyard workers examined, 22 had asbestos present in their lungs. Almost half of the engineering workers examined (7 out of 15) also had asbestos in their lung tissue.[19]

By the late 1960s, knowledge of the health hazards of asbestos was becoming widespread. British Rail announced in 1967 – the year that the Scottish Occupational Health Service visited Red Road – that it would never use asbestos insulation again because it was hazardous to workers. In 1972 doctors in the USA linked stomach cancer amongst insulation workers to asbestos exposure.[20] In 1977 a study of a group of laggers in Belfast reported that only 40 had survived out of 162.[21] And in 1980 the public heard that all the asbestos was being removed from the Royal Yacht *Britannia* which had been built in John Brown's Clydebank shipyard in 1953.[22] With rising media coverage exploiting this accumulating medical evidence – including

17. G. H. Roberts, Necropsy Studies of Asbestos Bodies in Glasgow (Doctor of Medicine Thesis, University of Wales, 1969), p. 295. This was broadly in line with other necropsy-based studies of urban areas in the 1960s (e.g. Pittsburgh; Miami; Cape Town) which demonstrated the existence of asbestos bodies in more than 25% of randomly selected specimen lungs. See Turner & Newall Archive, Memorandum on Asbestos and Asbestosis, December 1965, p. 10.
18. Roberts, Necropsy Studies, p. 294.
19. Ibid., pp. 22–6.
20. *Washington Post*, 5 October 1972.
21. P. C. Elmes and J. C. Marion, 'Insulation workers in Belfast', *British Journal of Industrial Medicine* (1977), 34, pp. 174–80.
22. *Daily Telegraph*, 29 June 1980.

several TV exposes of the asbestos issue – few were unaware of the dangers that asbestos posed by the late 1970s.

By this time, then, the link between asbestos and lung disease had been firmly established. A study by the West of Scotland Cancer Surveillance Unit (WSCSU) found that almost 6% of all male lung cancer cases in the West of Scotland between 1975 and 1984 could be linked to asbestos, but that most of them would not have been considered for compensation by the DHSS.[23] Along with the Cancer Prevention Society (CPS), the WSCSU quantified and monitored the alarmingly high rate of asbestos-related diseases on Clydeside and the increasing rate of deaths over time.[24] From less than one case per year in the early 1960s, *recorded* mesothelioma deaths rose to around 10 per year in the West of Scotland in the late 1960s and to between 30 to 40 per year by the early 1980s.[25] Mortality was much greater for men than women by a factor of around 10:1, and around a third of all mesothelioma deaths occurred before the age of 60.[26] There was also marked geographical clustering. The Glasgow Health Board (with 145 mesothelioma deaths between 1959 and 1979) registered double the incidence of mesothelioma deaths of Ayrshire and Arran, four times that of Argyll and Clyde and more than ten times that of Lanarkshire, the Forth Valley and Dumfries and Galloway. Clearly, the gender and geographical clustering reflected occupational exposure, especially within the shipbuilding, asbestos manufacturing and construction industries, which were most heavily concentrated in the Glasgow area.

The WSCSU and CPS research also indicated marked clustering within Glasgow itself, with the shipyards and most heavily industrialised areas of the city suffering the highest rates of the disease, especially Govan, Cardonald and Hillington, as well as Clydebank. A more detailed analysis of 247 deaths from asbestosis and mesothelioma in Glasgow over 1974–82 showed a wide range of the

23. H. De Vos Irvine *et al.*, 'Asbestos lung cancer in Glasgow and the West of Scotland', *British Medical Journal* 306, 1993, pp. 1503–6.

24. WSCSU, 'Mesothelioma in the West of Scotland' (Paper: November 1983); CPS, 'Preliminary Findings on Asbestos-Induced Disease, 1974–82' (1983). We are grateful to Dr Ian Symington for these references.

25. These recorded deaths in the 1960s do not tally with the 1967 chest clinic figures and suggest that death registration statistics considerably underestimate actual mortality by asbestos disease in this period.

26. The average age of death of all recorded asbestosis and asbestos-related cancer deaths (including mesothelioma) in Glasgow over 1974–82 was 65.

labour force affected, with highest incidence amongst construction
workers, insulation workers, maintenance and other fitters, plumbers,
pipe fitters, heating and ventilation engineers, gas fitters, carpenters,
joiners and electricians.[27] The report also showed that asbestosis
predisposed workers to contract lung cancer. This was confirmed by
further research by the WSCSU.[28] In the 1980s, there were around
700 officially recorded mesothelioma cases in west Scotland alone, a
situation which earned Glasgow the title of 'asbestos cancer capital
of the UK'.[29]

Clydebank was a particular blackspot, where, as we have noted in
Chapter 1, asbestos-related disease rates were more than eight times
above the West Scotland average in the late 1980s and amongst the
highest in Western Europe, having 512 times the UK average of
mesothelioma cases in 1990.[30] The three largest companies in
Clydebank – Turner's; John Brown's and Singer's – all exposed
significant proportions of their employees to asbestos. Turner's
manufactured asbestos products and even after closure in 1970 left
an asbestos waste dump that continued to contaminate the community
for a decade thereafter. John Brown's was one of the largest
shipbuilders on the Clyde, employing, at peak, around 3,000, where
asbestos was extensively used for insulation and fire protection. An
important factor was that the more evidently carcinogenic blue
asbestos was commonly used in the shipyards because of its superior
thermal insulating properties. White asbestos was a poorer insulator
when exposed to sea water and was much more extensively used on
land-based thermal insulation than in marine engineering and
shipbuilding.[31] Asbestos was also used in many engineering factories,
including the Singer sewing machine factory in Clydebank (which
employed several thousand workers) to insulate electrical motors,
wires and components.

27. CPS Report (1983).
28. H. De Vos Irvine, *et al.*, 'Asbestos Lung Cancer in Glasgow and the West of
    Scotland', *British Medical Journal*, no. 306, 1993, pp. 1503–6.
29. A. J. P. Dalton, unpublished paper, The UK Campaign to Ban Asbestos (1999).
    See also A. J. P. Dalton, *Asbestos, Killer Dust* (1979).
30. *Scotland on Sunday*, 7 August 1994.
31. K. Constantinidis, 'Asbestos Exposure', *British Journal of Clinical Practice*,
    June–August 1977, no. 7, p. 90.

The state steps in

State involvement in workers' compensation dates back to the introduction of the Workmen's Compensation Act in 1897. Path breaking though this legislation was, it would be wrong to see an upward curve of improvement regarding industrial compensation, as the pursuit of profit has always taken precedence over a need to reduce health risks at work.[32] As a consequence it was not until the 1897 Act was amended in 1906 that any real attempt was made to protect workers from industrial diseases – although even this was restricted to a limited range of toxic substances (see Chapter 2). The fact remained, then, that right up until the First World War, disability caused by the inhalation of harmful dust at work was neither prescribed nor compensatable.[33] Such were the limitations of the Workmen's Compensation Act that in 1938 William Beveridge remarked that 'the pioneering system of social security in Britain was based on a wrong principle and has been dominated by a wrong outlook'.[34] However, it was as part of this scheme that the first legislative effort to protect workers from the harmful effects of asbestos dust grew.

After the First World War, silicosis – common amongst grinders, potters, masons and miners – was included under the Workmen's Compensation Act, and this inclusion established a precedent for asbestosis being covered by the act 13 years later. With the passage of the Asbestos Industry Regulations of 1931, Britain became the first country in the world to introduce laws aimed at protecting workers from exposure to asbestos dust – Canada followed four years later. However, the problem lay in the fact that regulation of asbestos dust, the medical monitoring of workers exposed to the dust, and compensation arrangements for those disabled by asbestos, only extended to a restricted number of workers in specific occupations.[35] The main reason that this came about was that the government and the

32. See P. W. J. Bartrip and S. B. Burman, *The Wounded Soldiers of Industry* (Oxford, 1983).
33. See A. J. McIvor, 'Employers, the Government and Industrial Fatigue in Britain, 1890–1914', *British Journal of Industrial Medicine*, 1987, vol. 44; A. J. McIvor, 'Work and Health, 1880–1914', *Scottish Labour History Society Journal*, 24, 1989.
34. Quoted by N. Wikely, in A. I. Ogus (ed.), *The Law and Social Security*, p. 294.
35. G. Tweedale, *Magic Mineral to Killer Dust* (Oxford, 2000), p. 28.

employers decided that a widespread compensation scheme would be too difficult to manage, and too costly. The regulations, then, applied to those involved in the actual *manufacture* of asbestos, and workers employed in 'breaking, crushing, opening, grinding, mixing, or sieving' asbestos material were restricted to working eight hours a week in these 'scheduled' areas.[36] To keep a check on their health, these workers were now included under an Asbestosis Scheme which necessitated their appearing before a Medical Board for annual medical examinations. However, even with these annual check-ups asbestosis was a difficult disease to diagnose. More importantly, the Medical Boards were acutely aware of the consequences that a positive diagnosis would have on the employers and on the workers – for whom enforced unemployment in the 1930s would have been a disaster. Consequently, the number of workers suspended because of asbestosis remained quite small – in Scotland there were 80 medical inspections in the first year of the scheme and 2 suspensions. By 1940, there were just 142 suspensions across the entire industry in the UK.[37] Moreover, initially no medical panels of this kind had been put into place in Scotland, and when the STUC in 1932 asked the Secretary of State for Scotland to establish a Scottish-based Panel, the request was refused. [38] The Scottish trade unions also complained in the 1930s that compensation levels were set too low and that diagnosis by one medical referee was unfair and should be replaced by a system based on the judgement of three doctors.[39]

Despite the 1931 Regulations, then, a great many workers continued to be exposed to the deadly dust, and especially so in occupations that were not listed as scheduled areas. Most of the workers (around 90%) in Turner's Asbestos Cement factory in Dalmuir, for example, were not covered (see Chapter 3) and the manufacture of brake linings remained exempt from the regulations too. Moreover, the steadily growing number of workers who used the material on a daily basis – such as building trade workers, laggers, and plumbers – also remained beyond the protective arm of state legislation. This was recognised by the state regulators by World War Two, though nothing was done

36. House of Commons Employment Committee 1982–83, 'The Work of the Health and Safety Commission and Executive: Asbestos', Minutes of Evidence [87-I], p. 8 (Hereafter Employment Committee).
37. G. Tweedale, *Magic Mineral*, pp. 56–9.
38. *35th Annual Report of STUC Conference* (Glasgow 1932), p. 47.
39. STUC, *Annual Reports*, 1932, pp. 47–8; 1939, pp. 229–30; 1944, p. 16.

to address the problem for almost two decades. The Chief Medical Inspector of Factories commented in 1955:

> One very hazardous process, to which the Regulations do not always apply, is the removal of the old heat-insulation lagging. The handling of this very dry and dusty material presents a serious health hazard, which is all the more serious because the work is often done in confined spaces. Mush of this work is done in premises not subject to the Factories Acts, and in any case the operation does not take long. The persons who do it are, however, regularly engaged on it and are constantly exposed to risk.[40]

Unscheduled workers such as the laggers and strippers were allowed to apply for compensation under the Asbestosis Scheme – which curiously covered more workers than the Medical Scheme – but they first had to convince a Medical Board that their health had been affected, and this was difficult because their trades were exempt from the Medical Scheme.[41] The 1931 Regulations constituted an important step forward. It raised awareness of risk, widened the use of respirators and impermeable sacks in the industry, encouraged more comprehensive mechanisation of fibre-handling and the more widespread introduction of exhaust ventilation on the dustier machinery (such as the crushers, hopper, disintegrators and the looms).[42] Nonetheless, the structure of the protective and compensation legislation that came into force in 1931, was seriously flawed. Not only did it not cover most of those at risk, but, as the Chief Medical Inspector of Factories conceded in the mid-1950s, compliance with the legislation was 'variable' and effective policing of the legislation difficult:

> As would be expected from the diversity of processes to which the regulations apply, the premises concerned vary in standard from the best to the very worst. In recent years the large users of asbestos have improved their premises very much, and some smaller firms also have made improvements. There remain,

40. Annual Report of the Chief Inspector of Factories (FIR), 1955 (Cmnd 8), p. 142.
41. G. Tweedale, *Magic Mineral*, p. 70.
42. FIR, 1955, pp. 141–5.

however, some factories in premises where satisfactory
compliance with the Regulations is almost impossible.[43]

However, the evidence suggests that nobody *at the time* – including
the trade unions or the medical profession – protested strongly to
attain more comprehensive and effective coverage. Certainly there is
nothing in the *Glasgow Medical Journal* or Scottish Trades Union
Congress Reports to suggest otherwise (see Chapter 5).

In 1946 National Insurance replaced the older system of employer
liability, abolishing the Workmen's Compensation Act. The new
scheme covered the same workers as Workmen's Compensation –
with the inclusion of non-manual workers – but no longer allowed
employers the privilege of contracting out. Also, compensation for
asbestosis still meant following a difficult and frustrating path, and
by the mid-1950s the maximum payment was only £2 15s. (£2.75) per
week ...[44]

Moreover, there is evidence that Scottish workers were at a
particular disadvantage. Compensation payments were lower in
Scotland than elsewhere in the UK. In 1959 the STUC expressed alarm
that Scottish workers were receiving less in compensation payments
for industrial injury in the civil courts than their counterparts in
England. The maximum awards for cases in the Scottish Court of
Session rarely exceeded £5000 to £6000, and the main reason for this
was that judge trials in the English courts provided larger settlements
than Scottish jury trials.[45] It was also reported in the government
publication *Hansard* in March 1980 that the Glasgow Medical Boards
paid out less benefit for lung cancer than any other Board in the UK.
Moreover, the Society for the Prevention of Asbestos and Industrial
Diseases (SPAID) – established in 1978 – expressed its concern to the
DHSS in 1980 that it was difficult to obtain a *post mortem* in Glasgow
for those who had recently died of a suspected asbestos-related disease
– and a *post mortem* was the only sure way of legally establishing
that asbestos had been the culprit.[46]

The danger of asbestos dust was covered by the 1937 Factory Acts

43. Ibid., p. 142.
44. G. Tweedale, *Magic Mineral*, p. 75.
45. *62nd Annual Report of the STUC* (Glasgow, 1959), pp. 224–5.
46. Letter from Nancy Tate (Secretary of SPAID) to Dr R. S. Kennedy dated 22
    October 1980; also from N. Tate to Mr Reg. Prentice, DHSS, dated 21 October
    1980.

and the 1948 Building Regulations – the latter stipulating that adequate ventilation had to be made available or respirators supplied to all workers who 'in connection with any grinding, cleaning, spraying, or manipulation of any material in which there is given off any dust or fume of such a character and to such an extent as to be likely to be injurious to health'.[47] The Factory Act of 1961 also contained a similar proviso. This time respirators were not mentioned, but the need for 'adequate ventilation' was replaced by the stipulation that exhaust extraction equipment had to be used. Legal claims against employers could cite breaches of the 1931 Asbestos Regulations and/or of the Factory Acts.

Shipbuilding and ship repairing, though, were covered by their own regulations, which were first introduced under the Factory and Workshop Act of 1901. The way in which these regulations took shape in relation to the dangers of asbestos underlines the fact that profit was always the main concern. In 1945 the government first intimated a desire to bring the regulations up to date, but the process was delayed to such an extent that it was not until 1950 that a new draft was pre-circulated for comment. To the consternation of the asbestos companies this draft contained a clause stating that workers who worked 'in the vicinity' of any work that gave off hazardous dust had to be issued with a respirator. This, of course, would cost money. However, employer pressure initially managed to get the clause re-worded to include 'in the *immediate* vicinity'. (our italics) Moreover, when the new regulations finally came into force in 1960 the offending clause had disappeared completely. One leading asbestos manufacturer stated that this development was 'very satisfactory indeed' as the provision of respirators 'would no doubt have caused continual difficulties with other contractors and with the shipbuilders and might well have led to a substantial loss of asbestos insulation business'.[48] In view of the large number of Scottish workers who worked 'in the immediate vicinity' of laggers in the shipyards, the omission of this clause was to have serious consequences indeed. As late as the mid to late 1970s, then, those working in the vicinity of 'protected' asbestos workers remained much at risk. One asbestos specialist noted in 1977:

47. Employment Committee, p. 8.
48. Inaugural lecture by Professor N. J. Wikely at the Faculty of Law, University of Southampton, 4 February 2000. Also G. Tweedale, *Magic Mineral*, pp. 130–7.

Workmen not directly involved in asbestos applications may receive massive dust exposures; fitters, joiners and general labourers are not classified as 'asbestos workers' and they are unaware of the dangers of dust inhalations and do not use protective overalls and respirators.[49]

As far as regulating the workplace goes, supplying masks to exposed workers was perhaps the most obvious safeguard that the employers – or indeed the government – could have taken when the dangers were first realised. It was clear by the 1970s that masks were essential, and many Scottish employers were now duty bound to issue them. However, one lagger recalls:

As for supplying masks ... The only firm that ever gave us masks was Wright's Insulation ... Wright's Insulation sent down a bag of masks, a canvas bag that was covered in asbestos dust ... nae filters in them. I said 'What about filters?' 'Eh, you don't need any, put a bit of rag in it.' Well, before that, that's what we used to use; used to wrap rags round your face when you were working ... [50]

By the early 1980s there were several disposable masks available, but because asbestos fibres were so fine, only three were approved by the HSE for use with the mineral – two made by the 3M company, and one by Martindale.[51] Many employers, though, continued to issue their workers with unsuitable masks, and many of these were also uncomfortable to wear for any length of time because the straps cut into the back of the worker's head.[52] One respondent who worked with asbestos sprayers on contracts throughout central Scotland in the early 1980s remembers that although they were told to wear masks, they were uncomfortable to wear in a hot environment and were sometimes discarded.[53] We also saw in the last chapter how the joiners at Red Road found it difficult to work with masks – and that the protective suits were just impossible to work in. Moreover, even the approved masks were viewed by those in the know with some

49. K. Constantinidis, 'Asbestos Exposure', *British Journal of Clinical Practice*, June–August 1977, 7, p. 90.
50. Interview A14.
51. Employment Committee, p. 26.
52. Article by an asbestos worker in the *Morning Star*, 1 August 1970, p. 2.
53. Interview A10.

suspicion. One lagger remembers being issued with masks for the first time:

> At first they gave us wee Martindale masks. It was like a wee paper thing you put over your mouth. It's no worth a monkey's. A wee bandage with a wee bit of aluminium that you pressed in to your face ... And then you got another one that was a wee bit tougher than that, until eventually they brought out things that have got charcoal filters and a' that, and the goggles and the mask. But it didnae come overnight. [54]

However, many of those who were not directly involved in the insulation industry got no masks at all, as this sheet metal worker noted:

> They never gave you a mask. Even in the late 80s, some of they car ferries that came in from the Clyde Dock Engineering. You'd go down and get a staging up and get a couple of men to remove deckhead plates, and you'd find blue asbestos or asbestos. And you'd go tae the manager and say to him 'this'll need tae be sealed off'. 'Aye OK, right, fine. Just leave it the noo I'll contact you.' And you'd get a call the next morning at nine oclock: 'That area's safe come down'. They'd got guys in – scalers they were called – they just took it away and put it in bags, and that was it. And that was going on in about 1988 I think. And eventually somebody got a Factory Inspector in and they'd seal off the areas. But, eh, it didn't happen a lot. They'd seal off the areas and put the exhaust fans in with all the pucker cleansing stations and what have you. But when you walked about the ship, no one ever said 'Wear a mask'. [55]

And a heating engineer told a similar story of his experiences working with asbestos on the building sites around Scotland:

> The last firm I worked with supplied you with masks now and again ... but if you waited for the mask coming you would never get done ... They'd maybe give you two masks to last you a year sort of thing, you know. But eh, we accepted it ... But I don't say we were forced to accept it, but it was a general trend in the building trade that you just carried on with

54. Interview A22.
55. Interview A17.

the job, you know. And eh, to carry on with the job if you were waiting for things to be done, the job would never get done, you know.[56]

At the beginning of a new century the main asbestos problem in Scotland is no longer the dangers of using the material to insulate pipes and boilers, but the sheer amount of asbestos in buildings throughout the country. At the end of the 1990s it was suggested that the government should subsidise the development and distribution of cheap and effective masks for anybody who had to come into contact with the deadly mineral. However, the HSE did not have the finances to carry out such an undertaking, and the supply of masks has been left to individual private companies. Clearly, then, no lessons have been learned from history.[57]

For those who were exposed to asbestos dust inside, in a factory or workshop, dust extraction equipment was essential. However, the evidence we reviewed in Chapter 3 indicates that ventilation engineering prior to c. 1970 was crude and much exhaust ventilation was ineffective, even when this was fitted. This was even the view of Turner & Newall's own Medical Adviser. Another twenty years were to pass before comprehensive safety legislation, brought in to comply with EEC directives, came into force relating to the inspection and maintenance of exhaust equipment such as this.[58]

Underlying all this was employer reluctance to admit that there was any danger. For example, insulation engineers working at the construction of the giant BP chemicals plant at Grangemouth in 1977 asked their employers and the Factory Inspectorate for a written assurance that asbestos dust levels were safe. The workers subsequently refused to believe that the dust levels were accurate, and came out on an unofficial strike over fears for their safety. This was condemned by the management in the press: 'It is disgraceful these unofficial strikes by contractor's employees should impede the investment programme planned to safeguard the future of Grangemouth'.[59]

56. Interview A6. Robin Howie's research has shown that even in the 1980s the respirators in use were far from being totally effective and that even those strippers using the necessary precautions were exposed to an unacceptable level of risk.
57. BBC Radio 4, 'Asbestos: Too little too late', 15 October 1998.
58. Asbestos: Worker protection and further prohibitions. Proposals for Regulations and Guidance [Cd. 47 1992], pp. 25–30.
59. *Sunday Post*, 14 May 1978, p. 4.

By this time the Asbestos Regulations 1969 had come into force. These now encompassed all the processes previously covered by the 1931 legislation', but included other neglected processes such as the making of insulation slabs and mattresses. They were quite specific about ventilation, recommending that 'the processes be carried on under an exhaust draught or in some other equally safe way, or that protective clothing and respiratory protective equipment be provided for the use of the persons employed'. However, although the new rules went some way to giving more workers protection, they were only directed at those who worked in factories or other places to which the Factories Act 1961 applied. More importantly, the new safety standards were based on information provided by the major asbestos company Turner & Newall. According to their own research, the inhalation of two particles of asbestos per cubic centimetre of air in their factories resulted in only 3% of the workers contracting asbestosis over a certain period. However, this research was never independently verified, and it was later revealed that at least 10% of the workers had in fact contracted asbestosis.[60]

The first big media inquiry into working with asbestos occurred in the 1970s. In 1975 a TV programme implicated the Factory Inspectorate in the deaths of asbestos workers at the Cape Asbestos plant in Hebden Bridge in Yorkshire. The public outcry which this exposé brought about caused Michael Foot, the then Minister for Employment, to set up an inquiry, and this was led by the HSC chairman Bill Simpson. The first report of this Advisory Committee on Asbestos – or the Simpson Inquiry – dealt exclusively with the thermal insulation industry and appeared three years later. The inquiry reported that the heaviest death toll amongst all workers exposed to asbestos was amongst those in thermal insulating, and recommended that immediate action should be taken to protect them.[61] However, despite this warning, another three years passed before the HSE produced its Approved Code of Practice for Working With Asbestos Insulation and Asbestos Coating. The HSE also proposed that insulation engineers be licensed, and this was adopted in 1982. Moreover, despite the fact that the Inquiry stated that it had 'failed to identify a threshold below which there is no evidence of adverse effects', the Simpson Committee's recommendations were

60. *Glasgow News*, no date, p. 4.
61. Employment Committee, p. 16.

fairly tame.[62] A ban was placed on the import of blue asbestos –
which had already been banned voluntarily by the industry – and on
brown asbestos. Asbestos spraying was also made illegal, and the
stripping of asbestos was to be undertaken in future only by licensed
contractors. The six-monthly inspections introduced under these
Regulations did have a positive effect in picking up the early signs of
asbestosis, though once mesothelioma was detected there was nothing
much that could be done. An ex-lagger engaged on stripping work
commented on the certification system as well as making some telling
remarks about trading off exposure against higher earnings:

> When I worked with Cape's, before you could work with
> asbestos you had to get a wee certificate ... you had to go to a
> doctor and tell him that you were going to work stripping
> asbestos. You would pay for it yourself to the doctor and then
> Cape's would reimburse you for whatever you paid for the
> X-rays and the check-up. I've been doing all this and they were
> saying 'Aye, you're clear. Nothing's the matter with you.' ...
> You know, you were always getting clearance.[63]

Dust levels were also lowered as a consequence of the Simpson
Report, but dust counts were still to be determined by the old
membrane filter method, and not by electron microscopes as proposed
by some experts.[64] This was to have tragic consequences, and an
article in the *New Scientist* in 1978 reported that the method of dust
sampling – where particles were drawn through a filter and counted
with the aid of an optical microscope – could be as much as 50%
inaccurate.[65]

It was a similar story when determining the extent of asbestosis in
sufferers. A House of Lords Inquiry in 1982 heard that the Medical
Panels' methods of diagnosing asbestos diseases were out of date as
they relied on the optical microscope. The main evidence to support
this was that a gram of dried lung tissue viewed through such a
microscope revealed that there was only one asbestos particle present

62. Employment Committee, p. 11.
63. Interview A 16.
64. G. Tweedale, *Magic Mineral*, p. 246.
65. *New Scientist*, 8 June 1978, p. 645. Also, *Asbestos Bulletin*, 18, 6 (1977),
    p. 175. Only in the 1990s was technology developed that could measure dust
    fibres quickly and accurately. See *Times Higher Education Supplement*, 24
    September 1993, p. 5.

in the sample. However, 8.5 million particles came into view when the same sample was viewed under an electron microscope.[66] Some indication of how small an amount of asbestos dust is required to damage the body is the fact that by the 1990s the safe limit was judged to be ten asbestos fibres per litre of air, and that one scientist compared this to searching for ten sewing-machine needles in a space the size of Wembley stadium.[67]

The Health and Safety at Work Act of 1974 ensured that responsibility for workplace health was shared between employers and workers – and this applied to working with asbestos too – and brought two new organisations into being: the Health and Safety Executive (HSE) and the Health and Safety Commission (HSC). Long before the 1974 act came into force, though, the medical profession, the trade union movement, and several government committees, had argued that the state could only deal with workers' health head-on if an occupational health service was set up as part of the National Health Service (NHS).[68] The 1974 Act, though, by shunting responsibility on to the workforce and the employers, continued a long British tradition of limited state intervention in workplace health. More importantly, in 1977 the Safety Representative and Safety Committee Regulations were passed, which meant that trade unions were now allowed to set up joint employer/employee safety committees. However, the main drawback was that the legislation only applied to unionised workplaces, and from this time onward trade union membership dropped across Scotland, which meant that the number of workers covered by the new legislation dropped too.

Compounding this was the fact that the HSE – the body charged with ensuring the health of the workforce – and the Factory Inspectorate tended to emphasise *safety* at work as opposed to *health* at work. Before becoming part of the HSE in 1974, the Factory Inspectorate frequently issued safety publications, and organised lectures for shop stewards and trade union delegates on industrial *safety*. In the same way, the HSE initiated campaigns in the 1970s to ensure the safety of children on farms and building sites; published information on forklift truck safety; and began a campaign in 1979

---

66. *Asbestos Bulletin*, March–April 1982, p. 99.
67. *Times Higher Education Supplement*, 24 September, 1993, p. 5.
68. See R. Johnston and A. J. McIvor, 'Whatever happened to the occupational health service?', in C. Nottingham (ed.), *The NHS in Scotland* (Ashgate, 2000).

to encourage breathalising employees in certain industries. All
important safety issues. Even when Bill Simpson, who was in charge
of the Advisory Committee on Asbestos – and himself a former iron
moulder from Falkirk – visited Scott Lithgow's shipyard in 1977, his
main concern was for the safety of welders working in confined
spaces.[69] Such an emphasis, then, played down the fact that deaths
from occupational disease in Britain were running at ten times the
rate of deaths from occupational accidents, and that asbestos at work
was a major health risk.[70]

The proficiency of the Factory Inspectorate has often been called
into question. Trade unionists have expressed a concern that many
of the HSE personnel came from a management or university
background, saw things in management terms, and were soft on
employers.[71] Indeed, a Labour Research Department publication in
1975 stated that 'the law has not been enforced by those whose duty
it was to do so'. It was also the policy of the Factory Inspectorate to
try to persuade employers to comply with legislation rather than to
prosecute.[72]

Moreover, the Factory Inspectorate has also been critically under
strength. Even after the number of inspectors was increased – due in
part to pressure from the GMWU – in 1971 in Scotland 50 inspectors
were still responsible for 25,000 industrial premises. This meant that
on average an inspector made a visit to one of these establishments
once every four years.[73] An electrician with mesothelioma remarked:

> I've never ever met a Factory Inspector in 40-odd years of
> work. I've heard he was coming to the site … If there were an
> accident or anything, the buzz went round that the Factory
> Inspector's coming. I've still to meet the Factory Inspector in 42
> years, more, 47 years. And I've been in jobs where men were
> killed. Steel works, the Concert Hall … and I'm still to see the
> Factory Inspector.[74]

A shipyard shop steward convenor also noted the limited role

69. *Glasgow Herald*, 27 September 1977, p. 8.
70. S. Harvey, *Just an Occupational Hazard* (London, 1988), p. 15.
71. Eva and Oswald, *Health and Safety*, p. 53.
72. Labour Research Department Guide to the Health and Safety at Work Act
    (1975), p. 4.
73. *Glasgow Herald*, 25 June 1971, p. 14. *Morning Star* cutting, no date.
74. Interview A13.

played by the HSE, and especially in relation to safety rather than health:

> It was more accidents, you know, is the staging safe? Are you using proper ropes? Proper wires? They would check periodically, but you never heard anything about internal breathing or anything like that you know. [75]

Moreover, even when the Factory Inspectorate took action against companies who were contravening asbestos regulations, the level of fines was normally low. In 1971 Factory Inspectors examined an asbestos cement factory in Manchester, similar to the one in Dalmuir, and found that dust levels were 80 times over the safe level. The company were fined only £25. This was the first prosecution under the new 1969 Asbestos Regulations.[76] In 1975 Yarrow's Shipbuilders on the Clyde were fined a total of £80 on two charges under the same regulations.[77] An Aberdeen joinery firm were fined £50 for failing to provide exhaust ventilation in their factory where asbestos boards were being cut.[78] And a Paisley company was fined a mere £50 for failing to provide its workers with protective masks and clothing when they were demolishing a dye works riddled with asbestos.[79] The relatively low levels of fines imposed for breaches of health and safety remained the norm throughout the period, and in the mid-1990s the average fine imposed in the lower courts was just over £2000. Moreover, up until 1996 no employer in the UK had ever been sent to prison for failing to comply with industrial health and safety legislation.

The revised Asbestos Regulations of 1979 were superseded in 1983 by new measures stipulating that any worker involved in asbestos insulation or coating be medically examined before commencing employment with a firm, and at a maximum of two-year intervals thereafter. In 1984–85, the asbestos industry's voluntary ban was enforced by legislation which banned imports of both blue and brown asbestos. This followed European Union directives aimed at improving standards of occupational health. However, it was not until 1987 that the Control of Asbestos at Work Regulations finally

75. Interview A9.
76. We are indebted to G. Tweedale for this information.
77. Letter from HM Factory Inspectorate to J. Todd, dated 5 December 1978.
78. *Daily Star* cutting (no date).
79. *Daily Mail*, 15 February 1977.

acknowledged the full extent of the problem by ensuring that *all* workers exposed to asbestos (not just those in prescribed occupations and covered by the Shipbuilding Regulations) be protected and subjected to regular medical inspections. White asbestos, considered less insidious (in relation to mesothelioma), continued to be imported and manufactured until it too was banned by legislation passed in November 1999. This came just over a century after the initial official identification of asbestos as a health hazard by a government Factory Inspector and after a long campaign by pressure groups and the trade unions to get all asbestos legally banned.[80]

Fighting for compensation while struggling for breath

No amount of financial compensation can make up for a lost life or severely impaired health. Nonetheless, victims of asbestos-related disease have three main routes which they can follow in their efforts to secure compensation. The first is through the DSS and the state benefit system. Asbestosis, mesothelioma, lung cancer – when accompanied by pleural thickening or asbestosis – and bilateral diffuse pleural thickening, meaning thickening of the lining of both lungs, are all now prescribed diseases. Secondly, civil action can be taken for damages against employers. Thirdly, some sufferers can take advantage of the Pneumoconiosis etc. (Workers Compensation) Act of 1979. Under this Act payments are made from the Department of the Environment when former employers are out of business and do not exist to have a case brought against them. Prior to 1979 one of the main problems was attaining any compensation where a culpable business had closed down. All these routes to financial recompense for injury or death were fraught with difficulties. The pressure group Clydeside Action on Asbestos reported that less than half of their membership whom they judged to be eligible over the 1986–1990 period were compensated by the DSS. The main reason for this is the stringency of the DSS procedure in which claimants must satisfy a Special Medical Board that they are suffering from a *prescribed disease*.[81] A good example of this is that of a female French polisher

---

80. The 1999 UK asbestos import ban (which includes some exceptions – including power stations) came many years after the Scandinavian countries banned chrysotile (Norway in 1984; Denmark and Sweden in 1986).

81. This is fully explained in L. Lenaghan, *Victims Twice Over*, pp. 30–50.

who was exposed to asbestos dust in the shipyards. When she developed symptoms, an X-ray revealed that she was suffering from pleural thickening of her right lung. However, her appeal for Industrial Disablement Benefit was refused because only bilateral pleural thickening (within both lungs) was classed as a prescribed disease.[82] Moreover, a study by the Benefits Agency in the early 1990s found that in only 39% of cases did medical officers agree that claimants had pleural thickening – this compared to 75% positive diagnoses for all other prescribed diseases.[83]

The length of time taken to settle claims can also be excessive. When Ron Hill died in 1983 from mesothelioma caused through his work as a joiner at Red Road Flats 30 years earlier, his son complained to the local MP William McKelvey of the treatment that his father had received from the DHSS. McKelvey pursued this and eventually an Ombudsman's report in 1984 upheld the complaint. The Ombudsman's criticism of the DHSS was scathing. He noted that a DHSS circular had previously been issued to staff at all offices advising that asbestos-induced diseases, and in particular mesothelioma, be given the highest priority:

> In spite of this, the service which Mr Hill was given was desperately slow ... Mr Hill was deprived of whatever extra comfort the benefit might have brought him in his last months of life ... He claimed state benefit from the DHSS on 17th August 1982, but the Department's offer of settlement came on 29th July 1983, eight weeks after Mr Hill's death.

However, the *Scotsman* noted that the performance of the Ombudsman had been even slower: 'The DHSS took eleven and a half months to decide that Ron Hill suffered from asbestosis and the Ombudsman took thirteen and a half months to decide that eleven and a half months was too long'.[84]

Changes in the social security system have also meant a lower level of compensation for those injured at work. Much of this change reflects the transition of the economy from physical labour to service industry. The Industrial Injuries Scheme arose out of the Beveridge

82. L. Lenaghan, *Victims*, p. 30.
83. Department of Social Security Act 1992. Review by Industrial Injuries Advisory Council, 1996 [Cm. 3467].
84. *The Scotsman*, 27/11/84. Quoted in T. Gorman, 'The continuing use', p. 34.

Report and produced the National Insurance Act 1946, the National Insurance (Industrial Injuries) Act 1946, and National Assistance Act 1946. All of these came into effect on 5 July 1948. However, gradually the notion of an 'insurance' was eroded, and under the 1980 Social Security Act the National Insurance Advisory Committee was replaced by the Social Security Advisory Committee. More controversially, the Social Security No 2 Act of that year extended the minimum qualifying period for sickness benefit to at least four consecutive working days, and scrapped earnings-related supplements to unemployment benefit, sickness benefit, and maternity allowance – as well as reducing the amount of Supplementary Benefit payable to the families of workers on strike. Further evidence that the government wanted to shift the focus away from industrial claims came the following year when a government White Paper entitled 'Reform of the Industrial Injuries Scheme' recommended the abolition of Injury Benefit and the abolition of Special Hardship Allowance, Unemployability Supplement, Constant Attendance Allowance, Exceptionally Severe Disablement Allowance, Hospital Treatment Allowance, and Industrial Death Benefit. Injury Benefit was scrapped in April 1983. However, the other proposals were shelved because of public outcry.

After 5 April 1983, then, those who were off work because of illness or injury were no longer able to claim Sickness Benefit, but were entitled to an entirely new benefit called Statutory Sick Pay (SSP). This took the responsibility for paying a welfare benefit away from the state and placed it on the employers. However, the trade union-based Labour Research Department estimated that the new initiative would mean that most people would lose out by at least £25 a week, and that many employers would ensure that they only employed the fittest workers. Moreover, with the abolition of Industrial Injury Benefit those who would normally have qualified for the higher limit of benefit now had to make do with SSP for the first eight weeks of their incapacity, and only when they had been off work for 15 weeks were they able to apply for Disablement Benefit. Everything comes down to hard economics, of course, and by abolishing Industrial Injury Benefit the government hoped to save £5 million a year.[85] However, all these reforms were taking place just as the asbestos time bomb was exploding. Consequently, as the social security system changed to reflect the move away from old industries,

85. *Statutory Sick Pay*, Labour Research Department (1983), p. 6.

those who were damaged by the old industries became embarrassing anachronisms.

Things got worse. The Social Security (Incapacity for Work) Act 1994 replaced Sickness and Invalidity Benefit with Incapacity Benefit – for those who had paid enough National Insurance contributions – and brought in two tests to determine claimants' incapacity for work. Incapacity Benefit is a social security benefit for people who have worked and paid National Insurance contributions, but cannot work due to sickness or disability, and in 1995 it was paid at £62.45 a week. Those who had not paid National Insurance contributions could claim Severe Disablement Allowance. The system, then, seemed to be hostile to those with an industrial disability, and many sufferers of asbestos-related diseases were also frustrated that if they were in receipt of Disablement Benefit, other benefits – such as Income Support, Income-based Jobseeker's Allowance, Family Credit, Housing Benefit, Council Tax Benefit, Disability Working Allowance – were adversely affected. Moreover, the claiming system was quite complex, and an ex-DHSS employee who eventually had to fight his own claim for industrial disability commented:

> I think it's too hard for people. I mean, I worked in there for 32 years and I'd like to I think I've got enough malum. After the first time I was knocked back by the Medical Appeal Tribunal I was finished. And I consider myself quite a strong character. I gave up. So I'm just trying to figure out how many poor people who are probably not that *au fait* with paperwork get on.[86]

For those workers diagnosed as having pleural plaques civil compensation is the only route – as the condition is not included under the DHSS compensation scheme. One insulation engineer, though, who can only speak with the help of an oxygen mask, was repeatedly told by the DHSS that he did not qualify for benefit as he did not have an incapacitating disease:

> They didn't think that pleural plaques was an incapacitating disease. So, the brother law, he, he phoned up [the DHSS]. He says 'That brother in law of mine is sitting here without a bloody breath tae draw'. He gave him a few choice words

86. Interview A7.

didn't he? And they said, 'There's no need for that'. 'Nae
bloody wonder' he says, 'see this brother in law of mine sitting
here, he hasn't a breath tae draw and you says he's no
incapacitated'. He says 'You want to come and see him'.[87]

Disillusionment with the benefit system was echoed by others. For
example, a 53-year-old with pleural plaques, exposed to asbestos while
working in demolition, told of his struggle to secure state welfare for
his disability while, at the same time, trying to come to terms with
its medical effects. One of the most difficult things was the constant
pressure of having to prove that his disability was severe enough to
entitle him to state allowances. He had fought for five years to get
Motobility Allowance, and had this to say about the system:

> I went up tae a panel one time and there's three sitting there,
> and they're no supposed tae tell you the decision you know
> when you're there, but they just turned round and says 'Are we
> agreed with this' – now this was only cause it was dinner
> time – and the one at the end went like that [thumbs down].
> Now they're no supposed tae tell you till you go out and they
> discuss it. And he turned round after it and said 'I'll need tae
> go out and put money in my car'. That's all he was worried
> about you know, getting booked.

He maintained that a general disagreement among health
professionals over the severity of his disability seriously affected his
benefit entitlement, and had added significantly to the stress levels he
was already enduring:

> One will no agree with this, and then one will no agree with
> that, then back tae another, then another year tae wait. During
> that time the wife got put off on the sick: 19 months. So all we
> got then was £84 for the two of us, plus our £20 pension ...
> It's the doctors that does it. You go tae the doctor at the
> Southern and they give you a' the tests, and put you on this
> walking thing ... You've got tae be crippled before you can get
> that mobility money, you know. [88]

Civil compensation can be a long and complicated process and in
the past workers in Scotland have been particularly disadvantaged by

87. Interview A1.
88. Interview A7.

a tendency within the Scottish courts to award considerably less money for personal injury compensation than their counterparts south of the border in England. This was commented upon and criticised on several occasions in the 1950s and 1960s by the Scottish trade unions.[89] However, there have been several important legal decisions in Scotland that have made the situation easier for claimants. By far the most important of these was the removal of a loophole in Scots law that encouraged companies to drag out claims in the hope that the claimants died before the case went to court.

A prime example of this was the case of Charles Coyle, which we noted early in Chapter 1. To briefly recap: Coyle worked at the insulation trade in Glasgow as a sprayer for Turner & Newall between 1945 and 1954. In 1951, when he was in his late 40s, he developed a cough and later shortness of breath when walking uphill or climbing stairs. His doctor referred him to Glasgow's Belvidere Hospital and he underwent a chest X-ray which showed he had asbestosis. In 1955 his solicitor made a claim for negligence against his employers T&N. The company, though, fully realised that once Coyle had died his claim for damages would die with him and the widow would have to settle for a reduced amount, and a letter from his doctor in 1956 informed them that he did not have long to live. Charles Coyle died and his claim for damages – estimated by T&N's solicitors to be in the region of £4000 – died with him. The company made an *ex gratia* payment to his widow and children of £500.[90]

It was to be almost 40 years before this law was changed, and many more workers were to suffer the same fate as Coyle. By 1977 one fifth of the 500-strong Insulation Branch of the TGWU had asbestosis, and between 1980 and 1989 there were 700 mesothelioma cases in the West of Scotland alone. Most of these workers had claims against their former employers, and had the law not been changed, many of these claims would have died with them. One shipyard worker, who had helped build the *QE2*, died only one week before his claim for damages came to court.[91] One case was successfully hurried through the courts by an Edinburgh solicitor, and the claimant became the first Scottish mesothelioma victim to survive long enough

89. STUC, General Council, Minutes, 8 July 1959; 13 December 1967; 6 February 1968.
90. G. Tweedale, *Magic Mineral*, p. 110; also Letter from J. A. Crocket to Robertson Chalmers and Co., dated 9 May 1956. CAA Archive.
91. *Sunday Mail*, March 1992, p. 14.

to receive compensation. That was in 1988. He used the money to visit his relatives in South Africa for the last time before he died.[92]

The absence of clear and unequivocal medical evidence could also spike legitimate claims. In 1986 the widow of a Glasgow insulation worker, who had died aged 46 of lung cancer, sued her husband's former employers for damages. David Main had worked for two Glasgow-based insulation companies through the 1960s and '70s. Initially, the judge awarded £37,695 damages to Mrs Main, but this was overturned by the Appeal Court on the grounds that there was no medical evidence of asbestosis. This was despite the fact that the Appeal Court heard and accepted the evidence that *no* precautions had been taken by Wormald's or Wright Insulation 'to prevent or reduce the risk of exposure to asbestos dust and particles'.[93]

In the early 1990s – following pressure from legal firms and victims' pressure groups – the Scottish Law Commission circulated 45 legal firms in Aberdeen, Glasgow, and Edinburgh, and asked a key question: 'Do you agree that there may be an incentive in the present law for defender to postpone making settlement or reaching proof until after the death of the pursuer in order to minimise the amount of any compensation paid?' Although only 15 firms replied to the questionnaire, all but one agreed that there was such an incentive.[94] As a consequence of this the law was changed in 1993, and with the passage of the Damages (Scotland) Act of that year the immediate family of the deceased became entitled to claim for the distress and anxiety they had to endure 'in contemplation of the suffering of the deceased before his death'.

Another benefit to claimants with pleural plaques and other asbestos-related diseases is that 'Provisional Damages' can now be claimed from employers. This means that a relatively modest sum can be accepted as a settlement with the proviso that the case can be opened up again if more serious health problems are encountered. In one of the first such cases the European MP Alex Falconer successfully sued the Ministry of Defence for negligence in relation to withholding information on the hazards of asbestos and not providing proper ventilation at the Rosyth Royal Naval Dockyard where he worked stripping old asbestos insulation from 1969 to 1974. The settlement

92. *Glasgow Herald*, September 1988, p. 11.
93. *Glasgow Herald*, 15 March 1986.
94. Scottish Law Commission Discussion Paper No. 89, 'The Effects of Death and Damages', November, 1990, p. 6.

admitted MOD liability, and awarded Falconer 'token' damages of £100 with the proviso that the plaintiff was open to re-apply if his condition (pleural thickening in both lungs was diagnosed in 1982) worsened over the subsequent 30 years.[95] This is also what happened to one of the Glasgow insulation engineers we spoke to. In the 1980s he accepted £12,000 as final settlement compensation for his asbestos-induced disability. However, his condition deteriorated markedly thereafter, and he related the course of this deterioration as it was monitored periodically by the DHSS:

> In July this year I was 40% asbestosis, right. Then they pumped me up to 50%. The doctors down there [DHSS office in Glasgow] examined me and took X-rays and everything, right. So, I had 50%. Then I came back from holiday and I found a wee lump on my shoulder, and I went for a CT scan. I got a biopsy on this lump and they told me it was cancer on the lump, and a tumour in my lung.[96]

Pursuing civil litigation is difficult in other ways too. In many cases companies drag out the process for as long as possible in the hope that the claimant will run out of steam – in a great many cases eventually settling on the steps of the court. Moreover, when the case does go to court the claimant's solicitor has to prove without any doubt that his client was exposed to dangerous levels of asbestos dust at work, and have strong medical evidence that asbestos was the principal causal factor in bringing about ill health. A 75-year-old joiner who had worked with asbestos in the SCWS during the war struggled to get compensation from the state and from his former employer. He was told by the DHSS that he would need witnesses to verify that he had worked with the SCWS some 50 years earlier. Fortunately he discovered that all SCWS records were kept in the Cooperative's office in Manchester, and he was able to locate the names of his former workmates. However, even after establishing that he had worked in Shieldhall's furniture department – and after being diagnosed with an asbestos-related prescribed disease – the DHSS was still reluctant to pay him Disablement Benefit, and only pressure from Clydeside Action on Asbestos eventually induced them to do so. Moreover, his civil claim for damages against the SCWS hit the buffers

95. *The Scotsman*, 15 October 1987, p. 4.
96. Interview A21.

when the company denied that he had worked there. He expressed his frustration at the slowness of the legal process:

> They [his solicitors] seemed to have difficulty pinning the Cooperative down ... There seems to be a case of 'That's that. Put it away and forget about it'. Until we phone up and ask how things are going, then we discover that we need another expert. And that would be another £150 for an expert. And then I would need another CT scan, copies of which they would have got from the Royal Infirmary. Then the latest one ... we would need an expert from a Factory Inspectorate to assess the situation. Now, how on earth are you going to assess that away back in these days with the conditions that prevailed in the premises that we were working?[97]

A lagger who worked for just about every insulation company on the Clyde came up against the same reluctance when he initially launched a civil claim against Cape Asbestos:

> They claim that I never worked with them, but I done my gaffer with them for quite a number of years. But eh, eventually they admitted in court that they exposed me to asbestos and that I did work for them over the ... And the firms they bought over. So, I've a full work history now which I didnae have a couple of year back, which again was supplied by the Chase Manhattan Bank. You cannae get information on your working life here. You've got to send to America for it.[98]

A final injustice embedded within the system came with the introduction by the Conservative government in January 1989 of the Compensation Recovery Unit (CRU). This was a branch of the DSS created to claw back state benefits paid out to victims who were subsequently successful in claiming civil damages. This led to the situation where very large amounts of money were being recouped from people who were often seriously ill, as well as from the deceased's relatives. One Glasgow shipyard lagger, Andy Rae, received a £72,000 settlement but had £42,000 deducted after calculation of his sickness benefit, whilst in another case £30,000 damages was awarded by the court and £28,000 deducted to repay benefits by the

97. Interview A8.
98. Interview A14.

CRU. This vicious revenue-saving measure transferred vast sums of money from needy victims of asbestos and other occupational hazards into the government's hands. Over the financial year 1993–94 alone, some £82 million was recovered by the CRU. One asbestos campaigner, Tommy Gorman, described the legislation as 'callous', causing untold 'stress and anguish' and argued that 'the logic of this legislation is to discourage workers from making claims in the first place'.[99]

What is also clearly evident is that asbestos exposure, and hence asbestos-related disease, extended considerably beyond the shipbuilding, construction and heavy industries dominated by male workers. A small but significant number of cases occurred amongst office workers, school teachers, transport workers and cleaners. Women have been characterised as 'the forgotten victims'. The CPS study of 1974–82 recorded 25 female deaths from asbestos-related diseases in Glasgow. One Glasgow female mesothelioma victim was a secretary in an asbestos works and three others were employed directly in asbestos manufacture, one as an asbestos weaver, and another worked in MacLellan's Rubberworks as a 'helper' in the asbestos room. At least two Scottish women obtained compensation from the government as a result of proving their illnesses were linked to wartime work: in one case the contact with asbestos was in the manufacture of gas masks with asbestos filters, and in the other the woman was employed at the Royal Naval Dockyard at Rosyth in Fife from 1942 to 1945. A woman who died of mesothelioma contracted the disease whilst working as a cleaner in a bus garage, sweeping up the asbestos dust produced by the men who repaired and replaced the asbestos brake linings on the buses. Other female victims were employed as French polishers, in munitions, in offices, as cleaners and as teachers.[100] In 1992, £9000 was awarded to the widower of a Glasgow primary school teacher called Jeanette Sawyers who died of mesothelioma. This was the first ever case in which the DHSS acknowledged that a person who did not work with asbestos was nevertheless killed by it, and it was decided that the 'balance of probability' suggested that the teacher had been exposed to asbestos

99. T. Gorman, 'Action on Asbestos', in *Scottish Trade Union Review*, no. 67, November/December 1994, pp. 12–13. Several members of CAA describe the deleterious impact of the CRU legislation in the CAA video, 'Hidden Hazards'.

100. L. Lenaghan, *Victims Twice Over*, p 52.

during her 30-year career in several schools in the South Side of Glasgow. The case established a precedent and was a victory for Clydeside Action on Asbestos. However, the local Education Department disagreed with the decision, and argued that the teacher could have been contaminated by her father's overalls when she was younger – he was a sheet metal worker who had worked with a company who did lagging.[101] This was a possibility, as there was a growing number of cases of women dying of asbestos-related cancers throughout the UK simply through contact with asbestos dust brought home on the work clothes and overalls of their husbands, sons, or fathers – in 1993 a verdict of death by industrial disease was issued by Portsmouth Coroner's Court in relation to a woman who was adjudged to have been exposed to asbestos in this way.[102] Gorman has argued that the extent of the problem amongst women has undoubtedly been under-estimated because of the common assumption that this was a male problem associated with male-dominated industries.[103] Women, as a consequence, have found it more difficult to attain proper recognition of their illness as well as full compensation.

Clearly, then, as far as the asbestos tragedy in Scotland is concerned the state has not only failed to protect its workers from harm, but has also failed to ensure that they received speedy and adequate compensation for this harm.

It is difficult to be objective when considering the development of knowledge of the asbestos hazard and state policy towards asbestos regulation and asbestos-related disability compensation. On the one hand, state intervention in the UK was more extensive than in most other developed countries prior to the 1970s. However, the various regulations that came into force have tended to be piecemeal in relation to the gravity of the issue, and have frequently been blunted by the business interest. There is also a significant degree of misfortune involved in the history of asbestos in Scotland, and the fact that lung cancer was linked to asbestos only a year after the 1931 Regulations came into force is an example of this. However, in the 1960s medical knowledge of the dangers increased, but the pace at which this was

101. *Times Educational Supplement*, 20 November 1992.
102. T. Gorman, 'The Continuing Use of Asbestos', p. 38.
103. T. Gorman, 'Women and Asbestos' in T. Gorman (ed.), *Clydebank: Asbestos the Unwanted Legacy* (2000).

1   Manufacturing asbestos yarn and cloth in George MacLellan and Co., Glasgow Rubber and Asbestos Works, Maryhill, Glasgow, 1939. (*Courtesy of Mitchell Library, Glasgow*)

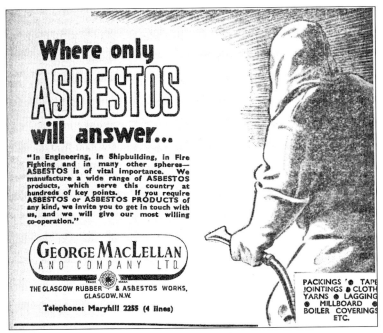

2   MacLellan's advertisement, *Glasgow Post Office Directory*, 1951.

3   Turner's Asbestos Cement factory, Clydebank, 1939. (*Courtesy of Mitchell Library, Glasgow*)

4   Making asbestos pipe joints, Turner's, Clydebank, 1938. (*Courtesy of Mitchell Library, Glasgow*)

5   Lorries loaded up with asbestos at Turner's, Clydebank, 1949. (*Courtesy of Clydebank Library*)

6   Stockpiles of raw asbestos at Turner's, Clydebank, 1960. (*Courtesy of Clydebank Library*)

7 Asbestos victims: a group of Turner's, Clydebank, workers in 1953. Most were reported to be suffering from lung-related illnesses in the mid-1980s. (*Courtesy of Clydebank Press*)

8 Asbestos victims: two of our respondents, Margaret and Owen Lilly. Both suffer from asbestos-related diseases (Margaret from washing Owen's overalls). (*Courtesy of Margaret and Owen Lilly*)

9   Asbestos insulation contractors: Bell's works, Newton Mearns, Glasgow, late 1950s. (*Courtesy of Glasgow City Libraries and Archives*)

10   Asbestos insulation contractors: Kitson's, Dobbies Loan, Glasgow, late 1950s. (*Courtesy of Glasgow City Libraries and Archives*)

11 The laggers' craft: ship's boiler-room, showing asbestos-insulated pipework by Anderson's, Glasgow, *c.* 1960. (*Courtesy of Glasgow City Libraries and Archives*)

12   John Brown's shipyard, Clydebank, 1949, showing HMS *Caronia* near completion. (*Courtesy of Clydebank Library*)

13   Asbestos exposure extended even to the finishing trades in shipbuilding, including the French polishers. *Queen Mary*, 1934. (*Courtesy of Clydebank Press*)

14   Construction of the QE2, John Brown's shipyard, 1966–67. Asbestos was extensively used at that time to fireproof the liner. (*Courtesy of Glasgow University Archives and Business Records*)

15   Locomotive construction, North British Locomotive Co., Springburn, Glasgow, 1924. In the foreground is an asbestos-lagged boiler. (*Courtesy of Mitchell Library, Glasgow*)

16   Fitting a Turner's asbestos cement corrugated roof in Glasgow, *c.* 1960.
(*Courtesy of Glasgow City Libraries and Archives*)

17   Insulation work at a school in Drumchapel, *c.* 1960. Asbestos was used
extensively as a fire retardant in Scottish schools in this period. (*Courtesy of
Glasgow City Libraries and Archives*)

18   The Red Road Flats, Springburn, Glasgow. Sprayed asbestos and marinite panels were heavily used in these flats, which were the highest in Europe when constructed in 1967.

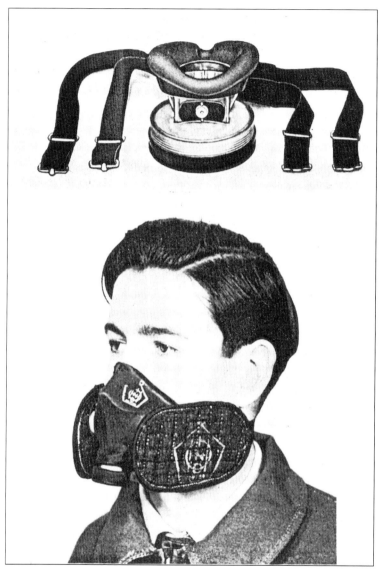

19 'State of the art' respirators (non-air line), authorised by the Ministry of Labour in the 1950s. Ironically, the filter in these masks was made of asbestos fibre.

20   'Best practice': demonstrating asbestos removal at the Hillington Training Centre, Glasgow, 1999. (*Courtesy of the Herald Picture Library*)

translated into protective legislation at workplace level was painfully slow. The 1969 Regulations in particular did not go far enough in protecting Scottish workers. However, the worst error in occupational health this century was the belief that the main danger of asbestos was in the dry-form processing of the mineral in the asbestos plants constructed in the pre-World War Two period. This mistake – recognised by the Factory Inspectorate as early as 1945 in relation to the shipyards – was to cost thousands of lives, and especially so in Scotland where most of the workers using asbestos were still not covered by protective regulations.

Underlying all this is the fact that occupational health has traditionally received a low priority in Scotland, and the institutional structure put in place in the mid-1970s – with the HSE and the HSC – has tended to continue this tradition by putting safety at work before health at work. The blame for the asbestos tragedy, then, can be left at a number of doors: the employers for not initiating proper safety procedures as soon as the dangers were realised; the government for favouring the business interest (evidence of this is the recent reluctance of a Labour Government to ban the import of white asbestos); and the trade unions and even the workers themselves to some extent for putting wages ahead of safety. However, only the state and the employers – and their insurance companies – can carry the can for the unfair system of civil and state compensation that has been in force throughout the period covered by this book. Sufferers of asbestos-related disease are victims. However, to achieve any level of compensation for their disability they have to endure a complex and at times distasteful process in which they are treated as the villains of the piece. The roots of this treatment are embedded deep in old attitudes fostered by nineteenth-century Workmen's Compensation procedure, and have taken a long time to wither. In the age of the welfare state, then, the asbestos tragedy stands out as a failure of state welfare policy. 'A man disabled during the course of his employment has been disabled while working under orders.' Therefore, if any remnant of the welfare state envisaged by Beveridge still remains, then the long and painful delay in compensating what one historian has called 'the wounded soldiers of industry' must be quickly removed.[104] The evidence provided by this study suggests that

104. P. W. J. Bartrip and S. B. Burman *The Wounded Soldiers of Industry* (Oxford, 1983).

DHSS industrial compensation procedure regarding asbestos-related disease – in which the onus is on the claimants to prove they have been affected to a significant degree by asbestos exposure – needs to be re-appraised. Unfortunately, such a re-appraisal cannot be undertaken by the new Scottish Parliament as the powers of the DHSS and the Employment Service still remain with Westminster. This is also the case with occupational health and safety, and it is to be lamented that Scotland's new government cannot as yet encompass these important fields.

CHAPTER FIVE

Opposing Camps? Employers, Unions and Pressure Groups

When you saw the conditions on the Clyde, it was like
fighting an atomic war with a bow and arrow, you know.
You hadnae a chance. [Clyde shipyard rigger]

In this chapter we examine how employers, workers and their
organisations in Scotland responded to the asbestos issue. As far as
the trade unions are concerned, it has been suggested that they did
not do enough to protect their members from occupational health
risks, and that they have historically concentrated on maximising
wages.[1] Trade unions have always been in an uncomfortable position
regarding occupational health and safety, as although they were in
the front line of defence against dangerous work practices, their main
rationale was to represent their members' interests, and this frequently
meant that wages and working hours were prioritised over
occupational health matters. Partly because of this, and partly because
medical knowledge was so slow in trickling down to shop-floor
level, the unions were relatively inactive regarding the asbestos
issue before the 1960s, and little was done, as Wikely and Tweedale
have shown, to modify the 1931 Asbestos Regulations and increase
worker safety.[2] Does this indictment apply to organised labour in
Scotland, or does the evidence suggest otherwise? What role did the
specialised pressure groups – including Clydeside Action on Asbestos
– which emerged in the late 1970s and the 1980s play in tackling the
problem?

1. For this argument, see P. Weindling (ed.), *A Social History of Occupational
   Health* (1985), p. 10; J. L. Williams, *Accidents and Ill-Health at Work* (1960),
   pp. 321–44. G. Tweedale, in *Magic Mineral* (2000) has also been critical of
   trade union inactivity on the asbestos issue.
2. N. Wikely, 'Asbestos and Cancer: an Early Warning to the British TUC',
   American Journal of Industrial Medicine, 22 (1992), pp. 449–516, cited in
   G. Tweedale, *Magic Mineral*, p. 171.

On their part, the employers and management have been charged with putting profits before workers' health and subjecting workers to dangerous working practices even when the dangers became known to them. The big UK asbestos manufacturer Turner & Newall has recently been the subject of an intense critique by G. Tweedale. This investigation was only made possible when the Chase Manhattan Bank forced T&N's papers into the public domain in 1995 – after T&N had fitted asbestos insulation to the banking company's New York headquarters. Tweedale's critique clearly shows that T&N adopted a head-in-sand approach to the whole issue of the dangers of asbestos, and that this giant UK asbestos multinational denied health risks, attempted to suppress research data in the 1950s that showed asbestos to be the cause of lung cancer, and fought tooth-and-nail to oppose the extension of protective legislation. Dust control measures were often ignored, medical inspections were infrequent and compensation levels were pitifully meagre. Other companies such as Cape Asbestos adopted a similarly callous attitude. The majority of asbestos-disease sufferers and their families received nothing in compensation before the 1960s, and until that time the average pay-out for a death was less that £300. To what extent was this pattern repeated with the asbestos manufacturers and users of the product in Scotland?

Employers, management and the asbestos problem

Well, at one time we used to call them the Masters' Federation, you know. But names change. We've met them, aye. Some good meetings, some bad meetings. But we've never went in and not came away with nothing. We've always came away with something ... We had to fight for everything we've ever got.[3]

Although a lot has been written about trade unions, the role of employers and management in occupational health and safety and the collective actions of employers have been given relatively little attention.[4] This is partly because of the dearth of records and the fact that private companies often operated in a more clandestine way than the more public and open activities of the trade unions. Unfortunately,

3. Interview A23.
4. For an account of the growth of employers' associations in the North of England and the West of Scotland, see A. J. McIvor, *Organised Capital* (Cambridge, 1996), and R. Johnston, *Clydeside Capital, 1870–1920* (East Linton, 2000).

a search for any surviving records of asbestos manufacturing companies in Scotland drew a blank. There are no surviving papers that we have been able to locate for MacLellan's, Tinto, Marinite or any of the pre-World War Two Scottish asbestos factories. Fortunately, however, there is some material in the main Turner & Newall Archive which refers to the activities of Newall's Insulation in Scotland and the Turner's Asbestos Cement factory in Clydebank, especially in relation to compensation issues. We have also uncovered and made use of some material from the shipbuilding industry, notably the Clyde Shipbuilders' Association records and the surviving records of the main employers' association in Scotland which organised the thermal insulation companies, including the lagging trades of Clydeside. These previously unresearched documents provide a valuable insight into employers' attitudes and policies in Scotland on the asbestos issue from the inter-war period onward.

Scottish employers in the nineteenth century were renowned for their competitiveness and individualism – the classic Victorian entrepreneurs. The ways in which they dealt with labour varied widely. As we noted in Chapter 2, there were some progressive, welfarist employers who genuinely attempted to regulate their working conditions to minimise the risk of injury and death to their employees. Robert Owen at New Lanark would be an example.[5] However, Scottish employers, especially those on Clydeside, developed something of a reputation for being tough on labour and their organisations in the nineteenth century. In the West of Scotland the prevailing capitalist culture before World War One was characterised by authoritarian, coercive managerial policies imbued with an anti-trade union attitude. Wages were lower than in other comparable industrial regions in the UK, and working conditions were extremely harsh in the heavy staple industries that dominated the Clydeside economy. This attitude to industrial relations was to some extent a reaction to workers' militancy on 'Red Clydeside', and one employers' association official linked to an organisation which ran a political blacklist – designed to keep labour activists out of employment – referred to Glasgow in the 1920s as 'the Red Capital of the Empire'.[6] However, Clydeside's hard-line managerial culture became diluted

5. See I Donnachie and G. Hewitt, *Historic New Lanark* (Edinburgh, 1993).
6. See A. McIvor and H. Paterson, 'Combating the Left', in R. Duncan and A. McIvor (eds), *Militant Workers: Labour and Class Conflict on the Clyde, 1900–1950* (Edinburgh, 1992), p. 143.

over time, although there were still some vestiges remaining in shipbuilding and engineering by the middle of the twentieth century.[7]

Scottish employers, like their counterparts south of the Border, also drifted towards collective organisation to protect capitalist interests in the face of accumulating pressures in the late nineteenth century. From the 1870s onwards the number of employers' associations throughout Britain grew in response to the increasing strength of trade unionism, and because of government 'interference' in production and growing foreign competition in markets. On Clydeside, this growth was quite marked, and by 1919 there were 180 national and local employers' associations operating in the area designed specifically for labour relations purposes.[8] One of these organisations was the Master Boiler and Pipe Coverers' Association whose member firms were closely associated with the use of asbestos as a thermal insulator.

The Secretary of this employers' association was the solicitor, Sir Thomas Biggart, of the Glasgow-based legal firm Biggart and Lumsden. Biggart was closely involved with Scottish employers' associations from the early 1890s, and his company was responsible for running the affairs of around 20 similar masters' organisations, including the Clyde Shipbuilders' Association and the Clydeside branch of the Engineering Employers' Federation – the North West Engineering Trades Employers' Association (NWETEA). Moreover, Biggart's involvement with employers stemmed from a definite capitalist class-consciousness – he was known to refer to the trade unions as 'the other side.'[9] In February 1931 Biggart sent a circular to all the member firms of the Glasgow Master Boiler and Pipe Coverers' Association and the North West Engineering Trades Employers' Association giving them full details of the impending Asbestos Industry (Asbestosis) Scheme. He warned them that:

> Although headed as applying to the Asbestos Industry only, the draft scheme, we are advised, is intended to apply to the

---

7. See R. Johnston, *Clydeside Capital, 1870–1920* (East Linton, 2000), Chapter 8; A. McKinlay and J. Melling, 'The Shop Floor Politics of Productivity', in A. Campbell, N. Fishman and J. McIlroy (eds), *British Trade Unions and Industrial Politics: Vol. 1, The Post-War Compromise, 1945–64* (1999), p. 229.

8. There had been only 22 in 1902. Directory of Industrial Associations in the United Kingdom, 1902 and 1919.

9. For an account of Biggart's activities see R. Johnston, *Clydeside Capital*, pp. 296–304.

processes defined in the scheme not only when carried on in asbestos works but also when carried on elsewhere.

Biggart was concerned here that many of the member firms were engaged in processes that were to be included under the new scheme: 'processes involving manipulation of asbestos ... the making of insulation slabs or sections ... the making or repairing of mattresses, composed wholly or partly of asbestos ... any other manufacturing process carried on in the same room ...' [10] Clearly, therefore, if they did not already know, the main Clydeside insulating masters were made fully aware of the dangers of working with asbestos in 1931, and were informed at that stage by their own secretary that the new regulations were intended to operate beyond the asbestos factories where the 'defined processes' took place. So, the asbestos manufacturing companies, the insulating companies and the engineering and shipbuilding firms on Clydeside were well aware of the dangers of asbestos long before World War Two.[11] Tweedale and Jeremy have shown how, throughout the period from the 1930s to the 1960s, Turner & Newall – the major asbestos multi-national company in the UK – pursued a policy of denial and minimisation of the risk, misinforming government regulators, trying to suppress research findings and paying out minimal levels of financial compensation whilst creaming off massive profits and paying bumper dividends to shareholders.[12] The Clydeside asbestos manufacturers and the asbestos insulating companies adopted very similar strategies. As early as November 1932 MacLellan's Glasgow Asbestos Works were lobbying Turner & Newall offering their support for a campaign to get the new Asbestos Regulations scrapped.[13] There were also some supporters in Parliament. The Glasgow Conservative MP Douglas Jamieson was congratulated by T&N for his albeit unsuccessful efforts to get the new Asbestos Regulations curtailed on the grounds that the cost to

10. Letter, Biggart, Lumsden and Co., Solicitors, to the members of the Glasgow Master Boiler and Pipe Coverers' Association, 19 February 1931; see also letter from Reid, McFarlane and Co. (Clydeside insulation contractors) to Turner and Newall, 20 February 1931, referring to the Biggart circular (Turner and Newall Archive, CAA, Glasgow).
11. See G. Tweedale, *Magic Mineral*; N. Wikely, 'Asbestos and cancer'.
12. G. Tweedale and D. J. Jeremy, 'Compensating the workers', pp. 116–17; see also G. Tweedale, *Magic Mineral*; *Scotsman*, 15 July 1993.
13. Letter Robert Turner, T&N, to K. MacLellan, Glasgow Asbestos Co., 3 November 1932 (T&N Archive, Manchester).

the employers of the Medical Panels was prohibitive.[14] Furthermore, the employers' records show that in 1951 the shipyard laggers were assured that 'there was no danger to health' involved in the spraying of asbestos.[15] Given the widely circulated warning from the Home Office about such dangers six years previously in 1945, this was being, at best, disingenuous.[16] In Scotland, as elsewhere, employers who used asbestos invariably denied any risk, then attempted to minimise the extent of the problem. In expressing their concerns over draft regulations suggesting the exclusion of young persons and the introduction of compulsory respirators in 1950, the Scottish insulation employers indicated their prioritisation of recruitment over ensuring the health and wellbeing of their labour force.[17]

The documentary and oral evidence for Clydeside (see Chapter 3) indicates quite unequivocally that there was no effective protection for most of the insulating workers (i.e. the laggers and sprayers) in shipbuilding at least until asbestos was formally added to the Shipbuilding Regulations in 1960. Those working beside these men were not protected by legislation until 1969. This was despite widespread knowledge of the dangers of working with asbestos, including Biggart's letter in 1931 and the Chief Factory Inspector's circular in 1945 (cited in full in Appendix 1).[18] Despite knowledge of the dangers to health that asbestos exposure entailed, the response of T&N was to reassure shipyards using its product that all was well and no special precautions were necessary. Thus, T&N wrote to the Fairfields shipyard on the Clyde in January 1946 denying the risk:

> We have pointed out that any such extension of the use of respirators is quite unnecessary ... I do not think that you need trouble about this question very much yourselves, as we are abundantly satisfied not only that we comply with the Regulations, and generally with the recommendations made in

14. Letter, Robert Turner, T&N, to G. Jamieson, MP for Glasgow District, 10 November 1932 (T&N Archive, Manchester).
15. Ibid., 11 April 1951.
16. Ibid., 4 February 1946; letter from A. W. Garrett, Chief Inspector of Factories, August 1945 (Turner & Newall Archive, CAA).
17. SIEA, Minutes, 2 November 1950; 11 December 1950. These draft regulations were dropped by the government after protests from the asbestos industry. The regulations were then shelved for almost a decade.
18. *Sunday Mail*, March 1992, p. 14. See also Channel 4 Scottish Eye TV programme, 'The cost of a ship' (1974).

the Chief Inspector's letter, but also that the risk referred to in that letter in point of fact hardly exists, or at most only to a completely negligible extent.[19]

Throughout the 1940s and 1950s, the records of the Scottish insulating employers' organisation show that they continued to obstruct the passage of further ameliorative legislation, assured workers that their work was safe, whilst coordinating activities with the English Thermal Insulation Engineers' Association and the asbestos manufacturers to oppose the extension of the Shipbuilding Regulations.[20] This successfully delayed the passage of effective statutory controls over asbestos use in the yards for more than two decades between 1945 and the late 1960s.

Throughout this period protection was frequently minimal, unenforced and ineffective – as the 1967 laggers' strike and much oral evidence (see Chapter 3) testifies. Meanwhile deaths continued. Bernard Stevenson, who worked for Clydeside insulating companies from 1909 to 1936 was diagnosed as permanently disabled with asbestosis in 1939 and died in 1942 of asbestosis, aged 52. Charlie Coyle died of asbestosis in 1956 aged just 48. The way in which his claim against Turner & Newall was dealt with indicates clearly the callous attitude of the asbestos industry at that time towards its disabled and dying workers (see full account in Chapter 1). By 1957, at least six Clydeside workers (three of whom were asbestos sprayers) employed by Newall's Insulation had contracted asbestosis.[21] Ten years later the number of laggers with asbestos-related diseases had risen to 53, and 14 had died, several of mesothelioma.[22] The men responded by taking action to protect themselves. In June 1967, 500 of Scotland's 700 insulating engineers went on strike over fears for their health.[23] It was reported at this time that 75% of the Clydeside insulating firms did not provide proper masks and only at the Rosyth Royal Naval Dockyard in Fife was protective clothing issued.[24] Even

19. Letter, Mr Grieve, T&N, to Fairfield Shipbuilding and Engineering Co. Ltd, 23 January 1946 (T&N Archive, Manchester)
20. SIEA, *Minutes*, 2 November 1950; 11 June 1958.
21. Newall Insulation Company Ltd, Asbestos Cases 1939–1957 (Turner & Newall Archive, CAA)
22. *Glasgow Herald*, 24 February, 1967, p. 24.
23. *Glasgow Herald*, 13 June 1967, p. 11; 19 June 1967, p. 16.
24. *The Newsletter*, 24 June 1967 (John Todd Papers; CAA Archive). At Rosyth, the protective clothing covered the workers completely, like a diving suit.

at Rosyth the precautions taken were ineffective, ventilating
equipment was inadequate and laggers were not warned fully of the
dangers when stripping out old asbestos insulating materials when
ships were being refitted in the late 1960s and into the 1970s.[25]
Moreover, after the immediate pressure of a trade-union campaign
or strike had passed, employers and management could subvert the
regulations or renege on agreed procedures. After the 1967 laggers'
strike, for example, the employers agreed to set up a Health
Committee and give the laggers medical inspections every two years.
The Health Committee met a few times, then didn't meet for four
years whilst the men had only one medical inspection in the decade
after the dispute.[26]

In the workplace, moreover, examples of employer and
management malpractice, which exposed workers to life-threatening
levels of exposure to asbestos, abound. Asbestos was sometimes
stripped clandestinely, frequently without proper sealing to prevent
contamination of the neighbouring work areas. Further, the waste
was often put into permeable bags and dumped illegally. It could also
be argued that, in general, management failed to propagate a safety
culture, and that workers were encouraged to cut corners because of
wage systems that incorporated bonuses or other incentives. One
worker at the Marinite asbestos factory in Springburn in Glasgow
recalled such direct managerial intervention:

> This machine they had, it was like a big eh ... cone. All you
> done was rip the bag with a knife, put the fibres into this
> fucking blower thing and it churned it up. You were looking
> up this funnel, and it would be all choked up, and you'd have
> – you know the likes of the gaffers who were in the factory at
> that time – and they would hit you with a rake. You'd say
> 'What's that for?' 'That's for getting the mix cleared out.'[27]

These kinds of practices were difficult to oppose when the heavy
industries were declining on Clydeside and there were plenty of folk
in a desperate enough position to work under any conditions.

Similarly, the policies of management at the Turner's' Asbestos
Cement Company at Clydebank from 1938 to its closure in 1970

---

25. See *Glasgow Herald*, 12 September 1988.
26. See John Todd's testimony in A. Dalton, *Asbestos Kills* (1979), p. 99.
27. Interview A 22.

contributed quite critically to exposing workers to lethal doses of asbestos dust. Turner's' claimed that working in the largely 'wet' processes of asbestos cement manufacture was safe. Hence, in the late 1930s T&N contracted out of its internal asbestosis insurance scheme in relation to such workers. How much of this was just public relations, however, is difficult to decipher from the extant records. The weight of evidence against the company suggests that they would have been aware of the risks in asbestos cement. Moreover, as Tweedale has shown, the medical surveillance schemes instituted by the parent company in Rochdale were less rigorously adhered to by the smaller satellite. Furthermore, management at Turner's Clydebank had a very slipshod attitude towards protection. Oral evidence shows that masks and respirators were either not provided for Turner's Clydebank factory workers, were ineffective or were available but the necessity of workers wearing them was not impressed upon those working in the dust on the shop floor – even when sweeping up (see Chapter 3). Workers were misinformed that the risk was minimal, associated just with one type of asbestos (blue) and with the 'dry' processes. Moreover, in compensation cases in the 1950s and 1960s, Turner's continued to deny the risks involved and suppressed evidence. In disputing James Docherty's asbestosis claim in 1956, the company noted that asbestosis 'can only develop as a result of long exposure over a period of many years'. Despite the prevalence of dust in the atmosphere in the dry-cutting processes identified by T&N's own Medical Adviser (Lewinsohn), the company still noted that a worker claiming compensation in 1968 was not at risk: 'McMeekan was not exposed to dust whilst in our employ, other than that dust which may normally be expected in the atmosphere'. In another case (Hugh McNicol), Turner's arranged a dust concentration test in the Dalmuir fibre store, finding an acceptable dust level of 0.5 fibres/c.c., well within the new limits of 2 fibres/c.c. laid down in the 1969 Regulations. However, the Regulations were more stringent for blue asbestos, though the works manager suggested in a note to TAC, Trafford Park that this should be kept quiet: 'I would point out for your information, although this may better be left unsaid elsewhere, that the Dalmuir fibre stores still contain some quantity of blue fibre, for which the acceptable 'safe' fibre concentration is reduced from 2 to 0.2 fibres/c.c.' [28]

28. Material taken from the compensation files of W. McMeekan; James Docherty and Hugh Nicol in the Chase Manhattan Archive, Manchester (we are grateful to Geoffrey Tweedale for providing this material).

Moreover, Turner's management appear to have done little, if anything, to take the initiative and change the culture of self-neglect on the shop floor, even long after the dangers of working with asbestos were well known. Internal T&N reports on the state of the asbestos cement industry in the late 1960s provide a damning indictment of the neglect of health and safety provision in factories such as that at Clydebank. The cost of making radical changes in such factories to comply with the new 1969 Asbestos Regulations may well have been one factor explaining the closure of TAC Clydebank in 1970 – along with the fact that such a strategy shed future liabilities too.

This inevitably left a grim legacy. An indeterminate number of ex-Turner employees suffer from or have died of asbestos-related diseases since the 1960s whilst a register of asbestosis cases kept by the TGWU recorded 177 members of a 600-strong branch suffering from some degree of asbestos-related disability over a seven year period, 1975–81. Seventy-three of these cases ended fatally, with the average age of the laggers who died just 58 years. In 1991 alone, it was reported that the laggers' branch of the TGWU on Clydeside had 46 fatalities linked to asbestos-related diseases.[29]

These deaths occurred primarily because employers and management had not acted sooner to prevent exposure to this killer dust, despite the fact that they had been aware of the dangers asbestos posed for a long time. The chronology of employer awareness went as follows: employers were aware of the danger of asbestosis in manufacturing workers by 1929–31; lung cancer in manufacturing workers by 1955; mesothelioma in manufacturing workers by 1964–65; asbestosis amongst insulation workers by 1945; lung cancer amongst insulation workers by 1955 (and perhaps before); mesothelioma amongst insulation workers by 1960–64.[30] Profit continued to be prioritised over workers' health. In 1968, Dr Gaze of the Asbestosis Research Council (ARC), continued to champion the cause of asbestos, reminding participants at an occupational hygiene conference in 1968 that asbestos insulation was essential as a fire retardant in saving lives at sea.[31] The ARC and Cape Asbestos later wrote denying the risks of short-period exposure:

29. *Sunday Mail*, 1 March 1992.
30. House of Commons Employment Committee 1982–83, 'The Work of the Health and Safety Commission and Executive: Asbestos', Minutes of Evidence [87-I], p. 8 (Hereafter Employment Committee).
31. See 'Discussion' section after P. G. Harries, 'Asbestos Hazards in Naval Dockyards', *Annals of Occupational Hygiene*, vol. 11, 1968, p 143.

Although the evidence in regard to crocidolite is still rather conflicting, there is a great deal of evidence from medically supervised long service employees in chrysotile and amosite mines, and in factories using these fibres, that lengthy exposures to low or moderate amounts of dust (say less than 5 fibres per cc) or exposure to large amounts of dust over short periods may not cause injury or even detectable morbidity.[32]

Tweedale has convincingly demonstrated how the ARC, funded by the asbestos companies, played a crucial role in dictating the research agenda on the asbestos employers' terms, maintaining the focus on asbestosis long after the cancer risk was evident and helping to delay and influence regulatory legislation in the companies favour. Its research, which became based in the Institute of Occupational Medicine at Edinburgh University, avoided potential critical epidemiological surveys, focussed unduly upon animal experimentation and was 'limited and pedestrian'.[33] The ARC was a pivotal element in the asbestos industry's armoury, and frequently defended the industry in the courts, the media and the scientific press. Even as late as the mid-1980s there were many willing to champion the cause of asbestos, including the trade journal, *Asbestos Bulletin*, which produced a special edition in 1987 which carried the following announcement:

We decided to dedicate this number to the defence of a unique mineral – asbestos. The emotional campaign portraying asbestos as a potential killer accelerates its substitution by inferior and more expensive man-made mineral fibres. Recent findings appear to indicate that any durable fibre of specific dimensions can be considered as a potential tumour hazard. We believe that a legacy of the past obscures great progress made by industry in harnessing the hazards of asbestos. We do not wish to minimise the risk involved ... but equally we are convinced that if properly handled this material – asbestos – can serve mankind in many ways and can make a great contribution to human safety ... In due course we revert to our

32. Ibid., p. 145
33. See G. Tweedale, 'Science or Public Relations?: The Asbestosis Research Council, 1957–1990', unpublished paper presented at the Work, Health and Illness Conference, University of Exeter, September 2000.

normal coverage and will continue to print good and bad news in an objective manner.[34]

Whilst the evidence on the employers' side is relatively thin, in the main, our findings concur with the critiques of Castleman and Tweedale in that Scottish employers denied risk and suppressed knowledge, opposed protective legislation, ruthlessly contested compensation, failed to warn workers and spread inaccurate information about the asbestos hazard.[35] Meanwhile, serious disability and deaths from asbestos-related lung cancer and mesothelioma continued to escalate alarmingly from the 1960s.

Scottish trade unions and asbestos

Effective trade unionism evolved slowly in Scotland. In 1892, only 3.7% of the adult population were trade unionists, and this compared with 5% south of the Border. Several reasons have been given. To some extent the growth of trade unionism – especially in the urban industrial conurbation of Clydeside – was held back by sectarianism amongst workers, by an inward-looking nationalism and by overstocked urban labour markets flooded with poor rural migrants from Ireland and the Highlands.[36] Clydeside employers were also notoriously anti-trade union. However, collective bargaining did strengthen over time as employers and workers increasingly realised that negotiation was better than outright conflict.[37]

The Clydeside engineering and shipbuilding industries have always been a bastion of highly skilled craft labour, and 60% of the total workforce in this industry was classed as skilled in 1914. However, even when workers had high levels of skill, effective trade unionism could still be hard to sustain.[38] In the early 1860s, for example, workers in the main British shipbuilding regions managed to increase their

34. *Asbestos Bulletin*, March–April 1987, p. 24.
35. B. Castleman, *Asbestos: Medical and Legal Aspects* (1996); G. Tweedale, *Magic Mineral*, pp. 277–93.
36. W. Knox, 'Class, Work And Trade Unionism in Scotland', in A. Dickson and J. H. Treble (eds.), *People and Society in Scotland, Vol. 3, 1914–1990* (Edinburgh, 1992).
37. R. Johnston, *Clydeside Capital* (East Linton, 2000); A. J. McIvor, 'Were Clydeside employers more autocratic?', in W. Kenefick and A. J. McIvor (eds), *Roots of Red Clydeside* (Edinburgh, 1996), p. 40.
38. W. Knox, *Industrial Nation* (Edinburgh, 1999), p. 206.

wages by picking off employers one at a time. However, in 1865 – during a downturn in trade – the situation was reversed, and this was especially so on the Clyde. Here, the bosses combined to defeat the workers over the issue of a nine-hour day, and by 1866 membership of the Boilermakers' Society had collapsed. The situation was so bad that two years later its Glasgow branch – which was now the strongest in Scotland – could only muster 41 members.[39] The union was also battered by determined national employer lock-outs in 1896–97 and later in 1922.

It was primarily because trade unionism was weak that shop stewards became so important in the Scottish workplace. During the First World War a powerful shop stewards' movement in the West of Scotland organised unofficial strike action that earned the region the label 'Red Clydeside'. After the war the power of the shop stewards declined somewhat, and the post-war years were marked by the determination of many Scottish engineering companies to minimise their influence and re-establish employers' right to manage without interference. Labour relations in the engineering industry, then, were largely confrontational for a significant part of our period.

The workmen were relatively well organised in asbestos marine lagging, engineering and construction by the post-Second World War period. The Glasgow laggers' branch (7/162) of the TGWU was one of the strongest in Scotland, with a membership of around 600 in the 1950s and 1960s, representing almost 90% of potential membership.[40] Initially, the trade of asbestos boiler and pipe lagging was carried out by unskilled labourers, as was asbestos spraying, which developed from the 1930s. On the Clyde, it was these insulation workers – who were members of the TGWU 7/162 Thermal Insulation Branch – who first started complaining about working conditions and the dangers of asbestos exposure during the Second World War. In 1951 the union claimed a substantial wage rise for asbestos sprayers in Scotland, on the basis of 'danger to health, the awkwardness of working with masks and the uncongenial nature of the work'. The employers rejected the claim, noting that as the labourers did the work after only one week's instruction, they did not merit a wage rise and that anyway the job was not dangerous.[41] Thereafter, the TGWU

39. Ibid., p. 117.
40. SIEA, Minutes, 1 December 1955.
41. Ibid., 11 April 1951.

waged a successful campaign in the 1950s to have the occupation of insulating engineer upgraded to skilled craft status, with a commensurate increase in earnings. In part, this was seen as a compensation for the hazards associated with asbestos work and in part as a way of raising occupational health standards by excluding inexperienced labourers from the work. From 1959, young asbestos laggers entering the trade became 'probationers' until they reached 18 years, when they undertook a three-year apprenticeship, becoming fully trained craftsmen at age 21.[42]

The Clydeside laggers also called for an investigation into health and safety in the thermal insulation industry but their requests were turned down by the local group secretary. One shop steward recalled how his branch had to fight even for basic amenities:

> There were no overalls. No boots. And you were swallowing it all the time, and so was all the people that were working near you. But they had a hut where they made mats only in it. Nae extractor fan or nothing ... At one time we didnae have any huts. We had to sit between decks on the ships. We had to go and fight for tae get a hut. You know, an ordinary hut. And in that hut was a' the material. And you were taking your tea during the meal breaks, and a' that material. And every part of the material had asbestos in it, a percentage.[43]

Another lagger recounted how the main fighting strength of the trade union was at branch level:

> Well, if you're talking about the unions. I always think the union is a mythical body. This branch done a lot. We happened to belong to a trade union. We fought ... I mean, we walked the streets for 26 weeks to get conditions. We were the ones that forced them to give us tables and chairs to sit down to have a meal with. Made them give us a changing room to hang our clothes up ...[44]

Around this time laggers in Belfast were taking up the mesothelioma issue too, and the TGWU gradually became more and more involved

42. SIEA, Minutes, 1 April 1952; 15 August 1956; 2 December 1958; 14 September 1959.
43. Interview A23.
44. Interview A22.

in ensuring that its members received adequate compensation.[45] There was also a new determination that workers, such as the lagger mentioned above, did not settle for low final payments. The Secretary related how this came about:

> Our legal department became a better legal department than it used to be. They began to get involved. Now what you have is that settlements are made on a pro-percentage rata basis. Whereas M could now go back and say that 'I'm now 90% or 100%' so there would be a further award. But he settled in these days for a one-off payment. And that bothers us all in here when you see M now.[46]

The main impetus for the trade unions to do something substantial about the unfolding asbestos tragedy in Scotland clearly came from workers in the insulation trade – which was excluded from the 1931 Regulations. In 1974 a conference of thermal insulation engineers called upon the government to bring about licensing of the thermal insulation industry. However, these requests, which were backed up by the TUC, were turned down. The GMWU was one of the most determined of the unions, and in 1974 lobbied the Simpson Committee then sitting to investigate the dangers of asbestos. In 1980 the union published a critique of the Simpson Report, and the following year it repeated its earlier request to the HSE that 53 recommendations made by the Simpson Committee be implemented.[47]

However, even the most vociferous of the unions were fully aware that if they pushed their demands too far, jobs would be at risk. For example, the GMWU's health and safety advisor commented: 'Asbestos workers could choose to settle for a 1 in 1000 risk, but that would mean closing down the asbestos industry tomorrow'.[48] Perhaps it is because of this that several workers look back on the trade unions' record on health and safety with jaundiced eyes. When an insulation engineer was asked about trade unionism in his industry he replied:

---

45. See O. Wade, *When I Dropped the Knife* (Durham, 1996). Also, D. O'Reilly *et al.*, 'Asbestos related mortality in Northern Ireland 1985–1994', *Journal of Public Health Medicine*, Volume 21, 1, pp. 95–101.
46. Interview A23.
47. Employment Committee, pp. 2–3.
48. Quoted in G. Tweedale, *Magic Mineral*, p. 249.

> It was an arse hole thing ... The insulating branch – I cannae
> remember the number – of the Transport and General
> Workers ... It's always been run by a shower of would-be
> gangsters. They were dishing money ... One branch secretary
> he fled to London. He'd done in all the funds and that. And
> the next one he went from rags to riches when he took the job,
> but he managed to keep his nose clear as far as the funds
> went ... Through the years they were supposed to pass out
> money to blokes that went on the sick and that, but they never
> ever done it. I never got a penny from the union in my life. [49]

It was members of the Insulation Branch who were prominent
amongst those who formed Clydeside Action on Asbestos, and this
organisation has done superb work in assisting many victims to claim
their rightful compensation. However, one lagger noted that in its
early days the personnel were less than savoury:

> When it first started up it was our crowd that took tae dae
> with it, and I wanted nothing at all tae dae with them. Because
> they were a shower of bloody rogues. I'm no kidding you. I
> could mention their names but I'd probably get dragged up for
> deprivation of character ... A clique. If your face fitted they
> helped you. If your face didnae fit you were out. [50]

Similar thoughts on trade union involvement were expressed by other
ex-workers. A Scottish lagger remembers his experiences of being in
charge of jobs in England when he needed union help:

> Anytime you had a dispute or anything I found that if you
> tried to call them [local trade union delegates] out they
> wouldnae come. So, what was going on was eh, just basically
> the guys on the job had to work it out for themselves whether
> they were going to do it or whether they wernae going to do it,
> you know. But, union help? Very disappointed with it. [51]

And a heating engineer who was a member of the Heating, Ventilation
and Air Conditioning Workers' Union, recalled that his union did not
have the strength to do much to improve worker safety, and that this

---

49. Interview A14.
50. Interview A1.
51. Interview A16.

would have been difficult anyway due to the displaced nature of workers:

> To my knowledge there has only been one strike in the heating
> trade, and they couldnae afford ... They termed it a catch
> strike ... They only could take out so many firms or so many
> jobs. Say for talking sake there was eh, say six jobs involved in
> heating in the town. Well, they'd take three of thae jobs out
> and the rest had to put a levy in to keep their wages up. The
> union hadnae enough money and the backing to support a full
> strike, you know, an all-out strike. So we had to work it on
> catch strikes, you know. And it only lasted, to my memory, I
> think it was three weeks, then we couldnae afford it after that.
> Packed it in. So the strike was just a no-go area. As I say we
> werenae a strong enough union because eh, it didnae affect
> any ... We knew we couldnae last. You know, we couldnae go
> out indefinite. We could maybe go out for a fortnight maybe,
> but the most I can ever remember was three weeks. [52]

However, another trade union activist now suffering from pleural plaques noted that things had to be kept in perspective:

> No one attached any great importance to it [asbestos]. They
> knew it wasnae good for your health. But there are so many
> things in shipbuilding that are bad for your health, you know. I
> mean if you get a guy in a double bottom welding. He's only
> got about two feet. And he's crawling in between right in the
> double bottom of the ship. And he's in a wee confined space
> no bigger than that settee you're sitting on and welding and
> burning you know. And he's getting all these fumes ... So
> there's so many things, that it's just another thing that you've
> got to overcome when you're in shipbuilding ... When you saw
> the conditions in the Clyde it was like fighting an atomic war
> with a bow and arrow, you know. You hadnae a chance. [53]

Although the trade union movement and the STUC had been vocal on the issue of a national occupational health service from 1946, with the passage of the Safety Representative and Safety Committees' Regulations of 1977, trade union pressure came to an end. The unions

52. Interview A6.
53. Interview A18.

were largely content that employer/employee safety committees could now be set up, and a heating engineer remembers how after years of exposure to asbestos a trade union safety representative arrived one day to give him and his colleagues a lecture on safety:

> They came up and gave us a lecture on asbestos. I said you're a wee bit late in the day. I mean that's 1996, 1995 ... I said 'health and safety? We're kidding ourselves on here aren't we?'[54]

And as a plater recalled his experiences of the new system:

> I was in Barclay Curles there, and they brought out a new system and they had to have a safety man ... And I was recommended to be the safety man on the ship there, and they had a meeting every month ... I was the only man that was in the ship. And when we got up there, there was an insurance man and everybody gave their opinion of what was dangerous. And I brought up asbestos. But at the same time the men that were in the engine shop, they werenae involved with asbestos ... and you couldnae get the backing of them.[55]

Looking beyond the specific industries and unions that were directly involved with the asbestos issue, how did the Scottish union movement react to the asbestos problem? The records of the STUC indicate that the Congress was very aware of occupational health and safety and, indeed, broader public health issues. From the 1930s the STUC campaigned, with some success, to increase the number of factory and Trade Boards inspectors and get reforms in workmen's compensation provision and a widening of the list of prescribed industrial diseases.[56] Congress was also actively involved in the post-war decades in lobbying the Minister of Labour and the Secretary of State for Scotland on a wide range of health issues, including the NHS, cervical cancer, dermatitis, radiation hazards, Factory Acts, the provision of general practitioners, and environmental pollution. Congress was also instrumental in raising awareness of occupational health and safety in general through the promotion of conferences, seminars, day schools and training schemes for union officials. The

54. Interview A7.
55. Interview A3.
56. STUC, *Annual Reports* (subsequently AR), 1939, p. 39; 229–30; 1940, pp. 190–1; 1944, p. 16; 1956, p. 240.

first of these took place in 1973 and several were organised at the STUC Education Centre at Treesbank thereafter.

From the 1950s, lung disease is a recurring theme in the STUC Annual Reports. The organisation threw its weight behind campaigns to eradicate tuberculosis through mass X-ray provision. The organisation also participated in a TUC campaign in the early 1950s to reduce the incidence of silicosis and pneumoconiosis in quarrying, iron foundries and mining. In its survey of iron foundry workers in 1951, almost 33% of workers examined were designated as 'suspected' cases of silicosis. Later it campaigned to get an Appeals Board established to provide some redress where workers' claims were rejected by the Pneumoconiosis Medical Panels.[57] This had a positive effect. In 1982, for example, a Glasgow painter won his appeal for Industrial Disability Benefit for asbestosis at the Appeal Tribunal (thus endorsing the views of his own doctor) after the Pneumoconiosis Medical Panel had refused his claim.[58] His exposure to asbestos was through brushing down and preparing four large asbestos cement roofs for painting.

However, given the evident interest and activity of the STUC on public health issues, and its clear awareness of the occupational dust issue, what is surprising is its lack of active campaigning on the asbestos problem in the three post-war decades to the 1970s. There is a silence on this issue in the STUC papers which is striking. Indeed, throughout the 50-year period from 1930 to 1980 there are only four direct references to asbestos in the STUC Annual Reports. The first, in 1968, is a comment from the delegate from the Glasgow District Trades Council which referred to the hazardous work practices at the Red Road building site. This followed representation to the Trades Council from the Amalgamated Society of Woodworkers a year before where the union had warned that the dangers extended beyond the workplace 'to the general public'.[59] The second, a year later, from the Midlothian Trades Council, noted the TGWU report on the high number of fatalities due to asbestosis and criticised the STUC for doing so little to address the asbestos problem. In 1974–75 the asbestos risk was noted in the Youth Conference section of the STUC Annual Report. However, the ambivalent attitude of the STUC towards

57. STUC, AR, 1964, p. 394; 1965, p. 72.
58. *Health and Safety at Work*, May 1984, p. 37.
59. Glasgow and District Trades Council, Minutes, 29 March 1967; 5 April 1967.

asbestos in this period was most evident, perhaps, at the 1976 STUC Conference in Perth. Before the conference started the insulation engineers from Clydebank circulated leaflets on the hazards of asbestos to the delegates before the conference got under way. This, though, was a breach of conference procedure, and the delegates were asked to ignore the leaflets. Several of them put the leaflets in their pockets, some crumpled them up, and one delegate – who went on to become a Labour MP – stood up and ceremoniously tore his into little pieces.[60] Worker unity, then, was hard to achieve at all levels and the evidence suggests that prior to the 1980s, the STUC did not take up asbestos dust consistently as a specific campaigning issue. Opportunities were clearly missed here to raise awareness and campaign actively for tighter and more effective regulations.

This was partly because the STUC failed to develop an ongoing relationship with occupational medicine prior to the 1970s. Significantly, the STUC did not have a Medical Adviser, as did the TUC (from 1960). It did occasionally call in Scottish medical experts to brief Executive officials on health issues – such as Dr Buchanan who advised Congress on occupational rheumatism – though there is no evidence in the STUC Reports or Minutes that they ever did so in relation to asbestos. Also noteworthy is that the STUC regarded the radical Socialist Medical Association (SMA) as a 'prescribed' organisation, refusing to allow its members to speak to affiliated unions and trades councils despite its evident interest in occupational health, including dust. In 1957 the SMA highlighted the massive incidence of chest disease in the UK (six times that of West Germany and twenty times higher than the Scandinavian countries), emphasising 'occupational factors' in their explanation:

> Many industries, particularly in this country where much
> old-fashioned plant is still in operation, are extremely dusty and
> those who work in them know that their chests suffer as a
> result ... Clearly we must make an earlier beginning if we are
> to tackle the root cause; every workman should be aware that
> dust and fumes at work are a hazard to health that must be
> controlled by proper preventative measures. No one should ever
> regard a cough as being normal.[61]

60. STUC, AR, 1984, p. 659. The earlier references to asbestos are at STUC, AR, 1968, p. 112–13; 1969, pp. 359–60; 1975, p. 220.
61. TGWU, Record, XXXVI, February 1957, p. 231.

The SMA went on to assert that the problem was 'largely unnecessary', that workers and unions needed to take more interest in such matters and (in a thinly veiled attack on trade unions' prioritisation of the wage packet) that 'in the battle for higher wages, better conditions must not be forgotten: amongst them clean air at work is clearly vital'. The organisation also appealed for 'more active co-operation with trade unions on health matters'. In Scotland, some of the Trades Councils tried to respond positively to this plea. In 1959, the Cowdenbeath Trades Council complained that the banning of the SMA 'serves only to weaken our Trade Union Movement'.[62] Thus an important avenue for raising awareness of occupational hazards to the workers themselves in the 1950s and 1960s was closed off.

There is also no reference at all in the STUC Annual Reports and Minutes of any discussion of the revision of the Asbestos Regulations over 1967–69. Clearly what was happening was that the STUC was delegating such issues to the TUC and not playing an active role in the campaigning process. A clear opportunity for the Scottish union movement to affect policy on occupational health in Scotland came in 1969, two years after the *QE2* Marinite *exposé* and the Red Road incident. A delegation from the STUC visited the Scottish Occupational Health Service in Dundee. The invitation was offered because 'the Director and his staff had believed that it would be possible for the General Council to influence trade unions to refer health matters for investigation to the laboratories'.[63] In response, however, the STUC informed SOHS that its occupational health matters were dealt with by the London School of Hygiene and Tropical Medicine. A chance to develop a more positive interface between occupational medicine and the unions in Scotland was thus missed.

This was doubly tragic because the Medical Adviser to the TUC at the time, Robert Murray, was relatively conservative on the asbestos issue, supporting regulation rather than a banning of the product. In 1967, Murray noted that 'no unacceptable risk at present exists' in the docks regarding asbestos exposure.[64] A year later, whilst promoting alternatives to asbestos he agreed with the ARC line that

---

62. STUC, GC, Minutes, 8 July 1959. The SMA provided 'many interesting lectures and films'.
63. STUC, GC, Minutes, 1 June 1969.
64. Cited in *Hazards*, 65, January–March 1999, p. 5.

'there were certain applications in which asbestos was essential'.[65] With reference to Red Road, Murray commented that he was grateful to Dr Sanderson of the SOHS for being 'able to demonstrate to the satisfaction of the building workers, after a strike, that by the use of certain methods it was possible to control the asbestos in the atmosphere to a reasonable level'.[66] Similarly, Murray tried to quell the fears of shipyard workers at the Fairfield's yard in Govan in 1969 by telling them that there were no hazards as long as proper precautions were taken.[67] His attitude to the workers was invariably patronising. Murray is on record as stating that companies such as Cape Asbestos, and Turner & Newall, were 'good firms', and his remark that 'workers would pick up asbestos with their teeth if they were paid enough' also won him few friends on Clydeside.[68] Murray went on to write a defence of the asbestos industry in the *British Journal of Industrial Medicine* in 1990.

The views of the trade unions' own medical expert may thus have helped to extend the use of asbestos and hence the exposure of many more people to this dangerous substance.[69] Moreover, what is also evident is that the STUC's main source of information on asbestos came from Murray. In September 1967 Murray's 'helpful information' provided on request on the asbestos issue was reported in the STUC General Council Minutes. This shows, firstly, just how uninformed the STUC was on the issue in the mid-late 1960s and, secondly, the extent to which they accepted without question Murray's interpretation of the problem, including that only blue asbestos was dangerous and that 'the risk is very much a matter of the degree of exposure to breathing the dust'.[70] Again, no action was taken by the STUC.

This contrasted sharply with the positive action taken against the asbestos hazard in the Clyde shipyards and on the building sites in the late 1960s and into the 1970s. In 1970 – the year after another West of Scotland study was published which made clear that the link

65. Harries, 'Asbestos Hazards', p. 143.
66. Ibid.
67. G. W. Roberts, 'Necropsy Studies of Asbestos Bodies in Glasgow and a Clinico-Pathological Study of Pleural Mesothelioma' (1969); letter from J. Bryson to Newall's Insulation Co. Ltd, dated 29 June 1970. CAA Archive, 100364.
68. *Morning Star*, 15 November 1974, p. 4.
69. For a more detailed critique, see Dalton, *Asbestos Kills*.
70. STUC, GC, Minutes, 13 September 1967.

between asbestos and mesothelioma was conclusive – shop stewards at Fairfield's shipyards refused to handle asbestos on safety grounds. This occurred at the same time as some workers in England were expressing publicly their concerns over the dangers of working with asbestos – including dockers in London in 1965 and the trade unions in the Royal Naval Dockyards who promoted the replacement of asbestos with glass fibre through their Joint Industrial Council in 1966–67.

Trade unionism, then, went *some way* to alleviating the asbestos problem for *some* of the Scottish workers directly affected by it. However, trade unionism could not be expected to protect the Scottish working class in general, and the evidence suggests that trade union involvement was patchy and that for a long time occupational health issues were not given priority. This was noted by a Dr Dingwall in a research paper on asbestos disease in 1988:

> Some unions have identified health and safety issues as a major policy concern. They run aggressive programmes to alert both current and retired workers to the possibility of obtaining compensation. Other unions have been relatively inactive. It is hard to resist the conclusion that if all unions were as active as the few, many more cases would come forward.[71]

The protective matrix offered by collective organisation was clearly more effective amongst the shipyard laggers, for example, than in the asbestos manufacturing plants. In Turner's Asbestos Cement trade unionism was non-existent, at least until the late 1960s. Similarly so with MacLellan's Rubber and Asbestos works in Maryhill, Glasgow, where there was no trade union until 1968.[72] The weakness of trade unionism in asbestos manufacturing in the post-war period is indicated in the fact that the industry had a statutory National Joint Industrial Council (NJIC – representing the UK) which negotiated wages and working conditions.[73] Moreover, the TGWU, which covered a whole range of miscellaneous and related occupations (including rubber, chemicals, concrete, cement, gas, paint, rayon and aerated water) did

71. *The Scotsman*, 5 January 1989, p. 5. Dingwall also went on to criticise doctors for failing to mobilise potential cases, sometimes failing even to inform elderly patients of their condition.
72. We are grateful to Pat Whitelaw, a shop steward at MacLellan's, for this information.
73. TGWU, *Annual Reports*, 1954, p. 103; 1958, p. 102; 1960, p. 197.

not record a significant presence in the asbestos factories in the 1950s, though it did represent such workers on the NJIC in this period.[74]

With the decline in trade union membership across Scotland, the increase in sub-contracting by large firms, and the upsurge in the number of small companies, the number of workers exposed to asbestos who were protected by trade unions declined from the mid-1970s. Moreover, although it was in the interest of the unions to ensure that their members were shielded from dangerous working practices, it was also in their interest to ensure that their jobs were protected too. Such a conflict of interest frequently acted against health and safety issues. For example, in 1979 the Scottish Secretary of the TGWU indicated that rather than implementing the TUC's proposals for phasing out the use of asbestos, the Scottish TGWU was committed to maintaining employment of asbestos workers, but 'would look after the families of those members who suffer from asbestos disease as a result'.[75]

The trade unions in Scotland thus had mixed responses to the asbestos hazard. One commentator noted in 1968 that: 'The position of the unions varied. There were some people who were so afraid of asbestos that they wanted the material banned altogether, while there were others, within the industry particularly, who appeared to handle it with impunity'.[76] In asbestos manufacturing in Scotland trade unions hardly had a presence until the late 1960s so workers went virtually unprotected. In construction and shipbuilding the unions were stronger. One of the first strategies of the unions in these workplaces was to negotiate additional wage payments to compensate for working in dusty work conditions (see Chapter 3). In the case of the Glasgow Boiler Coverers' Society and the Joiners' Society these date back to the 1910s, when agreements were struck with employers to provide members with 'dirty money' or 'stripping money' when engaged in cutting and working with asbestos lagging and panels such as 'asbestocel' and 'asbestoslab'. Clearly the dust was regarded as uncomfortable and injurious even at this time, even though the sources do not make it apparent that the specific risks of asbestosis were recognised. These collective agreements were periodically

74. TGWU, Record, 1958–59.
75. Letter from Nancy Tait (SPAID) to Raymond Macdonald, Scottish Secretary, TGWU, 6 February 1979 (John Todd Papers, CAA Archive, Glasgow).
76. Robert Murray, in 'Discussion' after Harries, 'Asbestos Hazards', 1968, p. 143.

re-negotiated and extended through to the 1950s and 1960s to cover other at-risk workers, including the electricians. At one level this shows a willingness of the workers and their unions to tolerate dangerous work practices as long as they were rewarded by higher wages. Whilst this can be interpreted as an example of the unions prioritising wages over health, there were also other motivations behind this policy. As the ASW delegate for Clydeside noted, the higher wage payments were designed to put pressure on the employers to introduce preventative measures, including dust suppression equipment, and were not meant as an *alternative* to proper control of the hazard (see Chapter 3). Moreover, the oral and documentary evidence clearly shows that workers and the unions were unaware of the *extent* of the danger prior to the mid-late 1960s when the clear association of asbestos dust with cancer became more widely recognised.

Furthermore, the unions' policies to a degree reflected the fatalism, stoicism and *machismo* culture of the men in the heavy engineering, shipbuilding and construction industries in the post-war decades. In union policy-making and campaigning, wages were invariably put before safety issues, and safety issues put ahead of health. Traumatic injuries and deaths at work got a higher profile than the longer-term effects of inhaling dust at work. The latter appeared a distant possibility, the former an immediate and real threat. The decline in trade union membership and retrenchment as de-industrialisation set in on Clydeside only served to exacerbate these tendencies within the Scottish trade union movement to turn a blind eye towards the longer-term hazards of inhaling asbestos dust at work: 56,000 jobs were lost in Scottish shipbuilding alone in the five years 1958–63 and the STUC Annual Reports are full of references throughout the post-war period to yard, pit and factory closures and the escalating crisis in heavy engineering and shipbuilding on the Clyde.

Those historians who castigate the trade unions for neglecting occupational health and safety have failed to recognise the real efforts that were made, especially at branch level, and have failed to put the issue sufficiently in context or to recognise that the unions largely reflected the fatalistic attitude of most members on health issues. It was difficult for the Scottish trade union movement to prioritise asbestos because the unions in this industry were relatively weak and disparate and the whole movement was facing retrenchment due to de-industrialisation from the 1950s. Moreover, despite the prevailing and unfavourable circumstances, the evidence of rank-and-file activity

on the asbestos issue stretching back to the Second World War by
the Glasgow branch of the laggers in the TGWU provides a significant
example of purposeful and radical action to safeguard members from
the harmful effects of asbestos. The unions most directly involved in
the use of asbestos could have done much more to protect their
members, and the STUC could have campaigned more vigorously at
an earlier period. A problem in Scotland, though, was that there were
not enough trade unionists working in asbestos manufacture to force
the unions to take the risks seriously – although the apathy of the
trade union movement south of the Border towards the problem
before the 1970s suggests that nothing much would have been done
anyway. The main dynamic for union intervention eventually came
from branch level: strike action, combined with the request by the
Insulation Branch of the TGWU's to the Scottish Occupational Health
Laboratory Service in 1968, along with the laggers' unofficial appeal
to the STUC in the mid-1970s, all testify to the concern felt by those
working directly with a material which day-by-day was being exposed
as a killer.

The asbestos pressure groups

Beyond the trade unions, and perhaps partly because of the limited
attention the unions gave to the asbestos issue, individual pressure
groups emerged to support victims and campaign for ameliorative
change. The first known asbestos self-help group was formally
established in London in 1978 by Nancy Tait, though she had been
active for several years after her husband died of mesothelioma in
1967. Her Society for the Prevention of Asbestosis and Industrial
Diseases (SPAID) was created to help sufferers of asbestos-related
diseases, 'often geographically isolated and in no physical or mental
condition to fight for the disability benefits and compensation to
which they are entitled'. SPAID also initiated medical enquiries into
mesothelioma which exposed the fallacies prevailing in the late 1970s,
effectively challenging claims that low exposure levels, white asbestos
and asbestos cement were all 'safe'. SPAID were also instrumental in
campaigning to get the ineffective diagnosis by optical microscopic
examination used by Social Security tribunals changed to electron
microscopy in the mid-1980s.

Nancy Tait's work extended to Glasgow, which she first visited in
1977 and regularly thereafter. Her main contact in the late 1970s was

a lagger, John Todd, who chaired the Glasgow TGWU Health Committee and the Insulating Engineers' branch of the TGWU. Todd had worked for most of the large asbestos insulation companies on jobs throughout Scotland, and was employed by Newall's Insulation in the 1930s and 1940s, and again from 1963 to1972. John Todd was a tireless campaigner on the asbestos issue in Scotland from the 1960s, though he found it difficult at times to generate full support from the TGWU leadership. He pressed the asbestos issue in all quarters – within the Factory Inspectorate, with employers and management, with MPs and local councillors, and within his own trade union. His complaints to the Inspectors – whom he castigated on one occasion for their 'laxity' – forced visits and inspections and fuller adherence to the Asbestos Regulations in site after site across the West of Scotland where TGWU members were employed, particularly in relation to the removal of old asbestos lagging. Breaches of the Regulations were common, including at schools, hospitals, shipyards, building sites and at Central Station, Glasgow (in 1975). Fines against factory crime were sometimes the outcome, though the penalties could be ludicrously low and clearly failed to act as an effective deterrent, as we saw in Chapter 4. Moreover, sometimes cases for prosecution passed from the Factory Inspectorate to the Procurator Fiscal were not taken further because of lack of evidence (e.g. against Glasgow Corporation in 1975). Todd also campaigned in the 1970s to expose the grim working conditions at the asbestos factory in Livingston, where the Asbestos Regulations were breached with impunity and the dust was found to be contaminating the local community. Todd's aggressive campaigning, forthright opinions and direct approach earned him a reputation for troublemaking amongst the Factory Inspectorate and his own union. Officials within the TGWU sometimes refused to provide information and Todd was denied access to the STUC's health and safety education schools as a consequence of his attack on the union's inaction on asbestos in the 1970s.[77]

Nancy Tait praised John Todd's work whilst also criticising the Scottish branch of the TGWU in the late 1970s for being uncooperative. 'I received many assurances', she noted in March 1979,

---

77. A. Dalton, *Asbestos Killer Dust* (1979), pp. 99–100. See also the John Todd Papers (Clydeside Action on Asbestos Archive, Glasgow). John Todd spent years as a POW of the Japanese in World War Two.

'but so far, only words, no action' from the Scottish TGWU. One grievance was that the union had not insisted on *post mortems* being carried out on their members who had died of an asbestos-related disease, and as a consequence the Pneumoconiosis Medical Panels had refused disability benefit. Another problem was that the TGWU had refused legal aid to widows of deceased laggers because they had allegedly fallen into arrears with membership dues. In at least one case non-payment was because no one contacted the member for his dues after he became ill. In her correspondence with the TGWU in 1979 Tait openly criticised the union for being insensitive and a Glasgow official for being 'aggressively unhelpful', not following up her advice to arrange supportive medical evidence through two named chest consultants in Glasgow. She noted that there appeared to be little support available to asbestos-disease sufferers and their families in Scotland: 'Their problems are made much worse because many don't know where to go for advice and help'.[78]

Clydeside Action on Asbestos (CAA) emerged in the mid-1980s and quickly became the main focal point for asbestos-disease sufferers on Clydeside. It established 'Britain's first walk-in asbestos self-help centre' in January 1988. The group was a charity initially consisting of several activists – including a number of shipyard laggers – who were also asbestos-disease sufferers, including the founding chairman, Robert Crockett, a 60-year-old joiner from Cumbernauld, who had worked on the Red Road flats. Sadly, Crockett did not survive to witness the opening of the new premises. Another founder member was William Harkness from Springburn, Glasgow, who had been employed at the Marinite factory making the asbestos boards that had been used on the QE2. Harkness had bitter experience of the state compensation system, having been refused any benefit for 12 years from the DHSS because he had received an *ex gratia* payment of £1,000 from the company after his enforced early retirement because of advanced asbestosis. He embodied the mutual help philosophy that constituted Clydeside Action:

> I am half dead. I can't walk anywhere. I have to get taxis all
> the time and I have a machine at home I have to use every day

78. Letters, Nancy Tait (SPAID) to Raymond MacDonald, Scottish Secretary, TGWU, 6 February 1979; 6 March 1979 (in John Todd Papers, CAA Archive, Glasgow).

to help me breathe. CAA have been a great help to me over the years and I am determined to be part of the group and help others in the same condition caused by that filth.[79]

Through the 1980s, 1990s and into the new millennium CAA continued to actively campaign to assert the rights of asbestos-disease sufferers, to raise awareness of the asbestos problem, to publicise the issue and to represent their constituency at medical panels and tribunals. By 2000, CAA had helped more than 1,000 victims of asbestos-related disease. By then about 40–50% of these clients had died because of exposure to asbestos.

CAA provided both a supportive environment and an active campaigning agency for asbestos victims on Clydeside. One of the voluntary CAA workers wrote in the mid-1990s that CAA filled a gap in social service provision because of 'the failure of the social and medical services to provide information and support for the growing number of victims'.[80] One of their key services is in utilising their expert, accumulated knowledge to guide disease sufferers and their dependents through the mass of paperwork necessary to receive entitled benefits, or to press a compensation claim. A widow of an asbestos victim commented: 'They helped us both accept what had befallen us ... Without the group, I doubt if we both would have held on to our sanity'. The work of the group is remarkable, given that it has operated with very limited funding, and has been heavily reliant upon volunteers. Supported by Mike Watson MP, Tony Worthington MP, the STUC and others, one important success for CAA in the mid-1990s was in getting the Compensation Recovery legislation scrapped. This had enabled the DHSS to recoup state benefits that had been paid out from any subsequently successful civil compensation claim (see Chapter 4). Tommy Gorman and other CAA activists played a key role in this campaign which mobilised wide support and ultimately demonstrated just how successful a relatively small lobbying organisation could be in getting a piece of major legislation repealed.[81] CAA also successfully campaigned to expose the ineffectiveness of asbestos face masks that led directly to an HSE enquiry (the 'Howie Report'). Thus the group not only raised

79. *The Scotsman*, 15 January 1988, p 6.
80. J. Lenaghan, *Victims Twice Over* p. 1.
81. See Tommy Gorman, 'Action on Asbestos' in *Scottish Trade Union Review*, 67, November/December 1994, pp. 12–13.

awareness and provided support, but also played a considerable role in the containment and prevention of asbestos-related diseases in the last two decades of the twentieth century. In this, they were aided by the trade union movement, who, belatedly, gave increasing priority to the asbestos problem in the 1980s and 1990s, spurred on by veteran asbestos campaigners, including Nancy Tait and Alan Dalton, author of *Asbestos Killer Dust* in 1979. In particular, the TGWU and the GMWU played central roles in campaigning on asbestos from c. 1980. Nonetheless, Alan Dalton, the National Health and Safety Co-ordinator for the TGWU, singled out the work of CAA as being of prime importance: 'More than any other organisation CAA has, with very slender resources, done more to prevent asbestos-related diseases than any other in the UK, including the trade unions'.[82]

Clydeside Action constitutes the core organisation, but since the late 1980s a self-help group has also operated in the worst-hit area of Clydebank. The Clydebank Asbestos Group was officially formed in 1992 and became part of a wider Clydebank Asbestos Partnership in 1998, with support from West Dunbartonshire Council. It provides a full-time, professionally staffed information and advice centre giving effective support for asbestos-disease victims in this major black spot.

The Clydeside asbestos pressure groups were also very active, along with a number of other pressure groups including SPAID, in campaigning over the years to get all asbestos imports into the UK banned. This was successful only in 1999, when the import and manufacture of chrysotile (white asbestos) was finally banned, some 100 years or so after the first 'official' discovery of the dangers to workers' health of asbestos fibres.

82. A. Dalton, *Letter and Appeal for Funding for CAA*, 31 July 1996 (TGWU, Glasgow Archive).

CHAPTER SIX

Blighted Lives:
The Impact of Asbestos

Up until now I thought trauma was a fad imported from
America and reserved for the middle classes. I am now wiser.
[Electrician with mesothelioma][1]

In this chapter we turn to look at the social effects of asbestos as
seen through the eyes of those directly affected, and explore some
important questions: How did victims first realise that their health
had been damaged? What impact did this have on their lives and
their families? What was the financial impact of their disablement?
To what extent did a reduction in earnings and a deterioration in
physical health caused through asbestos-related disease push the
sufferers below the poverty line and into what is now termed social
exclusion?

Doctors, diagnoses and physical disablement

There is no effective cure for any of the asbestos-related diseases.
Once you have it, deterioration is inevitable. As one doctor explained:

Once it ingresses into the human body we can't really stop it
doing the damage that it does. There can't really be any
prevention. And the damage it can do is irreversible and in
some can be catastrophic.[2]

A striking characteristic of asbestos-induced ill health is the long
latency period of the disease. Consequently, despite the fact that
people had worked with the mineral for only a brief period, the
symptoms could present 20, 30 or 40 years later. A retired fitter

1. Interview A13.
2. Dr Clark Mullen, CAA, 'Hidden Hazards' Video.

worked alongside laggers between 1943 and 1947 and can clearly recall his disbelief when he was told 50 years later that his shortage of breath was linked to his wartime job:

> All that time and it suddenly comes up. I daresay I've been a bit breathless, and that, you know. But I didnae associate it with anything ... I never realised it until the doctor told me. I coudnae understand it at all ... It was the doctor that said it tae me. He got me to get an X-ray. And eh, the next time he saw me he says 'You've been working with asbestos'. I said 'That was a long time, fifty-odd years ago'. 'You've been working with it.' He could see it in the X-ray.[3]

A plumber had a similar experience when he was unexpectedly diagnosed as having pleural plaques:

> I never discovered I had this until 1998 when I went by chance. The doctor sent me for an X-ray and the next thing a report came back. The first thing the doctor said to me 'I've got the report back and it says "this man must not smoke, he's got a touch of asbestos"'. That was my first inclination that I had it. And that was all that time, nearly 30 years till it raises its head.[4]

The retired joiner who worked with the SCWS in the 1940s and 1950s had been experiencing difficult breathing for some time, but had assumed that this was a symptom of old age. His wife remembers how he became alerted to the possiblity of the connection:

> We were sitting one night and you were reading the paper. And he said 'Look at that'. And people were claiming asbestos. And he says 'God I worked with that for years and I've no got it' ... And I says to him one day 'You know I'd swear you had whooping cough, only you've had it for too long. But you should really go and see about that cause TB's back'. And that was why you went to the doctor and they said 'We'll get you X-rayed'.

The X-ray revealed that the cough was indeed caused by asbestos, and progressively the condition got worse:

3. Interview A3.
4. Interview A2.

Oh, he used to be a lovely singer. But now he cannae. He can hardly talk some times never mind sing.[5]

The ex-shipyard rigger's asbestos-damaged lungs were so bad that he was unable to have a general anaesthetic during a major operation:

They sent the anaesthetist up to check that I was all right to go under the full anaesthetic and he says 'Oh no, we cannae. You're far too chesty. I wouldnae recommend a full anaesthetic'. So I only got a jag in the spine and then off, you know. So, you're lying there listening to them hacking away at your leg, you know.[6]

By far the worst of the asbestos-related diseases is mesothelioma. This cancer has an extremely long incubation period, and normally kills victims within a year of diagnosis. The experiences of an electrician from Lanarkshire diagnosed with the condition deserve to be recounted in some length:

I mind going down the garden and digging a bit of the garden and when I got to the end of a row I was tired. And I thought 'This cannae be old age already', you know ... And then, there's a lot of steps up there fae the bottom of the garden, and through time I started to feel breathless coming up the stairs for the first time, and that was unusual.[7]

The breathlessness and slowing down led him to make an appointment with his GP:

And he tested my chest again. And he then picked up the dullness at the bottom of my back. And he got on the phone then and he made an appointment with [a consultant] ... So we went down to see this doctor and he examined me, seen the X-ray, and again he asked me the question [have you worked with asbestos?]. Same story. 'Right', he says, 'We'll take fluid off the lung.' So that was another week, and I went down and after everybody else was finished in the theatre I got called in and he gave me the jag to take the fluid out the lung. And he says 'Right, we'll send that away'. And eh, they sent it away and a week later he phoned us to come down and see him ...

5. Interview A8.
6. Interview A18.
7. Interview A13.

He phoned me up the night before and he says 'I've got the results of these wee nasties ...'

What happened when he and his wife went to see the consultant was a shock for the couple beyond belief:

'Right,' he says, 'These wee nasties are what I suspected, and you have diffuse mesothelioma in your lung.' Now, you've got to appreciate that neither [my wife] or I ... we didnae know what it was. But now we know a lot more. Eh, so he then we must have asked the question, and it came out that it was a tumour. So the next question is: 'Can it be operated on?' 'No.' 'Is there any treatment?' 'No. We only treat the symptoms'. And I said, or [my wife] said 'What are the symptoms?' And he looked at me and he said 'He'll know when he gets them.' I'm looking at the man eye-to-eye and I'm thinking 'Is there a coded message there? Is he saying 'Don't for Christ's sake ask in front of your wife what the symptoms are', you know? I thought there was a coded message there that says 'Clam up pal'. And then the next thing I can mind of saying was 'Look, surely in this day and age ... Have the Americans no had a go at this operation?' Because I didnae know the nature of the tumour, right? He says 'Well, they did', he says, 'But', he says 'The results werenae that satisfactory so they really abandoned it.' He says 'You know, Steve McQueen had that'. And I'm looking at [my wife] and I'm thinking 'is that bugger dead?'

His wife took up the tale:

I asked 'How long has he got?' And he says 'He's got one year'. And then he looked him up and down and he says 'But he's a big healthy looking man, he could maybe last a bit longer'. And we couldnae understand whether he meant two months, or he's talking about ... And he stood up and he shook hands with us and said 'Cheerio'. And I went out to the car and collapsed. I couldnae believe it.

It would be wrong to suggest that everyone presenting to health professionals with mesothelioma had similar bad experiences. Moreover, it may well be that this consultant felt that he was giving his patient an adequate level of compassionate advice. It is also possible that the couple's perceptions have been coloured by the trauma that they have had to endure. However, what is important is that they considered that they were being treated in a way that was totally unsuitable to the seriousness of the situation. Therefore, the communication between the health specialist and the patient was seriously ineffective. Moreover, in this case the degree of information conveyed to the patient was especially limited, as he was told that there was absolutely no possibility of an operation. However, this was not the case:

> I couldnae come to terms with that bit of it. 'Surely there must be somebody?' And then that's how I got to the think about America, cause I know what they're like, you know. They're no feart to have a go at anything … So, the point about it is, we think we asked him all the right questions, and there's no doubt at all that he specifically told us 'No, there wasnae an operation. No, there wasnae treatment. And no chemo'. And I'm standing here today [Standing up and pulling up his shirt to reveal a large surgical scar] with a back opened; had an operation – there it's there – and with a wee bit of luck I might make it. And that was less than 20 miles away from the man.

What he had not been told was that although only two surgeons in the whole of the UK operated on mesothelioma tumours, one of them was based at a hospital just 12 miles away from where the consultant sat. The electrician's wife reflected on the unfairness of the whole system in which she saw millions of pounds being poured into AIDS, but limited resources being directed towards an industrial disease:

> All these men have only got two surgeons, and a man sitting there at that place and sending them home to die. And we are talking about joiners, electricians, plumbers, shipyards workers …

However, there are several reasons why so few surgeons are prepared to operate on the tumour. Firstly, mesothelioma had been until the 1990s such a relatively unusual condition, that few Scottish surgeons would ever have had the chance to see a single case. Secondly, the most recent research in the USA indicates that treating mesothelioma by surgery is not the best course of action. Only in certain cases – for example, where a patient is experiencing severe pain – would it be offered, and even then patients would have to fulfil certain criteria

– such as being under 65, and having the condition picked up in the early course of the disease. Because of these factors, and because of the medical uncertainty surrounding the best way to deal with the cancer, most people who presented with the condition were not offered an operation.

This was the case with an Edinburgh electrical engineer. He was exposed to asbestos while working on the demolition of Portobello Power Station in the 1950s, and later alongside laggers in Grangemouth. His widow remembers how his breathing had been poor for five years before mesothelioma was diagnosed. This was probably an asbestos-related condition. However, his doctor, who had not inquired about his job, assumed it was asthma.

> He had been getting worse and coughing up a lot of phlegm and all that, and I went away to France for a week to see a friend and when I came back I said 'How's your breathing been while I've been away?' And he said 'Terrible'. And I said 'Well you'd better go to the doctor'. And he did. And the doctor then sent him for an X-ray. So, he went for an X-ray and he came home and he said 'They've asked me if I'd ever worked with asbestos'. Of course we didn't know the implications then ... He started to get the fluid drained off his lungs, five litres they took off, although not all at once. Of course after that his breathing improved, but then it was kind of down hill after that.[8]

A quantity surveyor from Glasgow in his early 60s who also died of mesothelioma was exposed to the deadly dust when he worked on supermarket construction contracts throughout Scotland, and at an asbestos factory in Livingston. His widow remembered how the tragedy began to unfold:

> I was preparing the meal, and he came flying in a desperately agitated state. 'I've to get down to the hospital right away. Right away. They need to take fluid from my lung. That's why I'm having a job to breathe' ... We went racing down and he had, I think, two and three quarter litres of fluid removed from his lung. Now, that was in the August. He was back again four weeks later for another session of this and he was kept in for

8. Interview A23.

five days where they drained it absolutely totally. And then he was in again, and then again, and then again.

The seriousness of the situation gradually became clear, and eventually resignation set in:

> As every wife knows in this position, you do your best to bolster them and keep going for them and make light of things. And he took my hand and said 'I'm not going to see xxx as a bride' ... Then we went up to bed together and we just cuddled and we both cried. And it's the one and only time that I really saw my husband crying.

In this case, though, the medical profession came through with flying colours:

> The consultants at Ayr hospital were just fantastic. Because twice the consultant phoned me here at home, and he would begin with saying 'Is Mr xxx beside you?' In other words he wanted to know if the space was clear to talk. Eh, and he talked to me at home.[9]

The manner in which doctors give out information on asbestos-related conditions can vary from individual to individual, and this can have a marked effect on how they view their futures. For example, a retired site engineer first heard that he had an asbestos-related disease when his doctor telephoned him one day:

> 'Aye,' he says 'you were down for an X-ray'. I says 'Yeah'. 'Well,' he says, 'The X-ray's showing ... Have you ever been exposed to asbestos?' I says 'Och aye, all my life'. 'Och well', he says, 'you've got nothing to worry about. You've got a touch of asbestosis'. I says 'Oh aye, the usual, if I get cremated it'll take three days'. And he laughed like hell. 'Aye,' he says, 'It won't bother you really'.[10]

However, another man with exactly the same condition was painted a different picture:

> He says 'Its no really life threatening what you've got, but I couldnae guarantee in two or three years time that could

9. Interview A20.
10. Interview A10.

develop intae something'. He says 'It is related tae asbestos but it's what they call pleural plaques'.[11]

And a lorry driver who had been exposed on numerous demolition contracts only heard the word 'asbestos' when he and his wife were told that he had lung damage:

> They said 'Have you ever worked with asbestos?' You were there that day [to his wife]. She started greeting [laughs]. Didn't you? Wee tears in her eyes. She says 'What's happening?' I said 'I'm going to die'.[12]

Some victims also believe that there was a conspiracy of silence amongst Scottish doctors as many seemed reluctant to give out accurate information. A Clydebank man's father worked at Turner's Asbestos in Dalmuir and died of lung cancer:

> My father was friendly with the family doctor to such an extent that the doctor would come up and play chess with him. And he'd sit there and spend a happy hour together if the doctor wisnae too busy that particular day. The doctor in question was a chest specialist, a consultant tae dae with respiratory diseases and so on, and he never once mentioned asbestos. And it seemed to be the general policy to keep things secret from the patients at that particular time. Obviously the medical profession thought ... I mean they were so high-handed they thought that what you didn't know didn't harm you, and you had nae right tae know. They were the specialists.[13]

An insulation engineer had even more cause for complaint, as his doctor was also the factory doctor for the T&N factory at Dalmuir:

> When I mentioned to the doctor that I didnae feel well at first and was starting to go breathless – this was in 1984 – he says 'There's no such thing as asbestosis'. So, this was the man that was passing all these workers, and the bulk of them were dead. There's a lot of claims in Clydebank for the asbestosis, and a lot of them have only got a short time to go. But anyway, that

11. Interview A11.
12. Interview A4.
13. Interview A19.

man denied black ... The minute I started to claim, the top doctor in there went absolutely nasty. He says 'A good spell in Belsen.' I had started to put on weight. When I was working I was about 13 stone and I went up to about 16 or 17 stone. 'A good spell in Belsen would have done you the world of good'.[14]

Again, it could well be the case that several factors combine to distort these accounts and the point should be made that before the 1970s few community GPs would have been aware of the asbestos cancer risk and most would not have seen cases. Most would simply have been diagnosed with lung cancer and the identification with asbestos would not have been made. Again we need to beware of using hindsight to judge GPs whose knowledge and awareness of such matters would have been thin, indeed perhaps not much better than the victims themselves in many cases. However, the main thing is that these patients' perceptions of their doctors' conduct are clouded with doubt and unease. One Clydeside asbestos sprayer summed up this sense of alienation quite graphically, commenting that asbestos-disease victims were 'industrial lepers'.[15] Consequently, there has either been a severe breakdown in patient information or in the doctor/patient relationship. A marine engineer told his story:

My doctor informed me just four years ago that he knew back in '86 that I had pleuritic lungs, that I had asbestosis of the lungs, but the doctors were then told by the British Medical Council not to tell anyone. Now, my doctor told me that in strict confidence. He would not stand up in court and admit that. I mean he said that to me. He said 'I cannae admit but I'm telling you now'. And he showed me it in black and white. He showed me this in black and white that back in 1986 pleural plaque thickening of my lungs had been detected.[16]

A retired heating engineer remembers how he first started to notice breathing troubles, and how it took a long time to get to the truth:

I was short of breath going into some of the boiler houses to work. But you just put that down to too much heat. You were going in ... Maybe the boilers were off maybe an hour, but it

14. Interview A14.
15. Tommy Nelson, in CAA 'Hidden Hazards' Video.
16. Interview A12.

was still way above boiling point, you know, in the boiler house. And you were stripped down eh, to maybe your overalls, and you were stripping maybe asbestos. So between the heat and the atmosphere you didnae actually ... You just put that down to the general effect, you know. And eh, I think it was maybe 10 years ago that I first started getting pains. And I went up and they said at one time I had a scar ... I went up to the chest clinic in Stobhill Hospital for I think it was every month for three month, and they still didnae give me what I was suffering fae. They just said 'Oh you're all clear ...' And maybe two maybe three year ago I started getting pains again, you know, shortage of breath. And then a year past ... The doctor sent me up to the hospital [for an X-ray] and I had to ask her. I said 'Did you ever have any results from the X-rays?' She said 'Did you ever work in the shipyards?' I said, 'Before you go any further, is it asbestos-related?' She says 'Yes'. I said, 'Well I've worked with asbestos for years, you know on and off'.[17]

Some victims, as we have seen, also complain that their doctors did not link their past working experience to symptoms that were clearly pointing towards asbestos-induced health damage. For example, a boilermaker plater noticed that he was getting out of puff. His doctor at first diagnosed asthma and prescribed Ventolin and an inhalor. This didn't help, and after an X-ray he was told that he had 'a spot on the lung':

I told the doctor time and time again that I worked in the shipyards, that I worked with asbestos. But I got the impression I was speaking to deaf ears ... I've never been cheeky like, you know ... I've never been forward enough tae pull up a doctor ... But I said 'There's something wrong there', I said. 'If I've got a spot in my lung', I said 'How can the doctors tell you it's a spot or if it's asbestos?' My mind was starting to go that way. I said 'How are they going tae know?' So I finished up I said 'Now I better see what this is'. And that's when I made up my mind to go down tae ... Clyde Action [on Asbestos]. I went up to my doctor, and told my doctor what I was doing. I said 'Doctor, I'm putting in for a claim for

17. Interview A6.

asbestos', and I told the doctor. I said 'I've a feeling that's what I've got'. And the doctor just looked at me. And, you know, he never said a thing. I said 'If I put this claim in do you think there's any chance I could win or something like that?' So he looked up the files and my X-rays, and he just looked at me and he says, 'There's nothing to lose'.[18]

Poverty and social exclusion

As we noted in Chapter 5, with the introduction of the welfare state in the post-war period, it was widely assumed that poverty – characterised by an inability to pay for the means of survival – would be conquered. To a great extent this wish has been fulfilled, and 'absolute poverty' of the type found by Booth and Rowntree in their social surveys around 1900 (and still evident in some of the depressed areas such as Clydeside in the 1930s) has been almost entirely (though not completely) banished. However, from the late 1970s social investigators became interested in a new form of poverty which they called 'relative poverty'.[19] Relative poverty is difficult to define, but implies that people can be so poor that, although their lives are not threatened, they are still 'excluded from ordinary living patterns, customs and activities'.[20] More recently it has been argued that the notion of poverty should involve more than just a lack of material goods, and that social deprivation is an important factor too.[21] However, poverty still remains a difficult thing to define. The present-day DSS takes the view that it cannot be measured objectively, and there have also been numerous attempts by social and medical experts to define 'quality of life' with some degree of accuracy. The

---

18. Interview A3.
19. P. Townsend, *Poverty in the United Kingdom* (1979); D. Pichaud, 'Problems in the Definition and Measurement of Poverty', *Journal of Social Policy* (1987), 16, 2, pp. 147–64; P. Alcock, *Understanding Poverty* (Basingstoke, 1993); S. Hutton, 'Testing Townsend', in S. Baldwin *et al.*, *Quality of Life: Perspectives and Policies* (New York, 1994).
20. Quoted in S. Hutton, 'Testing Townsend', in Baldwin *et al.*, *Quality of Life: Perspectives and Policies* (New York, 1994), p. 180. See also J. Mack and S. Lansley, *Poor Britain* (1985); P. Townsend, 'Deprivation', *Journal of Social Policy*, 16 (2), pp. 125–46.
21. See, for example, D. Gordon and C. Pantazi, *Breadline Britain* (Aldershot, 1997). See also L. Fallowfield, *Quality of Life: The Missing Measurement in Health Care* (London, 1990).

latest buzz phrase, though, is 'social exclusion', and this term has been used more and more frequently to imply a depth of poverty beyond that caused by material deprivation.[22] The Labour government launched an assault on social exclusion in the late 1990s, and Scotland's own Social Exclusion Network was set up in December 1997. However, the problem of definition still remains, and there is an ongoing debate as to whether indicators of social exclusion should be chosen by government – in effect 'imposed' from above – or derived from the views of individuals or communities.[23] In any event, the phrase is much more useful than that of 'relative poverty' as it implies both financial and social deprivation.

Our survey of industrial disability sufferers in Scotland indicates quite clearly that contracting a progressively debilitating and potentially life-threatening asbestos disease invariably resulted in social exclusion. Many of those affected by asbestos fall into the category of the socially excluded for two main reasons: they cannot afford to pursue the same life patterns as they once could; and/or their poor health prevents them taking part in these accepted social norms. Moreover, this can frequently affect the lifestyles of partners too, as they become drawn into the role of carer – sometimes, as Lillian Nicolson noted, a 24-hour-a-day job.[24]

A few examples illustrate this: Thomas Williamson pleaded with his solicitor in 1968, just months before his death from mesothelioma, noting: 'I didn't think compensation took do long to come through, my wife had to give her job up, to stay in the house with me all the time'.[25] A 69-year-old retired insurance salesman who received his dose of asbestos exposure while an apprentice fitter in the shipyards can now no longer climb the smallest hill. 'Life', he says 'has got to be lived in the slow lane with no exertions of any kind.'[26] Similarly a one-time brickwork labourer with asbestos-damaged lungs is unable to socialise as he once could, as he cannot tolerate any smoky

22. See K. Duffy, *Social Exclusion and Human Dignity in Europe* (London, 1995).
23. Social Inclusion Strategy, Evaluation Framework Action Team Progress Report, June 1999, p. 3.
24. *Aberdeen Evening Express*, 9 July 1992. Lillian's husband, a shipyard electrician, had been disabled for 12 years from 1980 until his death from asbestosis in 1992.
25. Letter from T. Williamson, plumber in Turner's Asbestos Cement, Clydebank, 29 July 1968 (in Turner & Newall Archive, Manchester).
26. Interview A15.

atmosphere.[27] A 67-year-old retired labourer from Greenock used to enjoy sport and was looking forward to an active retirement. However, he now finds it difficult to do any jobs around the house, never mind take part in sport. This, understandably, has made him irritable, as does the fact that his lack of exercise has caused him to put on weight.[28]

There are some cases where asbestos-related disability has caused no adverse economic effects. This is especially true when the physical effects of asbestos exposure become apparent after the worker has retired. A 68-year-old ships' plumber with pleural thickening, caused by working in the Clyde shipyards yards as an apprentice in the late 1940s, falls into this category. Despite the fact that his lung damage slowed him down a bit and prevented him doing any part-time work, he considered himself to be quite well off because his wife worked, they had been careful with their savings over the years, he was in receipt of both Superannuation and Old Age Pension, and he had been granted £7000 in civil compensation.[29] Similarly, a 72-year-old costing clerk – exposed to asbestos when walking through a factory every day – was stoical about his financial circumstances:

> Due to the fact that I used money in the time I was earning to purchase my house, and I don't overspend. At the age of 70 I suppose I can't say I'm poorly [off], and my foresight probably bars me from benefits.[30]

And this was also the case with a 68-year-old retired marine engineer from Grangemouth who received a £10,000 out-of-court settlement for lung damage caused by asbestos exposure over the course of his working life. His disability did not adversely affect his life to any great extent – although he suffered more from colds and chest infections. Moreover, he now finds himself in the fortunate position of being able to go on holiday more often than he did before his industrial illness took effect:

> I still feel a fraud. I've got it, I mean there's no doubt about it. Eh, one of the consultants explained it as like, if I opened my, if my lungs were opened out like that, it's as if somebody had

27. Interview A7.
28. Interview A8.
29. Interview A14.
30. Interview A8.

got a lighted candle and went like that down it, and its like
candle grease ... It *is* asbestos-related but it's at the lower
scale.[31]

A retired engineer suffering from shortness of breath – caused through
exposure to asbestos in the shipyards in the 1960s – also has little
worry over finances. Having left his trade to go into the insurance
business some time ago, he now lives in a good-quality residential
area of Glasgow, and gets his full benefit entitlement – he also has
a civil claim ongoing against an employer:

> I've got that 30% Disablement. That's in the bank. I get £125 a
> month. Eh, it helps to pay my standing orders for the electricity
> and the insurance and things like that. I've got Motobility
> Allowance. I don't see a penny of that, cause that pays for the
> car.[32]

The majority, though, have been less successful in getting adequate
compensation for work-induced disability, and many were unhappy
at the treatment they received from the DSS. A 71-year-old sheet iron
worker who had been exposed to a lifetime of fumes and asbestos
dust was eventually diagnosed as suffering from asthma – which, as
we have noted, is a common initial misdiagnosis. Consequently –
despite the fact he was convinced that his illness was linked to asbestos
– because he does not suffer from a 'prescribed disease' he was refused
Industrial Disability and has no recourse to civil compensation from
an employer. He looked back upon his years of toil with some
remorse, and recalls how he tried desperately to work right up to
retirement age in order to secure as much as he could in the way of
pension entitlements:

> I was hanging on like grim death trying to get to sixty-five.
> I was nine weeks short of sixty five when the firm went bust.
> And I got a job with [withheld], and it was to go down to wee
> fishing boats and estimate things. And I would leave and get
> down about 6.00 in the morning, so that I could sit and wait
> till I came quite normal and then start to measure ... This
> skipper came aboard. He heard the noise – metal boat, you
> know – and he came to find out what was wrong. This was

31. Interview A11.
32. Interview A15.

quarter past six in the morning. I told him who I was and why I was doing this, and that I was very breathless. And he said that I could have collapsed on his ship and there might have been a claim against his insurance ... So they chopped me. Anyway, that was the end of that. They gave me a week's money in lieu of notice, like, and that was me finished. I went to the doctor and he said 'You should have been finished years ago. You shouldn't have been anywhere near work'. But there you are. So with working up until that it helped my national pension.[33]

However, like many damaged by the working environment, he was more concerned about the impact that his disability had upon his social life:

I've had no social life since about 1980. Eh, people unfortunately don't want to know you when you're, you're ill like, you know? And people stopped coming. I was very disappointed. They made the excuse that we were too far away and what have you. And we've been more or less on our own since then. Couldn't go tae pubs or clubs, cinemas, anywhere where they might smoke – I believe they don't smoke nowadays in them. And we're more or less hermits. With the exception of that car. As long as I can keep that car I can get out. We can get down to the esplanade, or we can get down tae Arrochar or something like that. If the ground is flat I can walk. As long as it's not too cold or too warm, or the wind's not going, I can walk a reasonable, maybe a couple of hundred yards.[34]

One of the pastimes that many of those stricken with an asbestos-related condition miss is dancing. The retired ships' plumber made this quite clear:

See my wife and I were great dancers. We used to love going to the dancing. Now if I dae one turn round the hall I'm buggered.

Similarly, the boiler maker plater who had a job convincing his doctor that his shortage of breath was asbestos-related, also missed the dance floor:

Well I used to like ... I was no a bad dancer. I liked dancing

33. Interview A9.
34. Interview A9.

and that. But you cannae dae that now because you're
breathless. Even bowls. When I play bowls there – and they say
bowls is an old man's game and that like you know – you're
puffing and panting just walking up and down. And if you dae
any climbing ... If you try to climb or dig the garden you can
only dae as little as possible. At one time I could work out in
the garden all day there like, you know, and think nothing of
it. But now you've got tae sit down. You've got tae sit down
for about an hour and enjoy the sunshine and take it easy. Sit
in the chair relaxing. Any, any, moving or any sudden jerking
or that ... Even getting out of bed in the morning you're
breathless. Even washing and that ... Walking down and
getting the papers you're breathless.[35]

And the insulation engineer from Glasgow, who now has to keep an
oxygen tank beside him at all times, misses nights out at his local
ex-servicemen's club where he and his wife used to go dancing every
Friday and Saturday night:

Oh she used to enjoy her dancing. So did I of course, otherwise
I widnae dae it. I enjoyed a wee drink and a wee dance.[36]

The 73-year-old Glasgow joiner who was exposed to asbestos during
the war in the SCWS's cabinet making factory maintained that
although he was not on the poverty line, his condition had caused
significant financial consequences. The constant need for taxi fares
was proving a financial burden on the couple, but it was the effect
that his disability had upon his and his wife's social life that caused
the most annoyance. He was a lifetime non-smoker, and had kept fit
by cycling, swimming, golfing, amateur wrestling and judo – indeed
he was fit enough at the age of 68 to restrain a hapless burglar in a
double leg lock until the arrival of the police. However, whereas
he and his wife used to be 'out every night' at various clubs and
functions – at which he was frequently called upon to sing – he was
now practically confined to the house. However, he counted himself
lucky that he was allowed to finish his working life before the effects
of the asbestos took affect:

It really didn't manifest itself seriously until I was almost

35. Interview A3.
36. Interview A1.

retired. So I didn't lose any work through it ... My insurance was there, and eh, the small pension I got from my years in the Education Department, so that I didn't lose any work ... I was also very active. I was an amateur wrestler and eh, was always golfing. So that probably kept me going. So I was fortunate that way that I got to my retirement age really before the worst of it hit me.

However, his wife was not as stoical about the situation:

He's all right sitting here – but if you'd had seen him last week it would have been a different story. But if he goes somewhere he's got to take a taxi. He's got to take a taxi back. And I'm the same. I've got fibrosis in my lungs. That man in the asbestos place he said 'You've probably got it as well'. I says 'With the carry on he's had I wouldnae be bothered'. And I've got angina. Different things. If we go anywhere ... If we go shopping ... If we go to Asda we've got to take a taxi and we've got to take a taxi back. And he's no worth ... And he's no worth ... In fact, we've to let the taxi man help me with the bags ...

She went on:

Well, see, he coughs all night and I've got to listen because he starts off with a hard cough and then he goes quiet. So I've got to listen. Then it starts again and that's all right. But see if he doesnae ... Well I've got to go in and pull him up off the bed ... He's actually been lying on the floor.[37]

A joiner from Greenock exposed to asbestos in the shipyards in the 1960s lamented:

Well put it this way, if my wife wisnae working I wouldnae have a social life. It's as simple as that, cause I couldnae afford it. With my wife working we get out maybe one night a week. Some weeks we don't get out.[38]

And a 74-year-old retired fitter from East Kilbride who had been exposed to asbestos while working in the shipyards told a similar story. Again, because he was retired when the illness took hold, the

37. Interview A8.
38. Interview A17.

impact upon his finances has been 'practically nil'. However, he too lamented the unexpected curtailment of his social activities, and the fact that he is not able to enjoy the retirement to which he had been looking forward:

> I've always been a walker, I've walked all my life and I'm still a member of two clubs. But I cannae walk with them now; I couldnae walk with them at all ... Aye, I used tae love it. In fact I still go down ... and collect their money for them, and give them a hand.[39]

When industrial disability strikes *during* working life there is more likelihood of severe financial disruption on top of a curtailment of accepted social activities. For example, a 60 year-old lagger from Clydebank saw his earnings drop from £300 a week to just £65 a week. On this income he could no longer afford new clothes or buy household goods as often as he had done.[40] In a similar way a 63-year-old painter from Irvine had to use up all the money that he had managed to put away for his retirement when he became unemployed through ill health. Consequently, he can no longer renew his car, nor afford to spend much money on petrol.[41] A 59-year-old marine engineer from Glasgow had managed to work his way up to a consultative position when the effects of his exposure to asbestos – some 20 years earlier in the shipyards – became serious:

> I lived in a beautiful detached bungalow in Crookston very comfortably. My wife and I lived ... company cars, steaks all the time, used to the good life, used to a good comfortable life. From that we went out in the street. I had to sell my house, get rid of my car, give up my job obviously because of my ill health. My wife went to stay with her parents and there was no room for me there. I had to live out of the car for several days. I then scraped myself up enough money to get myself into a wee hotel. Then fortunately I found a pal who had room to put me up for three months. I did get another job, but I was never comfortable in the job because my health was going down the hill. They paid me off. I couldn't blame them, and I wasn't surprised.

39. Interview A5.
40. Interview A14.
41. Written evidence in AOHP questionnaire 30.

Despite being in receipt of state disability benefits his financial circumstances remained dire:

> Financially we are up to our ears in debt, because for the last 18 months the lawyers have told me that my claim is just about to come up, and we've been borrowing frantically from the bank, my wife and I. We now owe, and I'll say the figure, we now owe about £12,000 to the bank ... Financially I'm crippled ... But I've got. I'm in a crazy situation. I'm disabled. I get Disability Living Allowance, disability this, disability that. I'm on Income Support. Basically I can't complain as far as the state's concerned. We manage, my wife and I. We manage to scrape by. I have credit cards. We rob Peter to pay Paul ...[42]

The 60-year-old heating engineer from Glasgow who noticed breathing difficulties while working in boiler houses also suffered a drop in income:

> I can go back tae 1990, I could clear, I was doing seven days, 12 hour shifts. I was working away fae home, we were taking in the region of £400 to £500 a week. And then when I was off you were taking about £48 a week. A normal year up until I stopped was maybe £17,000 to £20,000 a year. I was on £48 for six months, then they put me up tae £57. But off of the £57 they wanted rent.[43]

As a consequence his living pattern had been suddenly changed:

> Och, everything's different. But I've good days and I have bad days. If I get up in the morning I can be full of energy for a couple of hours. See come the afternoon? I'm tired, you know. It's got different effects, you know. I went to the swimming and I was just hopeless, you know. I ended up paddling about, you know. And at one time I was ... Oh I was never out the baths, you know. Never away from the swimming. Eh, I still try and walk a bit. But I've got to pace it, you know. I cannae walk as fast as what I normally did, you know. It has got different effects. I've got this wee pain in the back, you know. But we'll see what he has to say about it today. I thought it was just a draught, you know. But, it's no ... If I stand too

42. Interview A12.
43. Interview A14.

long – you know, doing a wee iron – it is sore, you know. If I
lie certain ways at night it gets sore, you know. Wear and tear
to the body and a', you know. [44]

The sudden shock of having to adjust to a drop in income was also
noted by a 69-year-old lagger from Clydebank when he was diagnosed
as suffering from pleural plaques.[45] And the drop in the income of
the lagger who had to sell his house in Oxford and move to a small
flat in East Kilbride was compounded by the fact that the DHSS
suddenly stopped paying him the Mobility Allowance and Care
Allowance upon which he had come to depend. This mix up resulted
in a drop in earnings of over £200 a month, and this pushed him into
a spiral of debt:

Oh I'm up tae the eyeballs aye. I owe them about what is it? I
think I owe them about five and a half grand. Well I thought I
could balance it out. You think you can balance it out you
know ... I was trying tae work it, you know. Get a loan, pay
off the credit cards ... But it doesnae work that way, you know.

Consequently the £5000 which his employers' insurance company
decided to offer him in compensation for his disability will only pay
off his debt. Once again, therefore, social consequences and economic
impact combine to severely alter life patterns and bring about social
exclusion:

Well, I've no got the same standard of life that I had, put it
that way. I cannae go out for meals or different things like
that. Don't dae much of that. You can forget that. A lower
standard of living if you want to put it that way, you know ...
You know, you need to adjust. You're on a different
wavelength, know what I mean? You've got a different social
life and things like that. Actually, it's depressing, you know.
When you think you're all right and then you've got to come
to the other aspect of it, you know. So, it can be depressing.
I've got this ... This is only a wee flat. But I've got to have
this because I get what would you say, flashbacks. And then I
rare up. Frustration. You want to take it out on somebody so

44. Interview A17.
45. Interview A14.

it's your wife. So she phones the police and you've got all that
squabble. So that's why I've got this place. [46]

A loss of esteem combined with a debilitating illness often leads to
frustration and violent mood swings. A lorry driver/labourer with
asbestos-damaged lungs made this quite clear:

> The depression's bad ... You just want to greet your eyes out
> and everything, you know. Then you kind of sort of reminisce,
> all your past life. You know, as if you're going to die, you
> know. And you remember all the good times. And you just
> think ... You can get a violent one. You just flash up stuff ...
> You're looking at a table or something – that table say – and I
> could just take my temper out on that and that would be me,
> and you just smash it, smash it to bits. You've got they
> thoughts in your head saying 'Right, that table, I must smash
> that ... I might be calm, you know?' ... Your mind goes to a
> different place, and you don't know. Then you take these
> tablets and they make you sick. [47]

Social exclusion can be caused by more than changed financial
circumstances, as the physical and emotional effects of industrial
disability play a role too. Removed suddenly from the world of work,
many people suffer a loss of dignity as well as missing the
companionship of former colleagues. A relatively young miner who
was forced to finish working in his early 40s because of dust-induced
lung damage expressed this psychological shock:

> I've got over it now, but it was a big blow to me to be told that
> I'd never work again. Eh, your pride's dented, ken. I mean when
> you're out and your wife's to come out and say to you 'Come
> on I'll get that ...' Wee jobs outside that you're no fit to do ...
> It definitely hurts your pride. Eh, you see folk going about doing
> things that you ken you'll never be able to do again. [48]

This illustrates how physical impairment usually prevents dust-disease
victims from pursuing former pastimes. The marine engineer cited
previously noted this too:

46. Interview A16.
47. Interview A4.
48. Scottish Oral History Centre, Pneumoconiosis in coalmining project, C2.

I have gone from one extreme to another. My wife, if she was here, would tell you the reason she married me. The expression she used for me was 'happy go lucky'. That's exactly the kind of bloke I was. But up until this, when I lost my job through illness, I led a very full social life. I went out regularly with my mates ... used to go to parties, used to have friends round to the house. I no longer do that. I have shut myself off from life completely.[49]

And the 64-year-old electrician, who underwent the operation for mesothelioma, also lamented the changes to his living patterns that his illness had brought about. On Saturday evenings the couple used to socialise with friends in the local pub. His wife looks back on those happy times:

We had a meal and a talk, and then they come back here and had a coffee and had a blether ... We've never been out fae July. Never been out the house. We've had no social life. Nothing ... We were invited tae our niece's 21st birthday. She's at university; having a big party, but we couldnae go, because if somebody was smoking we couldnae go near the smoke. And obviously he isn't able tae go. It's just been one thing after the other for six months. We've had no social life, nothing. Everything has just been crying every day. Every day. Cause I keep thinking back. All my thoughts are negative. I cannae see a future.

The strain of living every day with an asbestos-related disease from which – even after an operation – no one can hold out much hope of survival, is devastating. Although the couple try to think positively, they are easily reminded of the seriousness of the situation:

Or you get something in for your funeral expenses – see these folk that send you these things in through the post – or insurance. These things affect you. I like music. It was months before I could put my wireless on.[50]

Social exclusion, then, is an apt term to describe the circumstances in which these people find themselves: a social exclusion caused by one deadly mineral. The 60-year-old from Clydebank who worked at

49. Interview A12.
50. Interview A13.

Turner & Newall's asbestos factory, also found that the sudden shock of his marked drop in earnings compounded the physical effects of his serious industrial disability. Moreover, what makes things worse is that his wife sustained lung damage by washing his asbestos-covered overalls every week for 30 years. Understandably, the couple are bitter at the economic hardship they have been forced to endure:

> We used to live in reasonable comfort. We're living just sort of on the poverty line I would say. It's difficult. [My wife] is very *very* good at making ends meet. We get three different lots of money. This is absolute lunacy but this is the way it goes. We get Supplementary Benefit. The second one is Industrial Injuries, and then the wee monthly pension. So the Industrial Injuries and my works pension get taken off the Supplementary Benefit. So I've got three lots of money coming in, but it all amounts to the same as though I'm getting Supplementary Benefit ... And I feel a wee bit annoyed at that. Cause I feel I got the way I am through working for an employer; working damn hard tae earn a living. That employer did something wrong tae me and [my wife], and because I'm living below a certain limit I can only get Supplementary Benefit, so they take that off of me rather than let me have it. Now the government colluded in me getting in tae that bloody state, why should they not be paying for it? [51]

And their anger and frustration are multiplied by the curtailing effect that their illnesses have had on their once active life:

> I used tae dae a lot of hillwalking, always out in the country doing nature photography and stuff like this. I was getting a bit slower and a couple of times I noticed that [my wife] was walking faster than me ... The health aspect has had more impact than the financial aspect actually. The health aspect has stopped us going anywhere and daein things. We used to be running about all over Scotland. Everywhere we went we made friends. We could still dae that even though we're skint; but we canny dae it because of the ill health.

The couple had liked to jive to rock and roll music and socialised regularly. However, these days are now sadly gone:

51. Interview A19.

Och aye we had a lot of fun. And we've got a lot of memories,
and in here I'm still waiting to dae a' these things, but I cannae
dae them. [My wife's] the same. On a day like this I'd have
been up at Arrochar or something ...

The problem of social exclusion was exacerbated by the policies of
asbestos companies and the state welfare system. We have seen in
Chapter 4 that it was common before 1991 for the claim of the
victim to die if the victim did not survive to see the case brought to
court. Asbestos company solicitors and insurance companies thus
deliberately delayed cases claiming compensation, and widows could
find themselves receiving five to ten times less in compensation than
they would have received if the victim had survived until the case got
to court. In mesothelioma cases where life expectancy was almost
always less than a year after diagnosis the victim rarely survived to
get into court. Many sick asbestos workers were also denied state
benefits, especially before the mid-1980s, because of the stringency of
the DHSS's authorisation procedure.

Asbestos-disease victims were virtually powerless and had to watch
and feel their physical strength, breathing capability, and invariably
their morale, ebb away. The shock of learning of such disability, or
even being diagnosed with a fatal disease, could be traumatic – in
several cases in England leading directly to a nervous breakdown.[52]
Asbestos eroded people's health and often gnawed away at the very
root of people's dignity and pride. Death was invariably protracted
after a long period of physical deterioration – what one CAA volunteer
termed 'intolerable suffering'. Lillian Nicolson noted of her asbestotic
husband: 'During the last two years he was very ill. Right up to his
last breath he was in agony'.[53]

The diseases took lives and left many spouses, dependants and
other family members to cope with the trauma of premature death.
Describing such grief and the loss this entailed within families –
encompassing deep pain and often a sense of frustration, bitterness
and anger – is virtually impossible, but here lies one of the most tragic
aspects of the asbestos 'time bomb'. Brenda McKessock, whose
mother died of mesothelioma aged 67 in 1993, was moved to write
a book as a tribute and she expressed the loss she felt with these
words:

52. G. Tweedale, *Magic Mineral*, p. 73.
53. *Aberdeen Evening Express*, 9 July 1992.

My mother is dead. She was killed by asbestos. My dad was seventy years old in 1994. My parents should have been celebrating their Golden Wedding Anniversary in 1996. Instead my dad sits sad and alone in his house, surrounded by family photographs ... The victims are left to cope on their own. My mother didn't deserve to die the way she did. She did nothing wrong. She was brought up to believe that you should pay your own way in this world, be good to your family and owe no debts ... She wanted to enjoy her retirement and watch her grandchildren grow up. But she was robbed. There is not a day that goes by that I don't think about her. And I'm sad and I'm angry. Very angry.[54]

And because of the long latency period for such diseases, many more lives will be lost before the asbestos tragedy is over.

Asbestos in the community

Whilst mortality and disability are highest amongst asbestos workers, the consequences of asbestos went far beyond the workers who came into direct contact with the deadly fibres during their daily work. The wider community was directly affected in a number of ways. Asbestos dust, coming either directly from asbestos factories such as at Livingston or Clydebank, or waste tips, blew into the neighbouring streets. One estimate in the mid-1970s suggested that urban areas had around ten times the asbestos fibre content in the air compared to rural areas and that the immediate environs of asbestos processing plants had more than double the normal rate of contamination in urban areas.[55] One Clydebank resident noted how the end of Agamemnon Street adjacent to the Turner's asbestos factory was covered in white dust which settled on cars and window sills.[56] Turner & Newall's own Medical Adviser, Dr Hilton Lewinsohn, had referred to such environmental pollution around the TAC factories in the late 1960s, commenting on asbestos being used as a hard surface on roadways and car parks around the factories, and spilling from tractors so much that others were at risk:

54. B. McKessock, *Mesothelioma: The Story of An Illness* (Argyll, 1995), pp. 150–1.
55. *Asbestos Bulletin*, vol. 15, no 4, July–August 1974, p. 92.
56. We are grateful to Jim Cameron for this comment.

Not only are the drivers of the tractors at risk, but also the warehousemen, the office workers and others who use the roadway, as well as the community living in the neighbourhood of the factory, especially in the direction of the prevailing winds. The association of mesothelioma of the pleura with non-occupational exposure to asbestos dust is now well recognised – this is an unnecessary risk to the community and all possible measures should be urgently implemented to stop this hazardous procedure.[57]

Similar allegations were made about the environs of an asbestos works in Livingston by John Todd in the 1970s. As yet, we know of no successful legal action to claim compensation for asbestos-related disease contracted in this way in Scotland. However, in England a precedent has been set with a plaintiff, June Hancock, being awarded £65,000 in Leeds High Court in 1995 in such a 'bystander' case taken against Turner & Newall.[58]

Moreover, the wives, partners and families of asbestos workers in building, insulation and the asbestos factories were exposed to the risk of contracting asbestos-related diseases through contact with the dust on work clothes and overalls brought into the home. One occupational cancer expert, Irvine Selikoff, coined this 'family contact' asbestos disease. The first cases in the UK were identified in the mid-1960s in London in a survey which found eleven cases of mesothelioma amongst folk whose only contact with asbestos was through a fellow member of the household working directly with asbestos.[59] In Scotland, the first known cases of 'family contact' disease were identified in 1989. Amongst our respondents, two wives of Turner's Asbestos Cement workers commented independently on the dust brought into the home on work clothes.[60] Tragically, one of these now suffers from pleural plaques associated with this secondary exposure to asbestos dust caused by regular washing of work overalls.[61] The wife of a machine operator recalled in conversation with her husband:

57. H. Lewinsohn to J. K. Shepherd, Turner's Asbestos Cement Co., 10 December 1968. Chase Manhattan Archive, Manchester. We are grateful to Geoffrey Tweedale for this reference.
58. G. Tweedale, *Magic Mineral*, pp. 270–3.
59. T. Gorman, 'Women and Asbestos', pp. 132–3.
60. Interviews A19 and A23.
61. Interview A19.

See when you went into it and you came out that first day. When I said to you how did you get on, you said to me it was ok, it was a good job. I said why are you all white? He had pure black hair. Your black hair was pure white with the dust ... The man came home and he was pure white, actually white with dust. It was a nightmare, a pure nightmare.[62]

Her husband noted the lack of facilities to wash before returning home, contrasting the situation at Turner's with Singer's:

There was no such thing in it as a shower bath either when you finished working. Not at all. No, your hands and clothes were all cement and everything. If you washed your face you were washing the cement into it. I was in Singer's a wee while before that. That was a good clean job. I just didnae like it because it was shiftwork as well. You got a shower bath in Singer's.[63]

Dust being transported home by asbestos workers could also expose other people through incidental contact. One Turner's employee at Clydebank noted:

You were covered in wet asbestos cement. So you got on the bus with that and it started drying out and you were very popular with some of the bus conductors and so on. They thought the world of you sitting there making their seats all white, you know. We nearly all carried newspapers just tae sit on in the buses so it didnae affect too many people. But we didnae know we were killing them.[64]

How many incidental 'bystander' cases beyond 'family contact' have occurred in Scotland is not known, though there has been at least one case of a female bus conductor in Greenock contaminated in this way.[65] In his work on women and asbestos disease, Tommy Gorman has argued that the majority of female cases of mesothelioma in

---

62. Interview A22.
63. Interview A22. Research has shown that hair requires several washes before asbestos particles are entirely removed.
64. Interviewee A19.
65. We are grateful to Tommy Gorman for this reference. There is also a case of a bus conductor on the Turner & Newall route in Manchester who has recently contracted mesothelioma. We are grateful to Geoffrey Tweedale for this reference.

Scotland are likely to have been through such low-level environmental and indirect 'family contact' exposure, rather than through occupational exposure.[66] One consequence of this has been that it has been more difficult for women to obtain adequate state benefits because they rarely qualify for Industrial Disability Benefit and the DHSS are very cautious about officially recognising that mesothelioma can be caused by such low-level contact with the mineral.

There are currently millions of tons of asbestos in Scotland's buildings, and this has constituted a major hazard for the wider community. Many council houses and high-rise flats have extensive asbestos insulation, and people have become exposed when this is disturbed for stripping, or inadvertently when drilling through or knocking down walls, or undertaking other home improvements. At least one Scottish victim traces his mesothelioma back to contact with asbestos insulation when taking down a wall in his own home. Between 1982 and 1992 Strathclyde Regional Council alone spent £8.6 million on stripping asbestos from its properties.[67] However, bad working practices were common. For example, asbestos dust was found blowing around the school playground in Drumchapel in 1992. Although the school was closed at the time, local children still frequently used the playground. Action was subsequently taken against the contractor involved.[68] Press reports abound in the 1980s and 1990s in stories of asbestos exposure in these ways. To what extent this will result in growing 'bystander' mesothelioma deaths over the subsequent two decades is impossible to estimate. One point worth making, however, is that exposure in this way fell particularly severely upon the least advantaged sections of society. Not only were manual workers in the older industrial areas like Clydeside most likely to be exposed at work, but also the poorest families were most likely to be more heavily exposed because of asbestos in their housing schemes, multi-storey flats, schools and hospitals. Death and disability caused by asbestos was, in other words, predominantly (though not exclusively) a working class problem. Moreover, as with lead, the

---

66. T. Gorman, 'Women and Asbestos', in T. Gorman (ed.), *Clydebank and Asbestos: the Unwanted Legacy* (Clydebank, 2000), p. 135. See also T. Gorman, Hidden Hazard; Forgotten Victims: Some Aspects of Asbestos Abuse in Britain (Glasgow Caledonian University BA Dissertation, 1997).
67. *Times Educational Supplement*, 20 November 1992.
68. *Ibid*. See also the CAA, 'Hidden Hazards' video.

risk was particularly acute amongst the young who were exposed to asbestos dust in the environment.

What is clearly apparent is that the catalogue of failure that has characterised the whole asbestos tragedy in Scotland continues with regard to dealing with asbestos in the environment. In June 2000 it was revealed that the agency assigned the responsibility of monitoring the extent of asbestos in many of Scotland's buildings had failed in its task. Glasgow Scientific Services (GSS) operated under the command of the old Strathclyde Regional Council and – from 1996 – of Glasgow City Council. However, eleven other Scottish local authorities depended upon it to check their premises for the deadly substance, and GSS carried out around 8–10,000 property checks every year during the 1990s. In 2000, though, Renfrewshire Council discovered that five of its schools and a sports pavilion that had recently been given the all-clear by GSS were contaminated by asbestos – the pavilion contained so much dangerous asbestos that it had to be demolished. Consequently, the Council had to launch an operation to trace staff, pupils, and any contractors who had worked in the dangerous buildings to offer them advice and counselling.[69]

Finally, asbestos companies, shipyards and asbestos stripping firms frequently contaminated the local area with indiscriminate dumping of asbestos waste. In Falkirk, for example, there was a public outcry in the mid-1980s when it was discovered that children were playing on the site of an asbestos tip that straddled a public right of way.[70] The Turner's factory in Clydebank was also responsible for leaving a polluted site, including a large, uncovered asbestos waste pile, when the plant closed down in 1970. Throughout its existence from 1938 to 1970 all the waste asbestos cement from Turner's was put through a crusher and this, plus asbestos cement silt from the bottom of the maturing tanks in the factory, was taken from the plant and dumped down at the riverbank and the mudflats adjacent to the factory. The Turner's employee responsible in the 1960s for this asbestos disposal, Jack Walsh, testified in 1987 that 'all the ground between the factory and the river along the whole frontage was reclaimed by dumping asbestos waste'.[71] He estimated that this represented an area around 1,000 yards long by 40 yards wide by 7 yards deep. It appears that

69. See *The Herald*, 30 June, 1 July and 4 July 2000.
70. *The Scotsman*, 31 May 1986, p. 5.
71. *Evening Times*, 26 October 1987.

nothing was done to make the site safe for a decade after TAC closed. In 1980 this situation was exposed in the press. Commenting on the issue, Ted Rushworth, the Director of the Cancer Prevention Society, highlighted the cancer risk to the community that the dumped asbestos represented and expressed his amazement that Clydebank residents had tolerated such 'scandalous contamination' for so long.[72] Some asbestos removal was undertaken on the site in 1980 and a more extensive clean up job undertaken by the Council in 1985, costing some £400,000. This essentially involved covering the asbestos on site. Attempts to recoup the costs from the owners of the site, Monaville Estates, failed because they lacked liquid assets.[73]

This only partially solved the problem, which surfaced again when a private American health company approached the District Council and the Scottish Office in 1987 with a bid to purchase the site. Their proposal was to build a private 260-bed intensive care hospital, which incorporated a postgraduate medical education centre and a hotel on the Turner's site. Amidst much controversy and public protest, and the opposition of the Labour Party and the health unions, the Secretary of State for Scotland Malcolm Rifkind gave planning permission for the building of the private health facility which became known as Health Care International Scotland. Amongst the incentives offered to the health consortium was an agreement that the site be completely cleared of all asbestos waste, with the cost borne by the Scottish Development Agency.[74] Clydebank District Council was split on the issue and only granted planning permission for the asbestos removal at Dalmuir on the casting vote of the Chairman after a tied vote.[75] The asbestos was excavated, dumped in a dredged and deepened nearby disused dock basin (the Arnott Young Basin) and covered with concrete. The original projection was that the cost of clearing the site would amount to around £2 million. In the event there were major difficulties and costs soared. Subsequently, the total cost of clearing the asbestos-contaminated site at Dalmuir escalated to £8 million of taxpayers' money.[76] A final irony is that there is now a luxurious,

72. *The Scotsman*, 4 June 1980.
73. *Lennox Herald*, 20 December 1985.
74. *Glasgow Herald*, 8 March 1991; *Evening Times*, 12 March 1991.
75. Clydebank Health Care Campaign, Case for a Public Enquiry (Clydebank Library, ref. 362.11. L.C.).
76. Ibid. See also Clydebank Health Care Campaign, *Reply to Comments on an Asbestos Removal Scheme at Clydebank* (Clydebank Library), ref. 362.11.

state-of-the-art private health facility providing treatment and care for those fortunate enough to be able to afford it on the very site where the manufacturing of asbestos had contributed to undermining the health and destroying the lives of many workers.

The asbestos tragedy in Scotland really involves thousands of personal and family tragedies. The evidence in this chapter illustrates how the sudden realisation that seemingly mundane, almost forgotten, working practices have damaged an individual's health – often gravely – can be a stunning blow, and that people react to this blow in different ways. The impact which asbestos-related disease has on the families and close friends of sufferers is also severe, and this is often compounded by the fact that the victim has to fight a case for compensation for his or her illness while trying to come to terms with the illness.

Several conclusions can be drawn. Firstly, it is clear that the correlation between industrial disability and relative poverty deserves detailed investigation. Few sufferers of asbestos-related disease are plunged into *absolute* poverty by their experiences. However, their drop in income places severe limitations on their lifestyles, plunging them into *relative* poverty. Therefore, within their own frame of reference, the changed social and economic status of these individuals pushes them into the category of being 'excluded from ordinary living patterns, customs and activities'.[77]

The concept of 'social exclusion' is useful and valid in relation to most asbestos victims as it quite accurately conveys the cumulative effect – and constant interplay – of the financial, physical, and emotional factors that underlie work-induced disability. However, the difficulty still lies in determining when and to what extent people and groups are socially excluded, as individual perceptions, family and community support networks, and coping strategies, differ widely. Recent plans by the Social Exclusion Network, then, to conduct 2700 household interviews on an annual basis are along the right lines, as such research should make us more aware of these different perceptions – as well as illustrating how the workplace affects health. There was also a suggestion that a more direct experience of social

L. C. and J. D. Coull, Environmental Safety Guide, Comments on an Asbestos Removal Scheme at Clydebank (Clydebank Library, ref. 362.11. L.C.).

77. Quoted in S. Hutton, 'Testing Townsend', in S. Baldwin (ed.), *Quality of Life: Perspectives and Policies* (New York, 1994), p. 180.

exclusion would be achieved by policymakers if selected individuals were encouraged to keep a diary and take photographs. Such a 'bottom up' style of social investigation should also be encouraged.

Finally, this chapter has noted the deep ramifications of the asbestos tragedy within the wider community and environment, via 'bystander' and 'family contact' exposure as well as pollution from waste tips, asbestos company emissions, and the very buildings that people live, work, and play in. Such non-occupational exposure already accounts for much of the female disability and death through asbestos-related disease, and such cases seem likely to increase in Scotland over the next two decades.

CHAPTER SEVEN

Conclusion: The Legacy and the Lessons of a Public Health Disaster

If you put a guy into a car and push him down a hill with no brakes in it and it crashes at the bottom and kills him, you've murdered him. Well, it's the same with us. They made us work with poisonous materials that were killing us, and never told us. [Clydeside insulation engineer][1]

All developed industrial nations have an unfolding asbestos tragedy on their hands, and in many respects the story in Scotland is little different from elsewhere. Estimates of the number of workers liable to die of asbestos-related cancers in western Europe alone vary between 250,000 and one million by 2035.[2] For two generations of workers exposed between the 1920s and the 1970s this represents an occupational health epidemic of unprecedented proportions. One estimate suggests that 1% of all males in the UK born in the 1940s, the most at-risk group, will die from an asbestos-related disease. The asbestos tragedy in Scotland – where it is estimated that in the region of 20,000 will die – will constitute the country's worst occupational health disaster by far, with deaths continuing to accumulate into the 2000s and 2010s.[3] These startling statistics represent a monumental degree of suffering, pain, agony, deprivation and loss for individual victims and for their families. Consequently, the disaster is of such dimensions that it is impossible to adequately describe it and difficult to comprehend. In the UK, and indeed in most western European countries, asbestos manufacture and importation is now banned and

1. Interview A23.
2. J. Peto, 'Continuing Increase'; J. Peto, 'The European Mesothelioma Epidemic'; T. Gorman, 'Hidden Hazards, Forgotten Victims'.
3. Ibid. See also R. Howie, 'Asbestos, the Way Forward' and R. Howie, 'Asbestos-Induced Deaths in the UK', in G. A. Peters and B. J. Peters, *Sourcebook on Asbestos*, vol. 19 (Charlottesville, Virginia, 1999).

the removal of asbestos is strictly regulated. Elsewhere, though, in the developing world, the use of asbestos generally remains uncontrolled and environmental activists are currently campaigning to get a world-wide ban. There are lessons to be learnt here, both for asbestos consumers in the twenty first century and for Scotland and the UK in relation to how we deal with the grim legacy of this and, indeed, other occupational health problems.

What is distinctive, if anything, about the Scottish asbestos story? Whilst asbestos deaths have occurred throughout the UK, there are particularly high clusters in Scotland, both in the east – in the vicinity of Leith and Aberdeen (shipbuilding), Grangemouth (petrol refinery), the naval dockyard at Rosyth, and the shipbreakers and metal industries in Inverkeithing and Charlestown – and in the west. The industrial region of West Scotland emerges as a particular asbestos blackspot and one Clydeside town, Clydebank, had the highest asbestos cancer death rates in the whole of Britain at the end of the twentieth century. This, in itself, justified more extensive investigation. We have argued here that the long history of asbestos manufacturing in Scotland (going back to the 1870s), combined with the predominance of shipbuilding, shiprepairing, dockyards and heavy engineering on Clydeside, where asbestos was widely used as a thermal insulator, largely accounts for this. Our evidence indicates that occupational health standards in relation to asbestos were particularly poor in the Turner's Asbestos Cement factory in Clydebank and also in the Clyde shipyards and building sites. Widespread exposure to asbestos in these workplaces, especially from the 1930s to the 1960s, incubated a mesothelioma time bomb which is currently exploding across Scotland. Other shipbuilding and ship-repairing areas in Scotland also showed up high asbestos mortality rates, though it might be noted that at the Royal Naval Dockyard at Rosyth occupational health standards were somewhat better than in the private sector, with Rosyth being amongst the earliest of the Scottish ship-repair yards to ban asbestos spraying. The HSE statistics show that this pattern of mortality was replicated across the UK, with shipbuilding and repairing areas registering the highest death rates.

Whilst exposure was widespread, the other major at-risk groups were those who stripped and removed asbestos and construction workers, as the material was used extensively from the 1940s as a fire retardant in buildings. Here our evidence for Scotland indicates that there were few, if any, effective safety precautions before the

1970s. The Red Road Flats incident shows just how unaware building workers were of the risks to their health of working with asbestos before the mid-1960s. Not surprisingly, then, most (though by no means all) exposure in Scotland was occupational, with male mesothelioma deaths accounting for about 85–90% of all recorded asbestos-related disease deaths and female around 10–15%.[4] Nonetheless, a significant proportion of disabilities and fatalities have been caused by indirect exposure, so-called 'bystander' and 'family contact', caused, in some cases, by brushing and washing husbands' work overalls impregnated with the deadly fibres (see Chapter 6). Such 'environmental' exposure cases are certain to rise over the coming two decades.

To fully comprehend the unfolding asbestos tragedy, it is crucial to place it in its proper context. Working and manufacturing asbestos was one of many dangerous and life-threatening jobs. Throughout the twentieth century, employment in Scotland had an adverse impact upon health in many ways. This was true especially within mining, transport, construction and the traditional heavy metal working, engineering and shipbuilding industries that dominated the Clydeside industrial conurbation up to the 1960s. Workers in these industries were accustomed to hazardous work and frequent injuries, and this influenced attitudes towards risk, de-sensitising workers to the dangers of contact with asbestos. Moreover, evidence suggests that occupational health and safety standards may well have been somewhat lower in the industrial region of the West of Scotland after the Second World War compared to the rest of the UK, due primarily to the concentration and persistence of heavy industry in this region.

Asbestos is not just a recent problem in Scotland but is part of a long history of poor occupational health. Exposure of workers to asbestos in Scotland started a long way back, with the first companies being established in the 1870s to manufacture asbestos products in this country. As it was not until the 1920s that asbestosis was widely diagnosed and not until the 1930s that the carcinogenic properties of asbestos were suspected, few deaths would have been accurately

4. Such figures, derived from the HSE mesothelioma statistics, are likely to under-estimate somewhat the female incidence of such disease because of a tendency to misdiagnose female deaths, in turn linked to a reluctance to admit such deaths could be occupational given prevailing notions about female employment patterns and gender roles.

recorded as asbestos-related for the first 50–60 years or so of asbestos production and use in Scotland. Most would have been put down to heart failure, unspecified lung tumours, pneumonia, tuberculosis or the catch-all phrase for lung disease, 'phthisis'. The actual death toll from asbestos therefore will never be known.

It is also true that because nothing was known about the dangers of working with asbestos, as far as we can tell, until the late 1890s, then some lives were *inevitably* going to be lost. Thereafter, because there were only a few proven deaths for a further two decades or so, it is understandable, *given the context*, that little or nothing was done by way of prevention or control. Arguably, perhaps until the late 1920s when the first Asbestos Regulations were being prepared, those involved in the manufacture and use of the product cannot really be held responsible because medical knowledge was poor, asbestosis cases were few and awareness of the hazard was very incomplete. Consequently, the early, scattered references to the dangers of working with asbestos, from 1898 to the 1920s, need to be seen and understood within their appropriate setting – as Bartrip has convincingly argued.[5] In this period there were vastly more dangerous work processes that occupied the energies of the regulators and policy-makers, including coal mining, lead manufacture, iron smelting, shipping, the railways, cutlery grinding, metal mining and chemicals. Moreover, occupational medicine was in its infancy, whilst the pressures of the First World War and the interwar economic depression diverted the attention of the state from addressing industrial diseases.

In the pre-World War Two Scottish workplace, moreover, the prevailing ethos incorporated a widespread acceptance of very high levels of risk, of dirt, fumes, dust and danger. This was part of the customary order of things – the way work had always been done. On their part, employers' attitudes and strategies varied – capitalists were no monolithic group and some were clearly more concerned about the health and welfare of their employees than others. Nonetheless, the evidence indicates to us that both the asbestos producers and the primary users of the product in Scotland – notably the insulating companies – invariably and quite calculatingly placed profit before workers' health, neglected basic safety precautions, failed to educate and develop a safety-conscious workforce and intensified

---

5. P. Bartrip, 'Too Little, Too Late? The Home Office and the Asbestos Industry Regulations, 1931', *Medical History*, 42 (October 1998).

workloads to levels that seriously jeopardised workers' health and wellbeing. Moreover, even where there was a recognition that inhaling dust was unhealthy – and there were clear signs of such recognition even before World War One – there was a widely held view that there was an acceptable level of morbidity and even mortality.[6] This was especially so in the case of asbestos, where its advocates could point to the life-saving potential of the product as a fire retardant, especially on board ships. Hence the argument (and the paradox) that the 'magic mineral' protected lives, thus counter-balancing the undermining of health and loss of life amongst those who manufactured and worked with it.

Nonetheless, in our view this interpretation can only be taken so far. We do need to guard against the inappropriate use of historical hindsight and to get inside and understand the motives and attitudes of people operating within a specific historical context, with limited knowledge, attitudes and other priorities. However, there remains a strong case – indeed an irrefutable one in our opinion – to be made against both industry and the regulators for neglect and inaction on the asbestos issue from the mid-1920s. Such an indictment has been advanced persuasively by Brodeur, Castleman, Wikeley, Dalton, Howie, Gorman and, recently and most systematically by Tweedale.[7] Tweedale's comprehensive and masterly analysis of the massive Turner & Newall asbestos archive has demonstrated beyond doubt both the culpability of the asbestos manufacturers and users *and* the ineffectiveness of state action and legislation designed to address the asbestos issue. Despite making some efforts to control dust in its factories the dominant UK asbestos manufacturer, Turner & Newall, was 'strikingly irresponsible', as Tweedale puts it, in relation to the occupational health of its asbestos workers:

Turner & Newall provided significant opposition to the

6. See A. McIvor, 'Work and Health, 1880–1914', *Scottish Labour History Society Journal*, 24, 1989, pp. 58–9. For a general overview of occupational health and safety in this period see A. J. McIvor, *A History of Work in Britain, 1880–1950* (Palgrave/Macmillan, 2000), Chapter 5.
7. G. Tweedale, *Magic Mineral;* P. Brodeur, *Outrageous Misconduct: The Asbestos Industry on Trial* (New York, 1985); B. I. Castleman, *Asbestos: Medical and Legal Aspects* (New Jersey, Aspen, 4th edn, 1996); N. Wikeley, 'The Asbestos Regulations, 1931: A Licence to Kill?', *Journal of Law and Society*, 19 (Autumn 1992); A. Dalton, *Asbestos Killer Dust* (1979). For a different viewpoint, see P. Bartrip, 'Too Little, Too Late?'

government dust control and medical schemes between the
1930s and the 1960s; it neglected to implement such schemes
fully both in the UK and especially overseas; it failed to warn
customers; refused frequently to admit financial and moral
liability for the consequences of its actions; often paid only
token amounts of money for industrial injuries and deaths;
tried to browbeat doctors, coroners and the Medical Board;
sought to suppress research linking asbestos and cancer; gave
the government inaccurate data about disease amongst its
shipyard workers; and disseminated imprecise information
about the 'safety' of asbestos.[8]

This is a damning but not unfair indictment, given the evidence
which Tweedale has exhaustively unearthed in the T&N archive. Our
study of managerial practices in Scotland largely concurs with such a
critique. The Scottish thermal insulation companies who employed
the laggers were warned as early as 1931 by their own employers'
association solicitor of the dangers of working with asbestos. This
was reiterated by the Home Office in 1945 with a circular to shipyards
warning of the dangers to health of asbestos spraying. Nonetheless,
in Scotland, as we have seen, little was done by management to
safeguard laggers' health or to inculcate safety consciousness at the
point of production during the period from the 1930s to the 1960s.
Laggers and other asbestos workers, as well as those working around
them, continued to be assured that the work was safe. Before 1960,
masks were rarely made available and were often ineffective and where
they were issued it was to those directly working with the product,
such as some (though not all) of the sprayers in the 1950s and 1960s,
whereas those working in the 'immediate vicinity' remained unprotected. The abandonment of asbestos spraying as early as 1943 by
Fairfields shipyard in Govan (significantly, *before* the 1945 warning
circular) indicates both prior awareness of the dangers inherent in this
work and what could have been done by early, pre-emptive positive
action by the asbestos users/customers. But this was an exceptional
example. The Clyde Shipbuilders' Association appears to have blindly
accepted the assurances of the asbestos companies and insulators that
they were adhering to the letter of the law in their shipyards. Had
they directly engaged the laggers something more *might* have been

8. Tweedale, *Magic Mineral*, p. 279.

done. What certainly exacerbated the problem was the small-scale, diffused nature of asbestos insulation work in Scotland, undertaken by contractors (such as Newall's) and sub-licensees (such as Anderson's) employing just a handful of men. In such a context, government regulations were difficult, indeed almost impossible, to enforce; non-compliance was endemic and a high risk culture in the workplace allowed to doggedly persist. Moreover, the insistence by influential shipowners such as Cunard well into the 1960s that asbestos be extensively used in ship construction – as on the *QE2* – to maximise fire prevention only served to spread exposure widely within the shipbuilding fraternity, across the laggers, the joiners who cut the deadly Marinite, and other ship-finishing trades.

Our investigation of the labour process and work conditions at Turner's asbestos factory in Clydebank also provides clear evidence of serious malpractice in the manufacture of asbestos products in Scotland. Here there was neglect of dust suppression methods (including inadequate exhaust ventilation), lack of medical surveillance and ineffective medical monitoring of at-risk workers, together with crude, outmoded work practices which maximised dust generation on the shop floor, as well as little provision of masks and respirators. Management also suppressed information, as in the case of blue asbestos in the Turner's warehouse in the 1960s, and misinformed workers that white asbestos was harmless. Much of this was admitted by T&N's own medical adviser, Hilton Lewinsohn, in the late 1960s. Criminal negligence and managerial malpractice were also clearly evident in building construction and asbestos stripping operations in Scotland. Ranging from not informing workers they were in contact with asbestos, to bringing in cheap casual labour, instructing workers to cut corners, offering large bonuses to strip 'dry' and keep quiet, to failing to supply adequate numbers of mechanical sawing machines with exhaust ventilation (as at Red Road). Some workers were even told that the magnesia in the dust was good for them. Moreover (with the possible exception of Fairfield's shipyard), we have found no evidence of employers and management pro-actively encouraging health-consciousness in relation to asbestos, something which they were morally and ethically obliged to do (as Lewinsohn argued), given their superior knowledge, intelligence and positions of authority in industry. The available evidence suggests quite the opposite. Taking short cuts which involved serious health risks in order to maximise production was condoned, even encouraged.

Furthermore, the industry can be indicted for not developing safer substitutes or even banning its more toxic product – crocidolite (blue asbestos) – earlier. The development of the Rocksil (rock-wool) mine near Stirling by Cape Asbestos in the 1950s perhaps indicates awareness that alternative insulating materials needed to be developed, but the process was painfully slow. Significantly, it was almost a decade after the Wagner article in 1960 unequivocally associated asbestos with mesothelioma before the industry banned crocidolite. This contrasted sharply with the decisive action of ICI in the 1960s when they immediately removed their curing agent for tyres (NONOS X) when it was discovered to be a carcinogen causing bladder cancer.[9] Moreover, the deliberate delaying of compensation litigation until the claimant died – as in the case of Charlie Coyle – indicates a callous disregard for human suffering by both the producers and the primary users of asbestos. Profit was, quite clearly, being placed before workers' health and wellbeing. And in asbestos in its heyday from the 1930s to the 1960s, profits, as the T&N balance sheets indicate, were massive. A great many shareholders, then, lined their pockets from the suffering of those who worked with asbestos.

After the asbestos employers and management, the government also must bear a portion of the blame because of the limited coverage of the 1931 Regulations, weak enforcement and, crucially, the failure to extend the Regulations until the late 1960s to encompass the majority of workers at risk. These flaws in the regulatory system were the result of many factors, including an under-resourced Factory Inspectorate, ineffective deterrents for factory crime, economic considerations, the failure of the medical profession to openly criticise asbestos manufacturing, and a muted response on the part of the trade unions to the asbestos issue prior to the 1970s. This was very much evident in Scotland. A number of our interviewees testified to never having seen a government health and safety inspector. Our oral testimony brings forth clear evidence that life-threatening practices continued within the workplaces on Clydeside long after the dangers of asbestos were known and safety regulations introduced. Such evidence casts serious doubt on the effectiveness of voluntary industry regulation and state regulation to control exposure to asbestos in the workplace, from the original measures in 1931 right through to the 1980s. Clearly, the 'softly, softly' approach of the Factory Inspectorate

9. We are grateful to Robin Howie for this information.

and the principle of shared responsibility, enshrined in the 1974 Health and Safety at Work Act, failed to protect Scottish workers from the hazards of asbestos. Prosecutions meted out in the Scottish courts against factory law offenders were infrequent and fines ludicrously low. Significantly, no one, to date, has been imprisoned for breaches of Health and Safety laws in relation to asbestos offences in Scotland. Corporate crime was (and remains) very inadequately policed whilst safety continues, on the HSE's' own admission, to be take priority over health. Prior to the late 1960s, the state proved too willing to accept the restrictions upon legislation demanded by the asbestos industry. Within the asbestos debate, then, our work on Scotland tends to confirm the 'pessimistic' interpretations of Tweedale and others. This *was* a case both of legislative initiatives that were 'too little, too late' and of ongoing managerial and employer indifference, evasion and criminal negligence.

The situation was worsened by the problems of policing health and safety legislation in what were relatively small companies and by the deleterious effects of deregulation in the 1980s and 1990s. Scottish workers were also at a disadvantage in other respects. The different legal system north of the Border made it more difficult until the 1990s to obtain a *post mortem*, and thus to definitively prove asbestos lung tissue damage. Moreover, compensation awarded to victims of asbestos-related diseases in the Scottish courts was substantially lower than awards made in the English courts. This contributed, in turn, to the relative poverty and social exclusion faced by many Scottish victims of asbestos disease and their families.

The escalating asbestos catastrophe could perhaps have been kept within bounds if there had been effective opposition and pressure from either the medical fraternity or the trade unions, especially in the crucial period from the 1930s to the 1960s. Whilst there were critical voices and clear evidence of rank-and-file campaigning, especially within the TGWU, neither the doctors nor the unions provided the critical dissenting mass necessary to radically change policy.

Tweedale has noted the marked absence of doctors in the UK who spoke out against the asbestos risk.[10] In part this was because ordinary GPs were rarely well informed about asbestos-related disease before the 1970s. Moreover, by controlling, to a large extent, the type of

---

10. Tweedale, *Magic Mineral.*, pp. 282–3.

research undertaken (predominantly through the industry-funded Asbestosis Research Council), the asbestos industry helped to maintain a 'closed circle' where diffusion of medical knowledge was contained within a relatively narrow group of specialists. In Scotland, our survey of the medical journals has shown that they devoted little attention prior to the 1970s to occupational diseases and virtually ignored the asbestos issue altogether. Industrial medicine was poorly developed, with few but the very largest companies in Scotland directly employing full-time works doctors. Thus medical surveillance and epidemiological studies were rare in the asbestos sector in Scotland prior to the 1970s. In the case of the laggers, promises of medical surveillance after the 1967 strike were renaged on by employers. At Turner's Clydebank, a part-time and relatively unsympathetic local GP provided a poor service, which was critically undermined by the lack of confidentiality in Turner's medical records. Regular medicals were unheard of in the building trade. A measure of the weakness of occupational medicine on Clydeside was demonstrated at Red Road in the mid-1960s, when a mobile occupational health and dust-screening unit had to be called in from Dundee to test asbestos dust levels on the building site. This unit developed from a Nuffield-funded experiment in Dundee – the Scottish Occupational Health Service (SOHS) – which provided a co-operative service covering a large number of small firms. Such a service might well have made a difference in Glasgow, but despite pioneering occupational health schemes established by Glasgow Corporation in the 1950s and 1960s, no organisation was established which systematically investigated asbestos diseases or the occupational dust problem as a whole. The Glasgow shipyard laggers appealed to the Scottish Occupational Health Service (SOHS) to come in and monitor their working environment. Mair's unit in Dundee apparently made one attempt to do this, but gave up after being refused access by the thermal insulating firms they approached. Medical research thus took place piecemeal, by interested individuals in hospitals and cancer research groups. This reflects a wider problem built into the very structure of the British health service, where occupational health occupies a quite separate and subordinate sphere despite pleas from many quarters in the 1940s and into the 1950s that an Occupational Health Service be integrated into the NHS. We have argued elsewhere that had such a streamlined service been created, then occupational health would have been given a higher priority within the NHS, and that the probable outcome would have been that the asbestos problem, and death toll, would have been substantially reduced.[11] The one isolated example before the 1970s of the cavalry coming in was when the SOHS mobile van was dispatched to Red Road.

Most studies of the asbestos catastrophe in Britain now emphasise the failure of the trade unions – and especially the TUC – to protect workers from this threat. Thus the lack of an effective workers' counterpoise to the power of the asbestos companies *contributed* to the scale of the disaster. This has turned into a recurring thesis in the literature emphasising the unions' indifference to occupational health and accompanying commitment to the wage packet. Whilst this is, in our view, an interpretation that cannot be accepted without serious qualification (see, for example, the vigorous campaigning on occupational health by the cotton and the miners' unions from the late nineteenth century), the evidence in relation to asbestos is quite convincing, and, again, appears to be supported by the Scottish experience. Our examination of the STUC reports indicates lack of interest in the asbestos issue up to the 1970s. The emergence of the asbestos pressure groups, such as Clydeside Action on Asbestos, was, in part, a reaction to the evident failure of the trade unions to represent effectively the needs of asbestos victims in this region. However, as we have seen, there was significant activity at branch level in Scotland and some evidence of direct action on the asbestos issue, particularly within the well-organised laggers' branch of the TGWU on Clydeside. Initial reactions to the hazard prompted collective bargaining initiatives, including the negotiation of 'dirty' money bonuses to compensate for the dangers of working with the material. By the mid-to late 1960s, though, as the cancer risk became evident, laggers and building workers downed tools in order to improve work conditions, with some, albeit limited, successes. However, even this was not enough to generate a widespread campaign within the Scottish trade union movement, spearheaded by the STUC, to get the killer material effectively controlled or even banned.

Why was this? The capacity of the unions to effectively address the asbestos issue was severely constrained by the circumstances they found themselves under in post-war Scotland. With de-indus-

---

11. See R. Johnston and A. McIvor, 'Whatever happened to the Occupational Health Service?', in C. Nottingham (ed.), *The NHS in Scotland* (Aldershot, 2000).

trialisation, the collective bargaining power of the union movement in the heavy industries was substantially reduced. Unions faced tough decisions about how industrial action could affect job security, and, rightly or wrongly, on occasions, unions tolerated dangerous work conditions because they feared industrial action would precipitate company closures. Trade unionism was relatively weak, moreover, in the small, fragmented thermal insulation, heating engineering and asbestos factories – indeed, it was virtually non-existent at Scottish manufacturers such as MacLellan's and Turner's before the late 1960s. Moreover, to some degree the unions were reflecting the high acceptance of risk – especially in relation to the longer-term problems of occupational health, as distinct from safety – which characterised the industrial workforce in the traditional urban conurbations such as Clydeside. In such workplaces a *machismo* work culture prevailed, at least up to the 1960s. In this environment workers were expected to tolerate high levels of risk through peer pressure as well as managerial expectations. To step out of line would be an affront to masculinity – a sign of weakness. In this context trade unions sometimes appeared as intervening unnecessarily in workers' lives – indicated in the example of Glasgow building workers at one site telling their own TGWU official to 'fuck off' and not interfere when he warned them in 1967 of the long-term risks to their health from inhaling asbestos dust.[12]

However, only very rarely were workers themselves to blame for contributing to their own ill-health and mortality from exposure to asbestos. The notion of contributory negligence needs to be understood within the prevailing work culture and context of the time, taking into account the economic realities impinging upon industrial workers in this period with rising unemployment, wage insecurity and de-industrialisation, and workers' lack of authority and power in the workplace. Moreover, for much of the period under review workers were simply not aware of the dangers of working with asbestos. Our oral testimonies confirm that long before the danger was realised, asbestos 'fell like snow' from above, hung like a fog in shafts of sunlight, and was something to be fooled around with on the shop floor.

Having said this, it is important to recognise that the prevailing workplace culture provided an environment conducive to the

12. Interview A23.

incubation of life-threatening occupational disease. The oral evidence we have accumulated does indicate that workers were intensively socialised and habituated into accepting a high level of risk, and even death, in heavy industrial employment in areas like Clydeside. Danger was accepted as part of the customary fabric of working life in shipbuilding, construction, mining and factories, and injuries were relatively frequent, right up to the 1960s. The contraction of shipbuilding and the heavy industries in Scotland from the 1920s may have worked to perpetuate and fossilise such attitudes, making workers (especially the lesser skilled) even more willing to tolerate dangerous work practices for the sake of employment. The oral testimony shows that attitudes to work and to occupational hazards varied widely, as we might expect amongst a diverse section of folk, and that toleration of danger at work clearly diminished over time as awareness of the long-term consequences grew. This is also connected to the emergence of a more health-conscious society from the 1970s. However, a kind of stoic fatalism emerges from much of the oral testimony of shipbuilding, construction and asbestos factory workers, combined with a *machismo* work culture which saw moaners as being 'soft'. Moreover, the effect of a volatile and insecure labour market, combined with the short-term economic incentive built into the wage system, could frequently outweigh concerns over health in the longer term. Retrospectively, a number of our respondents ruefully mourned their willingness to cut corners and expose themselves to risk because bonuses were offered or wages were high or they needed a job. In this respect, however, it needs to be emphasised that workers' freedom of action was constrained by the economic imperatives of an unpredictable labour market and the basic needs of having to provide for a family. Workers were reacting, in effect, to wage systems and inducements offered by management who themselves had a moral obligation to ensure work conditions were safe and, indeed, to make their employees more aware and thus to develop a more health-conscious environment at the point of production. In Scotland, over the crucial period from *c.* 1930 to the 1960s, with few exceptions, there is little evidence that either the asbestos manufacturers or the primary users (such as the insulation sub-contractors) fulfilled these basic moral responsibilities. Again, we are back to the point that profit was being put ahead of workers' health and wellbeing.

Significantly, voices were raised very early on, even before World

War Two, criticising limited state action and the restricted scope of
the Asbestos Regulations, and recognising the existence of
life-threatening exposure in work processes such as spraying which
lay beyond the scheduled trades. These included Reginald Tage, an
independent occupational health specialist, and Sir Thomas Legge,
Chief Medical Inspector of Factories, who commented in 1934 in
relation to asbestos that 'it is impossible not to feel that opportunities
for discovery and prevention were badly missed'.[13] Thus what could
have been a contained crisis, of the proportions, say, of cotton
spinners' cancer or byssinosis, became a public health disaster of
massive, indeed unprecedented, magnitude.

The disastrous legacy of all this, indicated in sharply rising
asbestos-cancer death rates, has already been commented upon at
length. However, the asbestos catastrophe actually consists of
thousands of individual tragedies; of ordinary people's lives being
turned upside down and destroyed. What we have tried to do here
is to probe behind the statistics, drawing upon participant testimony
to open up layers of experience in relation to the impact of
asbestos-disease. This methodology has its strengths, but could be
subject to some criticism. In concentrating on interviewing victims of
occupational disease, we have been aware of the subjective nature of
the testimony, and of interviews where, on occasions, respondents
have told us what they think we want to hear, and of repeated
narratives from respondents which have reiterated criticisms of
employers, management, state officials, doctors and the trade unions.
To some, our focus on victim testimony will be interpreted as
unrepresentative and distorted. Nonetheless we felt it vital that an
account of the asbestos tragedy fully incorporate the perspective of
the victims – of those who personally witnessed exposure and the
effects of asbestos. The historians job is to analyse and interpret
surviving sources and in this respect people's memories are invaluable
fragments of evidence, though clearly this material needs to be treated
sensitively, using the normal conventions of cross-verification and
corroboration. Oral testimony is no less valid evidence, in our view,
than any other sources. We have filtered through the oral evidence,
pointed up exceptional cases and experiences, whilst consciously

13. Thomas Legge, *Industrial Maladies* (Oxford, 1934), p. 191; on Tage, see
    N. Wikeley, 'Asbestos and Cancer: An Early Warning to the British TUC',
    American Journal of Industrial Medicine, 22, 1992, pp. 449–54.

seeking to verify information by multiplication – asking the same or similar questions of all or most of our respondents – and corroborating views where possible against the documentary evidence, especially in relation to working conditions and the politics of occupational health, where the sources are more abundant and we have been able to exploit the T&N archive, newspapers, HSE material, trade union and employers' association papers. Furthermore, to some degree the victim-orientation of our oral history interviewing is counterbalanced by the fact that we have not been able to interview those likely to have been most embittered and alienated – the many thousands of workers who have paid the ultimate price for their contact with asbestos and have already died. Moreover, the *documentary* evidence on workplace culture and how asbestos affected people's health and social lives is relatively thin, so the oral interviews provide a new and vital perspective, essential, we would argue, to developing a full understanding of this industrial catastrophe.

Victims, dependants and their families have had to deal with the trauma of diagnosis, curtailment and loss of employment, physical deterioration and, invariably, the deeper psychological implications of dependency and loss of self-esteem. The courage displayed during this ultimate crisis in people's lives is striking, and, as interviewers, we have been deeply moved by the strength and heroism of such folk who have been visited by this modern-day blight. Most faced certain, painful death, when diagnosed with mesothelioma, with quiet stoicism. Others, frequently dependants, responded with understandable bitterness and anger directed against a system that cruelly robbed them of their loved ones. Many dependants and partners were forced to make their own personal sacrifices, some giving up careers and becoming full-time carers when the asbestosis became critically debilitating, or the cancer too painful to cope with. Some, especially older workers, appear to cope with this watershed in their lives better than others.

Lifestyles invariably changed, and often quite radically, when the curse of asbestos touched people's lives, though each individual case was different. A minority of our respondents indicated that they were not adversely affected in economic or social terms by their disability. However, our oral testimony has shown that for most asbestos disease victims in Scotland, social isolation and relative poverty have been the inevitable outcome of their disability. This slide down into what sociologists now term 'social exclusion' was especially evident as the asbestos tragedy unfolded – though legislation, especially from the

1960s (addressing occupational health and compensation), undoubtedly, on balance, *ameliorated* the predicament of victims. In the 1990s the scrapping of Compensation Recovery (in 1993) and the changes in the legal system which enabled a civil claim to proceed on the same basis beyond the death of the claimant have had positive effects. As have the pro-active campaigning and representation of victims by the asbestos pressure groups such as CAA, the campaigns of the unions since the 1970s and a more sympathetic treatment of victims by Local Authorities (for example, Glasgow City Council and West Dumbartonshire Council). Nonetheless, it remains the case that because of the physical symptoms of asbestos disease, the inequities of the benefit system and the hidden losses of unemployment (such as pensions schemes), combined with the difficulties asbestos victims continue to have in gaining civil compensation, *most* victims continue to experience 'social exclusion'. Indeed, our argument here is that victims of industrial disability (such as asbestosis and mesothelioma) are a neglected group in the socially excluded fraternity and merit more attention within the 'social exclusion' literature. Clearly such victims are invariably cut off from usual living patterns and activities, such as walking, sport, gardening and dancing. People's sense of loss is perhaps sharpened, moreover, by the material affluence that surrounds them as real wages and standards of living continued to rise in the UK in the second half of the twentieth century. Thus asbestos victims have found themselves let down by the social and medical services and have invariably had to face a gruelling struggle to attain compensation at a time when their health and capacity was being undermined – whilst 'gasping for breath'. In this sense, as one Scottish asbestos campaigner noted in the early 1990s, they were 'victims twice over'.[14]

The *exposés* of the asbestos health crisis in the press and the media from the 1970s and the campaigning of asbestos victim pressure groups (such as SPAID and CAA) from the 1980s, together with delayed and belated pressure from the trade union movement, played a large part in changing people's attitudes towards the asbestos risk. This energising of the anti-asbestos campaign resulted in tighter, more effective regulations and eventual banning of practically all asbestos manufacture and imports in the UK in November 1999. The tragedy is that it took over a hundred years from the first official recognition

14. J. Lenaghan, *Victims Twice Over.*

by a UK government Factory Inspector in 1898 before this was achieved. In Scotland, as elsewhere, the asbestos problem will remain with us for some time, however, because of the millions and millions of tons of the 'magic mineral' deeply embedded within buildings, ships and machinery, and because of the continuing rising death toll from asbestos-related diseases such as mesothelioma. This grisly and harrowing legacy of the past is a fact of life that we now have to live with. What urgently remains to be done is to ensure that society is fully aware of the asbestos tragedy and that no-one is further endangered through removal operations. Also that the victims of these diseases and their dependents are more generously compensated to help assuage the slide into relative poverty, social isolation and demoralisation that disability and knowledge of a fatal carcinoma can have. Sadly, however, no amount of financial compensation can ever recompense people for such serious disability or loss of life.

The evidence in our view points squarely to a quite disgraceful prioritisation of profit and production over workers' health. In effect, society tolerated a certain level of death and disability, and for far too long employers and managers were allowed a virtual free hand by a cautious state unwilling or unable to implement the tough measures needed to protect citizens effectively, both in the workplace and in the community. Scotland now has its own Parliament, and whilst powers in relation to occupational health and safety are not yet fully devolved, the country does have an opportunity to tackle the problems of industrial disability-induced social exclusion and lethal work practices. This is a debt we owe to those who have suffered and died gasping for breath over the past century or so from asbestos-related diseases. More than anything else, it is absolutely imperative that the lessons of the past are fully absorbed so that such a tragic experience is never repeated.

Monkey Dung and White Mice
(by Francis Devine, 2000) [1]

See me,
I cannae breathe me

I cannae kick a ba' wi' the gran' weans,
cannae dance nae mare,
cannae pitch a bool.

It wiz thon monkey dung.
Doon the Yard,
they laggers would work o'er us
high on the piping gantry.
First thing they would turn the batons,
feart for tae fa',
an' thon monkey dung would shoo'er doon.
Like sna it wiz,
clouds o' it,
ye couldnae see yer hon afore yer face.
It would be all oo'er ye –
in yer e'en mooth,
gaggin' ye'd be.
After that it would just spatter doon a' day,
wee gubby blobs that would dry oot an' pooder.

White mice we wiz ca'ed –
Jimmy McGlashan, Shug Doolan, ma'sel –
Hickory, Dickory an' Dock,
that wiz us.
We'd laugh aboot it
but ye'd be telt aff on the bus

---

1. Francis Devine is a trade union official working in Dublin, co-editor of
Saothar, Journal of the Irish Labour History Society and author of a collection
of poems, *Red Star, Blue Moon* (Dublin, 1997)

leaving the seats a' stoor.
We'd bring the *Record*
an' lay it oot oo'er the seats,
like auld Jessies an' their best settees.
Doon in Quinn's Vaults
ye'd no be left alane
so ye went hame,
shook aff the dust,
got the wife to beat it aff.
The telly would be a' scum.
We thought to be vexin' folk –
had nae notions we wiz killing 'em.

Wee Shug went first.
Lung cancer they said.
Loved his Woodbines,
fifty, sixty a day man
so he wiz, Wee Shug.
They telt him it wiz the fags.
Then Jimmy wiz diagnosed
wi' mesothelioma –
see hoo that big word just rolls aff the tongue?
I can even spell the bastard thing!
Fifty-wan Jimmy wiz.
Noo Senga, his partner,
she's struggling,
no weel at a',
wheezin' an peely wally,
in an' oot the Infirmary.

They're a' away –
Rab Sleton, Luggie Fleming, Malky John.
A' deid.

See me,
I cannae breathe me.
I cannae pish wi' oot the oxygen.
I cannae gae doon the toon,
drink wi' the boys.
Years since I wiz at Paradise.

Aye, it wiz the monkey dung,
thon fucking sna.

An' the worse thing is –
they kent fine,
they kent fae years afore a' us wee mice started to croak.
They kent
but didnae tell us,
let the monkey dung keep shooerin' doon.

Aye, I bet they a' breathe fine,
nae tight chests,
nae sleepless nights,
nae gas cylinders by the doonstair bed.

Fact is –
it wiznae the dust at a' –
Fidel Broon was richt,
it wiz Capitalism
but then that's no
a Prescribed Occupational Disease,
no yet anyways.

See me,
I cannae get ma breath me –
but I can still fight.

Aye,
still fight.

Appendix 1. Factory Inspector's Letter to UK Shipbuilders and Repairers, August 1945

(Clyde Shipbuilders' Association, Minutes, Mitchell Library Archives, Glasgow)

Ministry of Labour and National Service
Factory Department
St James Square
London, SW1
August 1945

Dear Sir,

Asbestos Insulation Aboard Ships

I am concerned by the considerable development during the war years in the use of asbestos, either alone or as a part of a mixture, in the Shipbuilding and Shiprepairing Industries mainly for the purpose of heat and sound insulation, and the accompanying increase in the number of workers exposed to risk of injury to health through asbestos.

If the risk is found to continue, the question will arise of including some statutory requirements on the subject when the Factories Act Regulations for constructional and other work in ships are being revised and extended, or of issuing a further code of regulations dealing particularly with the issue of asbestos. I would, however, emphasise that, while asbestos dust may not have any apparent effects at first, experience shows that, particularly if the workers are exposed to the dust in substantial concentrations, serious results are apt to develop later. It is therefore important that, even if the work will only be temporary, all reasonably practicable steps should be taken to reduce the risk to a minimum.

I suggest that protection can be secured on the following basis:

1   In some cases preparatory work, e.g. the making up of insulation
    mattresses, to which the Asbestos Industry Regulations, 1931,
    apply is carried on in a shed in the shipbuilding yard or near
    the dockside; in such cases those Regulations should, so far as
    the provisions are applicable, be carefully observed in practice.

2   On board ship steps should be taken, in accordance with the
    spirit of the Regulations, to prevent unnecessary concentrations
    or accumulations of asbestos dust – for instance by having good
    ventilation arrangements in confined spaces, damping down
    dust, and clearing up asbestos debris and accumulations of dust
    as soon as practicable.

3   The provision of a respirator (Home Office Mark No. 584042
    or other approved type) for each workman engaged in the fitting
    or removal of any dry insulating material containing asbestos,
    on board ship.

4   The provision of a similar respirator for all persons engaged in
    the spraying of asbestos or asbestos mixture at work ancillary
    thereto which renders them liable to exposure to dust or spray.
    During spraying, no other person should work in the same
    compartment unless also provided with a respirator.

5   No person under 18 should be employed in any process giving
    rise to asbestos dust or in any compartment or enclosed space
    where such a process is being carried on.

6   Specific arrangements for supervising the maintenance, care and
    use of respirators.

I may say that these arrangements have been accepted by the
Shipbuilding Employers' Federation and by the Trade Unions
concerned, and I therefore hope you will be prepared at once to accept
the precautions suggested.

>   I am, Sir,
>   Your obedient Servant,
>   A. W. GARRETT
>   H. M. Chief Inspector of Factories

Appendix 2. Clyde Shipbuilders' Association Circular Letter to Members, January 1946

(CSA, Minutes, Mitchell Library Archives, Glasgow)

Clyde Shipbuilders' Association
105 West George Street,
Glasgow
Circular Letter S. No. 46–20

22 January 1946

TO THE MEMBERS OF THE ASSOCIATION

Dear Sirs,

Increased Use of Asbestos on Board Ship

In August, 1945, the Chief Inspector of Factories issued a Circular Letter direct to firms who were known to be concerned with the use on board ship of asbestos or mixtures containing asbestos, directing attention to the precautions which should be taken to protect workpeople against the risk of injury to health through asbestosis. Attached, for handy reference, is a copy of the Chief Inspector's Circular, from which it will be observed that the precautions suggested by him had been the subject of consultation with the Federation and the Trade Unions.

At the request of the Confederation of S. & E. Unions the question of the practical application of these precautions was discussed at an informal meeting held yesterday between the Association Executive Committee and the representatives of the Confederation. The Union representatives indicated that while they were interested in the general observance of the precautions, they were particularly concerned to ensure that the recommended safeguards were carried out by sub-contracting firms whose workpeople were employed in shipyards.

The Employers indicated that, so far as they were aware, the precautions recommended by the Chief Inspector of Factories were being given effect to by all Shipbuilding and Shiprepairing firms; but they undertook to request the members of the Association to direct the attention of sub-contractors to the precautions, so as to ensure their strict observance on all appropriate occasions.

I am accordingly desired to request that you will bring to the notice of your sub-contractors the precautions outlined in the attachment hereto, and ensure that they are adopted on all work of the nature specified which is undertaken in your establishment.

        PLEASE NOTE

                Yours faithfully,
                William Lawson
                Secretary.

Appendix 3. Report of Central Conference between the Shipbuilding Employers' Federation and the Amalgamated Society of Woodworkers, 1 October 1954

(CSA, Minutes, Mitchell Library Archives, Glasgow)

Shipbuilding Employers' Federation,
1, Chester Street,
Grosvenor Place,
London, SW1

Circular Letter No. 141/54
Conference and Works Board Report No. 4/54

Joiners working with Marinite – claim for special allowance – Clyde district

It was explained by the representatives of the Joiners' Society that the claim related to the use of Marinite, a material with an asbestos base. While the reference to Central Conference related to the Clyde district there had been difficulties also in other districts, and it was hoped that a decision on the Clyde case would also dispose of outstanding claims in these districts.

Their claim for a special allowance was based on the grounds that Marinite was damaging to tools, and that when cut created clouds of fine dust, containing about 40% silica. That caused discomfort to the workmen and was injurious to their health. Subject to certain conditions the Clyde employers had offered to pay an allowance of 1½d. per hour; but the Society, though they accepted the conditions governing payment of the allowance, felt that the amount of the allowance offered was inadequate. The Union agreed that the proper course was for the employers to provide adequate ventilation and dust extraction, in which case, assuming that the employers were providing the tools, no allowance would be payable under the terms of the Clyde offer. One purpose the Society had in requesting that the allowance be increased was to penalise those employers who failed to provide such facilities. The allowance they had in mind was 3_d._ per hour.

On behalf of the Federation disagreement was expressed with the idea of attempting to penalise employers who failed to provide adequate ventilation and dust extraction facilities. It was recognised that the conditions that were encountered during the cutting of Marinite were by no means desirable, but the only wise answer was to provide adequate ventilation and dust extraction facilities. One should never approach a matter such as this on the basis of how far one could compensate men by payment of such an allowance. Regarding the question of damage to tools, it could be argued that no allowance was warranted on this basis but the offer which had been made by the Clyde employers and which had been accepted in principle by the Society did provide something in respect of the use of workmen's tools when engaged on Marinite.

After further discussion and an adjournment the Society's representatives were advised that the Board, having reviewed the whole position and having noted the acceptance by the Society of the conditions governing the payment of any allowance, were prepared to recommend the Clyde Association to amend their offer by increasing the allowance from 1½_d._ per hour to 2_d._ per hour.

This offer was accepted by the Society's representatives ...

Appendix 4. Marinite Agreement, Clyde Shipbuilders' Association and the Amalgamated Society of Woodworkers, 1 October 1954

(Glasgow University Archives and Business Records Centre, UCS1/91/145)

1 An allowance of 2*d.* per hour is to be paid to joiners and woodcutting machinists during periods when they are actually engaged on the cutting of faced or unfaced Marinite with power driven or hand operated tools.

2 The allowance of 2*d.* per hour is to be paid to joiners and woodcutting machinists when working with faced or unfaced Marinite in the immediate vicinity of men who are actually engaged on the cutting of such material.

3 No other allowance will fall to be paid in respect of the cutting of faced or unfaced Marinite. In particular, men who qualify for the allowance of 2*d.* per hour under this settlement will <u>not</u> be entitled to the extra of ¾*d.* per hour which is payable on certain types of insulation work nor for the allowance of the same amount which is granted to compensate for damage to tools during the cutting of specified hard materials.

4 The allowance of 2*d.* per hour is to compensate for the discomfort arising from the dust created during the cutting of the Marinite and also takes account of any exceptional wear occasioned to the workmen's tools used during the operation. Accordingly, where it is agreed that equipment used in connection with this operation is so designed (e.g. with dust collecting facilities) as to preserve normal atmospheric conditions, and at the same time the cutting tools are supplied by the employer, the allowance will not be payable.

Appendix 5. Report on the Asbestos Dust Survey Carried out at the Red Road Building Site, Glasgow, for the Corporation of Glasgow, May 1967. Prof. A. Mair, J. T. Sanderson and T. D. Guthrie

(Turner & Newall Archive, Manchester Metropolitan University)

In May 1967, the Occupational Hygiene Unit of the Scottish Occupational Health Laboratory Service Ltd carried out an atmospheric survey at the Corporation of Glasgow's Red Road building site. The survey was designed to assess the health risk to operatives handling asbestos products during the construction of multi-storey flats.

Several very large multi-storey flats are being erected at the previously mentioned building site. The buildings are constructed using a complex arrangement of steel girders. Because of the risk of these structures twisting during the event of a fire, the girders require to be completely encased with asbestos products. In addition, the whole of the exterior of these buildings consists of asbestos cement sheeting.

The girders and ceilings are all faced with ASBESTOLUX boarding, a material approximately ½ inch thick, supplied in 4 feet by 4 feet panels, and consisting of 20% by weight amosite and chrysotile asbestos. Most of the Asbestolux panels require trimming by means of a hand sawing operation, which visibly creates a considerable dust cloud. To attach these trimmed panels to the main supporting girders they are first tacked into position with nails, screwed into wooden blocks situated in the girders, then surplus material from the edges removed with a surfoam tool. Although the visible dust created by these processes is not great, the operative's head tends to be extremely close to the dust source. The dust generated also drifts downwards from the girders (which are at about ceiling height) into the breathing zone of the workers. These two points are extremely important and also apply to the process of fixing the panels to the main ceiling.

Although a squad of men have apparently been appointed to the task of damping down and sweeping up the Asbestolux sawdust as it is produced, no-one was seen carrying out this task in any of the areas investigated. Indeed in some rooms the quantity of waste on the floor could easily be described as considerable. Only one man was seen engaged in sweeping up waste material and this was being carried out in a room immediately prior to painting. No dampening of the dust was observed.

Of the fairly large number of men employed on 'dusty' operations during the survey, comparatively few made use of the respirators provided by the Corporation Safety Department. None of these men wore any special protective clothing apart from the overalls normally associated with men carrying out joinery operations.

The concentrations of asbestos dust found during the survey are recorded in the Table and are expressed in particles per cubic centimetre (p.p.c.c.) of air.

Scale

Fibre lengths	*No. of p.p.c.c. (fibres)*	*Assessment environment*
5 microns	More than 4	Very unsatisfactory
5 microns	2–4	Unsatisfactory
5 microns	1–2	Fairly satisfactory
5 microns	0.5–1	Satisfactory
5 microns	Less than 0.5	Very satisfactory

Table Showing Asbestos Dust Levels Found During the Survey

Operation	*Remarks*	*p.p.c.c. (asbestos) more than 5 microns in length*
Trimming Asbestolux panels	Dry panels; reasonably good natural ventilation	10–11
	Dry panels; very good natural ventilation	4

Fixing Asbestolux sheets to main girders	Dry panels; reasonably good natural ventilation	3
Fixing Asbestolux sheets to the ceiling	Dry panels; poor natural ventilation	8–13
'Shooting' asbestos blocks to the metal ceiling	Dry panels; poor natural ventilation	13–16
	Dry panels; very good natural ventilation	5
Sweeping up waste material	Poor natural ventilation undamped waste	37
General background level between dusty operation	Poor natural ventilation	5
	Reasonably good natural ventilation	2
	Very good natural ventilation	1
Clean room prior to painting	Poor natural ventilation	less than 1

DISCUSSIONS OF RESULTS AND RECOMMENDATIONS

It is readily seen from the Table that every single dust generating operation produces asbestos dust levels in excess of the acceptable value shown in the hazard assessment scale. In the vast majority of cases the acceptable level is grossly exceeded. Even when the natural ventilation is described as very good, the asbestos dust concentrations are higher than they should be and involve some degree of risk to the operatives.

By far the dustiest operation, and the one involving the most risk to health, is the sweeping up of the dry asbestos waste (sawdust, etc.). If possible, this should take place using a portable industrial vacuum cleaner in preference to a brush and the waste should be thoroughly dampened beforehand with water containing a small amount of detergent, or with damp sawdust (wood). Provision of a suitable respirator is essential for the protection of the 'sweeping up squad' as even the vacuum cleaner and dampened waste measures may not effect the necessary reduction in atmospheric dust.

In general, the following recommendations are made:

(a) Where trimming and surfoaming operations take place, the panels should be dampened either by spraying the complete board with water containing a detergent or by making use of a drip-feed system over the cutting area. If possible, use should also be made of a portable dust extraction system. However, if this is impracticable, all operatives should be encouraged to make effective use of their respirators.

(b) All operatives should be provided with suitable protective clothing that can be kept in a clean, dust free condition. Such clothing should be free from turn-ups, open pockets etc., and should be laundered frequently by a suitable industrial laundry service.

(c) It is essential to make use of an efficiently organised waste removal squad. Waste must not be allowed to accumulate in rooms and ideally it should be removed as soon as possible after the trimming operation. Regular checks on the efficiency of this squad should be carried out by the site Safety Officer.

(d) When asbestos blocks are nailed to the ceiling using the Multi-Gun, the operatives must make use of their respirator. The younger employees appear to be the most reluctant people to wear these devices and they in particular should be instructed in the need for such precautions.

(e) Wherever possible the trimming and surfoaming operations should be carried out in the room with the best natural ventilation. Rooms having windows should have these opened to their fullest extent.

(f) Where work is carried out in unventilated rooms such as the bathroom, the operatives should be instructed to wear their respirators in addition to carrying out the other precautionary measures, such as damping all panels etc.

Medical Viewpoint
From the medical point of view the risks to health are from (a) asbestosis or (b) diffuse mesothelioma of the pleura or peritoneum ... The latent period between first dust exposure and appearance of the mesothelioma may range from 15 to 50 years with a mean of about

30 years. The total effects of the two dusts which are present, amosite and chrysotile, might be considered on the evidence so far adduced, as not likely to cause mesothelioma and if it did, to take a much longer period to do it. This reasoning however, with regard to the cancer risk is largely hypothetical. The medical evidence in regard to asbestosis however, we can put forward much more convincingly, and state a very real hazard exists in the present instance.

Your Authority should be aware that there are in being Draft Asbestos Regulations and after discussion and agreement with the various employers and trade unions, etc., the Ministry of Labour will demand that these precautions must be adopted as the accepted procedure in all handling of asbestos. It might be wise to obtain a copy of these Draft Regulations, and while all recommendations might not be ultimately adopted, it would obviously be highly desirable if you could institute *all the suggestions* contained in the Draft, or if not, as many as are humanly possible, having regard to all the factors, human, medical, practical and economic.

In the long-term, medical supervision, including x-rays of the chest, and lung function tests, of all exposed workmen would seem necessary and/or desirable, but this is a matter which might be discussed at a later date.

SUMMARY

A survey has been carried out at the Red Road building site, Glasgow, to ascertain whether the atmospheric concentration levels of asbestos dust generated during the erection of the multi-storey flats, are likely to prove hazardous to the health of certain of the site operatives. The results of the survey indicate that a health risk to the operatives does exist and methods of mitigating the hazard are discussed in the report. It is suggested that another survey be carried out when the recommendations contained in this report have been fully implemented.

Bibliography

PRIMARY SOURCES

1. ORAL TESTIMONY

Interviews with 31 Scottish asbestos-disease victims (and on a few occasions their spouses) constitute a major part of the source material for this book. The respondents were located through an initial trawl of clients on the books of Clydeside Action on Asbestos, supplemented with additional contacts supplied by those interviewed, by the Scottish Transport and General Workers Union, Clydebank Asbestos Group and the asbestos campaigner, Tommy Gorman. Most of those interviewed also provided additional information on a standardised questionnaire. We decided from the outset to offer anonymity to protect the identities of those interviewed.

List of respondents

Interview A1	Retired insulation engineer – male – born 1920.
Interview A2	Ex-ships plumber – male – born 1931.
Interview A3	Retired boilermaker plater – male – born 1927.
Interview A4	Ex-lorry driver/labourer – male – born 1946.
Interview A5	Retired fitter – male – born 1924.
Interview A6	Retired heating engineer – male – born 1940.
Interview A7	Retired civil servant – male – born 1941.
Interview A8	Retired joiner – male – born 1926.
Interview A9	Retired sheet metal worker – male – born 1928.
Interview A10	Ex-asbestos sprayer – male – born 1948.
Interview A11	Retired marine engineer – male – born 1931.
Interview A12	Retired marine engineer – male – born 1940
Interview A13	Ex-electrician – male – born 1935.
	Wife of above – born 1938.
Interview A14	Retired insulation engineer – male – born 1930.
Interview A15	Ex-engineer – male – born 1930.
Interview A16	Retired insulation engineer – born 1943.
Interview A17	Ex-joiner – male – born 1945.
Interview A18	Ex-shipyard rigger – male – born 1922.
Interview A19	Ex-asbestos factory worker – male – born 1939.
Interview A20	Widow of quantity surveyor, born 1935.
Interview A21	Widow of electrical engineer, born 1933.
Interview A22	Retired insulation engineer – male – born 1933.
	Retired insulation engineer and asbestos factory worker – male – born 1937.

TGWU convenor – male – born 1946.
Retired insulation engineer – male – born 1931.
Interview A23 Retired insulation engineer – male – born 1917.
Interview A24 Ex asbestos factory worker – female – born 1930.
Interview A25 Ex-asbestos factory worker – male – born 1940.
Interview A26 Ex-asbestos factory worker – male – born 1936
Wife of asbestos factory worker – born 1939

The typed interview transcripts (and questionnaires) are deposited in the Scottish Oral History Centre Archive (deposit SOHCA/016), History Department, University of Strathclyde and are available for public consultation.

2. MANUSCRIPT SOURCES
Clydeside Action on Asbestos Archive, Glasgow

This is a voluminous archive of asbestos-related material accumulated over the last twenty years of campaigning. Much remains to be catalogued. The main collections consulted were:

The Turner & Newall Archive (consisting of more than 50 box files of copied documents provided to CAA from the Chase Manhattan Bank solicitors in 1995–96)

John Todd Papers, Clydeside Action on Asbestos (3 box files of papers)

Turner & Newall Archive, Manchester

An extensive collection of documents on microfilm and fiche relating to this leading UK asbestos company is held by Manchester Metropolitan University. We are grateful to Geoffrey Tweedale for providing access to many pertinent documents relating to Scotland, especially from Newall's Insulation and the Turner's Asbestos Cement Company, Dalmuir.

Clyde Shipbuilders' Association, Minutes, Correspondence etc. (Mitchell Library Glasgow Archives, TD 241)
Glasgow Master Boilermakers and Pipe Coverers' Association, Minutes (Glasgow University Business Records Archive, UGD 339/2/41)
Scottish Insulation Engineers' Association, Minutes (Glasgow University Business Records Archive, UGD 339/2/41)
Glasgow and District Trades Council, Minutes (Mitchell Library)
Scottish Trades Union Congress, General Council Minutes (Glasgow Caledonian University Archives)
Glasgow Corporation, Minutes, 1967–68 (Mitchell Library Glasgow Archives DTC 8/20)
John Brown and Co. (Shipbuilding), Specifications; Letter Books, Minutes (Glasgow University Business Records Archive, UCS/1)
Articles of Association of Phoenix Asbestos Manufacturing Company (Glasgow City Archives, Mitchell Library, Glasgow, Ref. SRA,T/BK–167/2)
Letter, K. and G. MacLellan to H. T. Kinloch, 23 March 1949 (Glasgow City Archives, Mitchell Library, Ref. TD512/37)

3. NEWSPAPERS AND JOURNALS
Aberdeen Press and Journal
Asbestos Bulletin
Clydebank Press
Daily Mail
Daily Record
The Engineer
Evening Express
Evening Times
Forward
Glasgow Chamber of Commerce Journal
Glasgow Herald
Glasgow Medical Journal
Glasgow News
*The India Rubber Journal: Organ of the Rubber, Gutta Percha, Asbestos &
  Plastics Industries*
Morning Star
The Newsletter
Scotland on Sunday
The Scotsman
Scottish Daily Express
Scottish Medical Journal
Scottish Trade Union Review
Sunday Mail
Sunday Post
The Times
Times Educational Supplement
Transport and General Workers Union Record

4. OFFICIAL PUBLICATIONS, REPORTS AND DIRECTORIES
Annual Reports of the Chief Inspector of Factories
Annual Reports of the Scottish Trade Union Congress
Annual Reports of the Transport and General Workers Union
Asbestos: Worker protection and further prohibitions. Proposals for Regulations
  and Guidance [Cd. 47 1992]
Departmental Committee on Industrial Diseases, 1907
Department of Employment, *British Labour Statistics: Historical Abstract* (1971)
Department of Social Security Act 1992. Review by Industrial Injuries Advisory
  Council, 1996. [Cm. 3467]
Health and Safety Commission, *Occupational Heath and Safety, the Way Ahead*
  (1977)
House of Commons Employment Committee 1982–83, 'The Work of the Health
  and Safety Commission and Executive Asbestos', Minutes of Evidence, 1984.
Kelly's Directories of Merchants, Manufacturers and Shippers (England, Scotland
  and Wales)
Post Office Directories of Glasgow
Royal Commission on Labour, 1891–93

5. UNPUBLISHED PRINTED SOURCES
Cancer Prevention Society, 'Preliminary Findings on Asbestos-Induced Disease, 1974–82' (1983)
Dalton, A. J. P., Memorandum to Select Committee on Environment, Transport, and Regional Affairs (1999)
Dalton, A. J. P., unpublished paper, 'The UK Campaign to Ban Asbestos' (1999).
Gorman, T., 'Hidden Hazard Forgotten Victims: Some Aspects of Asbestos Abuse in Britain' (Glasgow Caledonian University, BA Dissertation, 1997)
Greater Glasgow Health Board, Occupational Health Service, 'Red Road Construction Workers' Survey, 1985–86' (Unpublished Report, May 1986)
HSE Consultation Document 1998
HSE Epidemiology and Medical Statistics Unit, Merseyside, 'Mesothelioma Area Statistics, 1986–1995'; 'Mesothelioma Deaths by County and Occupation, 1976-1995'
Higgison, A., 'Asbestos in the Risk Environment' (Glasgow University, BA Dissertation, 1999)
Mair, A., Sanderson, J. T. and Guthrie, T. D., Report on the Asbestos Dust Survey Carried out at the Red Road Building Site, Glasgow, for the Corporation of Glasgow, May 1967.
Roberts, G. H., 'Necropsy Studies of Asbestos Bodies in Glasgow' (Doctor of Medicine thesis, University of Wales, 1968)
Scottish Law Commission Discussion Paper No. 89, 'The Effects of Death and Damages', November, 1990
Social Inclusion Strategy, Evaluation Framework Action Team Progress Report, June 1999
Tweedale, G., 'Science or Public Relations?: The Asbestosis Research Council, 1957–1990', paper to the Work, Health and Illness Confernce, University of Exeter, September 2000
WSCSU, 'Mesothelioma in the West of Scotland' (Paper: November 1983)
Wikely, N. J., 'Asbestos in the Shipyards', inaugural lecture at the Faculty of Law, University of Southampton, 4 February 1997
Woolfson, C., and Beck, M., 'Fatal and Major Injuries to Employees: The Scottish Anomaly', unpublished paper given at First Scottish Trade Union Research Network Conference, June 1999

6. TV AND VIDEO
Channel 4 Scottish Eye TV Programme, 'The Cost of a Ship' (1974)
Clydeside Action on Asbestos, 'Hidden Hazard, Forgotten Victims' (video, 1995)
Clydeside Action on Asbestos, 'A Struggle for Breath' (video, 1996)
BBC Radio 4, 'Asbestos: Too Little Too Late', 15 October 1998

SECONDARY SOURCES (BOOKS AND ARTICLES)

All places of publication are London, unless otherwise stated.

Alcock, P., *Understanding Poverty* (Basingstoke, 1993)
Arlidge, J. L. *Diseases of Occupations* (1892).

Bartrip, P., *Workmen's Compensation in Twentieth Century Britain* (Aldershot, 1987)

Bartrip, P. 'Too Little, too Late? The Home Office and the Asbestos Industry Regulations, 1931', *Medical History*, no. 42, 1998

Bartrip, P., and S. Burman., *Wounded Soldiers of Industry* (Oxford, 1983)

Blackburn, S. 'Working Class Attitudes to Social Reform', *International Review of Social History*, XXXIII (1988)

Bridge, J. C., 'Remarks on Occupational Dust', *British Medical Journal*, 21 December 1929

Brodeur, P., *Outrageous Misconduct: The Asbestos Industry on Trial* (New York, 1985)

Castleman, B. I., *Asbestos: Medical and Legal Aspects* (New Jersey: Aspen, 1996)

Checkland, S. G. *The Upas Tree: Glasgow 1875–1975* (Glasgow, 1976)

Clydebank Burgh Council, *Official Handbook, 1960*

Constantinidis, K., 'Asbestos Exposure – its Related Disorders', *The British Journal of Clinical Practice*, 7 (1977)

Dalton, A. *Asbestos Killer Dust* (1979)

De Vos Irvine, H.,. Lamont, D. W. Hole, D. J. and. Gillies, C. H., 'Asbestos Lung Cancer in Glasgow and the West of Scotland', *British Medical Journal*, no. 306, 1993

Dilke, M. S. and Templeton, A. A., *Third Statistical Account of Scotland* (Glasgow, 1959)

Doll, R., 'Mortality from lung cancer in asbestos workers', *British Journal of Industrial Medicine*, 1955

Duffy, K., *Social Exclusion and Human Dignity in Europe* (1995)

Elmes, P. C. and Marion, J. C., 'Insulation Workers in Belfast. A Further Study of Mortality due to Asbestos Exposure (1945–75)', *British Journal of Industrial Medicine* (1977), 34.

Fallowfield, L., *Quality of Life: the Missing Measurement in Health Care* (London, 1990)

Foster, J., Woolfson, C. and Beck, M., *Paying for the Piper: The Piper Alpha Disaster* (New York, 1996)

Fraser, W. H., *A History of British Trade Unionism, 1700–1998* (Basingstoke, 1999)

Glasgow Labour History Workshop, *The Singer Strike, 1911* (Clydebank, 1989)

Glasgow Labour History Workshop, 'Working in Singer', *Scottish Labour History Society Journal*, vol. 25 (1990)

Glasgow of Today, Businessmen and Mercantile Interests (Mitchell Library, Glasgow Collection, 1888)

Glendinning, M. and Muthesius, *Tower Block* (1982)

Gloag, D., 'Asbestos – can it be used safely?' *British Medical Journal*, 282, 14 February (1981)

Gold, C., and Cuthbert, J., 'Asbestos – A Hazard to the Community.' *Public Health*, Vol. 80, No. 6 (1966)

Gordon, D., and Pantazi, C., *Breadline Britain* (Aldershot, 1997).

Gorman, T., 'Action on Asbestos', *Scottish Trade Union Review*, 67 (November/December 1994)

Gorman, T., 'The Continuing Use of Asbestos in Buildings', *17th Proceedings of the Building Institute Summer School*, Glasgow 1995

Gorman, T., 'A case study of the settlement process', in Peters, G. A. and Peters, B. J. (eds), *Sourcebook on Asbestos*, vol. 20 (Charlottesville, Virginia, 1999)

Gorman, T. (ed.), *Clydebank, Asbestos the Unwanted Legacy* (Glasgow, 2000)

Gorman, T., 'Women and Asbestos', in Gorman, T. (ed.), *Clydebank, Asbestos the Unwanted Legacy* (Glasgow, 2000)

Greenberg, M., 'Knowledge of the Health hazard of Asbestos Prior to the Merewether and Price report of 1930', *Social History of Medicine*, no. 7, 1994

Harries, P. G., 'Asbestos Hazards in Naval Dockyards', *Annals of Occupational Hygiene*, 11, 1968

Harries, P. G., 'Asbestos Dust Concentrations in Ship Repairing', *Annals of Occupational Hygiene*, 14, 1971

Harvey, S., *Just an Occupational Hazard* (1988)

Hiett, D. M., 'Experimental asbestosis: an investigation of functional and pathological disturbances. Control animals and exposure conditions.' *British Journal of Industrial Medicine*, 2, 1973

Howie, R., 'Asbestos induced deaths in the UK', in Peters, G. A. and Peters, B. J. (eds), *Sourcebook on Asbestos*, vol. 19 (Charlottesville, Virginia, 1999)

Howie, R., 'Asbestos, the way forward learning from past mistakes', in Gorman, T. (ed.), *Clydebank, Asbestos the Unwanted Legacy.*

Hutchins, B., and Harrison, A., *A History of Factory Legislation* (1911)

Hutter, B. M., 'Regulating employers and employees: health and safety in the workplace', *Journal of Law and Society*, 20, 4, 1993

Hutton, S., 'Testing Townsend', in S. Baldwin *et al.*, *Quality of Life* (New York, 1994)

Jack, I., *The Sea* (1998)

Jeremy, D., 'Corporate responses to the Emergent recognition of a Health Hazard in the UK Asbestos Industry: the case of Turner and Newall', 1920–1960, *Business and Economic History*, no. 24, 1995

Johnston, R., *Clydeside Capital 1870–1920: A Social History of Employers* (East Linton, 2000)

Johnston, R., and McIvor, A. J., 'Incubating death: working with asbestos in Clydeside shipbuilding and engineering, 1945–1990', *Scottish Labour History*, 34, 1999

Johnston, R., and McIvor, A. J., 'The social impact of industrial disease: A workers' perspective from oral history evidence', in Donnelly, M. (ed.), *Proceedings of the First Scottish Trade Union Research Network Conference* (Glasgow, 1999)

Johnston R., and McIvor, A. J., 'Pushed into social exclusion: asbestos-related disability and relative poverty on Clydeside', *Scottish Affairs*, 32, summer 2000

Johnston, R., and McIvor, A. J., 'Whatever Happened to the Occupational Health Service?', in C. Nottingham (ed.), *The NHS in Scotland* (Aldershot, 2000)

Jones, H., 'An Inspector Calls' in P. Weindling (ed.), *A Social History of Occupational Health* (1985)

Kinnersley, P., *The Hazards of Work* (1973)

Knox, W. W., *Industrial Nation: Work, Culture and Society in Scotland, 1800–Present* (Edinburgh, 1999)

Law, A., 'Neither Colonial or Historic: Workers' Organisation at Rosyth Dockyard, 1945–95', in Lunn, K. and Day, A. (eds), *History of Work and Labour Relations in the Royal Dockyards* (1999)

Lenaghan, J., *Victims Twice Over* (Glasgow, n.d., *c.* 1994)

Mack, J., and Lansley, S., *Poor Britain* (1985)

McIvor, A. J., 'Manual Work, Technology and Industrial Health, 1918–1939', *Medical History*, no. 31, 1987

McIvor, A. J., 'Employers, the Government and Industrial Fatigue in Britain, 1890–1918', *British Journal of Industrial Medicine*, 1987

McIvor, A. J., 'Work and Health, 1880–1914', *Scottish Labour History Society Journal*, 24, 1989

McIvor, A. J., 'Women and Work in Twentieth Century Scotland', in A. Dickson and J. H. Treble (eds), *People and Society in Scotland*, vol. 3 (Edinburgh, 1992)

McIvor, A. J., *Organised Capital* (Cambridge, 1996)

McIvor, A. J., *A History of Work in Britain, 1880–1950* (2000)

McKinlay, A., *Making Ships, Making Men: Working in John Brown's, Clydebank Between the Wars* (Clydebank, 1989)

Melling, J., 'Scottish Industrialists', in T. Dickson (ed.), *Capital and Class in Scotland* (Edinburgh, 1982)

Muriel, L., *et al.*, 'Mesothelioma of Pleura and Peritoneaum Following Exposure to Asbestos in the London Area', *British Journal of Industrial Medicine*, 1965

Oliver, T., *Dangerous Trades* (1902)

O'Reilly, D. *et al.*, 'Asbestos-related mortality in Northern Ireland, 1985–1994', *Journal of Public Health Medicine*, vol. 21 (1999)

Peto, J., *et al.*, 'Continuing increase in mesothelioma mortality in Britain', *The Lancet*, vol. 345, 4 March 1995

Peto, J., 'The European mesothelioma epidemic', *British Journal of Cancer*, vol. 79, 1999

Rosato, D. V., *Asbestos: Its industrial applications* (1959)

Slaven, A., 'William Ewing Birrell', in A. Slaven and S. Checkland, *Dictionary of Scottish Business Biography*, vol. II (Aberdeen, 1990)

Smith, C., 'Dangerous Trades', *Economic Review*, October 1905, vol. XV

Smout, T. C., *A Century of the Scottish People* (1987)

Summers, A. L., *Asbestos and the Asbestos Industry* (1919)

Townsend, P., *Poverty in the United Kingdom* (1979)

Tweedale, G., *Magic Mineral to Deadly Dust: Turner and Newall and the Asbestos Health Hazard* (Oxford, 2000)

Tweedale, G., 'Sprayed Limpet Asbestos' in Peters, G. A. and Peters, B. J. (eds), *Sourcebook on Asbestos*, vol. 20 (Charlottesville, Virginia, 1999)

Tweedale, G., and Jeremy, D., 'Compensating the Workers: Industrial Injury and Compensation in the British Asbestos Industry, 1930s–60s', *Business History*, vol. 41, April 1999

Tweedale, G., and Hansen, P., 'Protecting the Workers: The Medical Board and the Asbestos Industry, 1930s–1960s', *Medical History*, no. 42, 1998

Vincent Day, St-V., 'On Asbestos', *Institution of Engineers and Shipbuilders in Scotland*, 5 December 1871 (Glasgow, 1872)

Wade, O., *When I Dropped the Knife* (Durham, 1996)

Wagner, J. C., 'Asbestos in Experimental Animals', *British Journal of Industrial Medicine*, 1963, 20, 1, pp. 1–12

Wagner, J. C., 'Asbestosis Carcinogenisis', *British Journal of Cancer*, 32, 258 (1975)

Weindling, P., (ed.), *A Social History of Occupational Health* (1985)

Wikeley, N., 'The Asbestos Regulations, 1931: A Licence to Kill?', *Journal of Law and Society*, 19 (1992)

Wikely, N., 'Asbestos and Cancer: an Early Warning to the British TUC', *American Journal of Industrial Medicine*, 22 (1992)

Wikeley, N., 'Turner and Newall: Early Organizational Responses to Litigation Risk', *Journal of Law and Society*, 24 (1997)

Wohl, A., *Endangered Lives* (1983)

Woolfson, C., and Beck, M., 'Deregulation: the contemporary politics of health and safety', in A. McClogan (ed.), *The Future of Labour Law* (1996)

Wyke, T., 'Mule Spinners' Cancer', in A. Fowler and T. Wyke (eds), *The Barefooted Aristocrats* (Littleborough, 1987)

Index

Disablement Benefits, 134–8
Docherty, James, 155
dockers, 20, 33, 116, 167, 169
doctors
 and asbestos, 73, 183–5, 217–18
 company, 46, 73, 90, 184–5
 diagnoses, 78, 179–87
 see also medical officers, nurses
Doig, Sandy, 30
Dolbey, Norman, 82
Drumchapel, 204
Dumbarton, 26
Dundee, 28, 58, 218; *see also* Scottish
 Occupational Health Service
Dunfermline, 28
dust measurement, 114, 130, 130–1,
 155, 237–8
dust and occupational health, 36,
 43–5, 166–7;
 see also asbestos, asbestosis,
 cancer, mesothelioma,
 pneumoconiosis
dust protection, *see* masks, protective
 clothing, respirators, ventilation

Edinburgh
 mesothelioma deaths, 27–8
Elderslie Graving Dock, Scotstoun, 81
Electrical Trades Union, 91
electricians, 5, 120, 179–80
emphysema, 56, 78
employers
 and asbestos, 148–58, 212–13
 and occupational health, 45–7,
 148–9, 212
employers' organisations, 150–1; *see
 also* individual employers'
 association entries
Engineering Employers' Federation, 87
engineering industry
 and asbestos, 16, 20, 21, 22, 25, 87,
 118
English Thermal Insulation Engineers'
 Association, 153
environment and asbestos, 6, 20, 75,
 115–16, 118, 120, 154, 165, 173,
 201–8
European Economic Community, 59,
 128, 133
extractors, *see* ventilation
eye injuries, 46, 58

face masks, *see* masks
Factory Act (1901), 53, 125
Factory Act (1937), 51–3, 56, 69, 125
Factory Act (1961), 125, 129
factory environment, 35–6, 53–5
 see also Turner's Asbestos Cement
factory inspection, 3, 47–8, 52, 54, 84,
 106, 112, 123–4, 128–9, 131–3,
 145, 173, 216–17, 229–30
Fairfield's (shipbuilders), Govan, 86,
 89, 168, 169, 214, 215
Falconer, Alex (European MP), 140
Falkirk, 205
family contact
 asbestos-disease, 144, 202–3
Faslane (naval base), 18
fatigue
 at work, 32–6
 in World War One, 50
 see also Industrial Fatigue
 Research Board
Ferguson, Nancy, 78
Findlay, J. and Co., Doune, 12
Fort William, 106
French polishers, 22, 25
Fullarton, Jimmy, 101

Garrett, A. W., 230
General and Municipal Workers'
 Union, 132, 161, 176; *see also*
 Transport and General
 Workers' Union
general practitioners, 73, 185; *see also*
 doctors
Glasgow
 mesothelioma deaths, 26
Glasgow Asbestos Co. Ltd, 12
Glasgow Boiler Coverers' Society, 170
Glasgow Corporation
 and asbestos, 57, 218
 and occupational health, 101, 104,
 173
 and Red Road Flats, 99–104,
 236–40
Glasgow District Trades Council, 97,
 165
Glasgow Master Boiler and Pipe
 Coverers' Association, 16, 150–1
 see also Scottish Insulation
 Engineers' Employers'
 Association

109, 129; *see also* asbestos
    stripping
Lilly, Margaret, 78
Lilly, Owen, 78
'Limpet' asbestos, *see* spraying
Livingston
    asbestos factory, 74, 202
locomotive manufacture, *see* North
    British Locomotive Co.
lung disease, *see* cancer,
    mesothelioma, pneumoconiosis,
    respiratory disease

MacDonald, Bobby, 100
machismo work culture, *see*
    masculinity
MacLellan, George and Co. Ltd,
    Maryhill, Glasgow, 12–13, 143,
    149, 151, 169, 220
Main, David, 140
Mair, Alex, 58, 96–7, 101, 218
management and asbestos, 154–8; *see
    also* employers
Management of Health and Safety at
    Work Regulations (1992), 59
managers, 25
Marinite, 18, 89–90, 92
Marinite Agreement (1954), 233–5
Marinite Co. Ltd., Glasgow, 14, 19,
    99, 149, 154
masculinity at work, 61, 81, 171, 220,
    221
masks, 70–2, 75, 87, 92, 98, 102,
    105–6, 109, 126–8, 155, 175
McInnes, Brian, 27
McKelvey, William (MP), 135
McKessock, Brenda, 200
McMeekan, William, 21
McNicol, Hugh, 155
McQueen, Steve, 23, 180
Meanan, Joseph, 85
medical examinations
    and Asbestos Regulations, 122
    in construction, 218
    and Factory Act (1937), 51, 53
    in shipyards, 91, 117, 218
    at Turner's Asbestos Cement,
        72–3
Medical Inspector of Factories, 123;
    see also Doig, Sandy and Legge,
    Thomas

Medical Officer of Health (Glasgow),
    113
medical officers, 73; *see also* doctors
Medical Panels, 68–9, 73, 85, 122,
    124, 130, 134–5, 152, 165, 174
Medical Research Council, 82
medicine, occupational, 46, 72–3, 166,
    218; *see also* doctors,
    Lewinsohn, Scottish
    Occupational Health Service
mercury poisoning, 40
Merewether and Price Report, 114
mesothelioma, 23, 24, 179
    asbestos manufacturing, 78–9, 119
    building workers, 22, 25, 103–4,
        119–20, 239–40
    carpenters, *see* joiners
    cleaners, 22
    Clydebank, 26–7, 28, 78, 120
    compensation, 139–40, 200
    Devonport, 93
    Edinburgh, 27–8
    electricians, 120, 179–80
    engineering, 22, 25
    environmental exposure, 202,
        203–4
    'family contact', 144, 202–3
    female deaths, 26, 78, 119
    French polishers, 22, 25
    Glasgow, 26
    heating engineers, 120
    Hill, Ron, 103, 135
    hospital consultant, 24
    ICI, 21
    insulators, 22, 120, 139, 153
    laggers, *see* insulators
    managerial, 25
    McKessock, Brenda, 200–1
    metal workers, 25
    mortality, 24–8, 119–20
    plumbers, 25, 120
    professionals, 25
    quantity surveyor, 74
    railways, 22
    Red Road Survey, 239–40
    Scottish towns, 26–8, 119
    secretary, 22
    shipbuilding, 22, 25, 103–4, 119
    short exposure and, 114
    surgery for, 180–2
    textile workers, 22

see also individual trade union
  entries
Trades Boards Act (1909), 35, 47, 48
Trades Union Congress, 34, 161, 166,
  170, 219
Transport and General Workers'
  Union, 2, 100, 139, 156, 159–62,
  169–70, 173–4, 176, 217, 219–20
transport workers, 22, 25
tuberculosis, 44, 165
Turner & Newall, 148, 151, 155–6,
  168, 213–14
  archive, 2, 242
  and Chase Manhattan case, 2
  and Coyle case, 7–8
  doctor, 90
  and Factory Act (1961), 129
  and Hancock case, 202
  insurance scheme, 68
  origins, 13
  profits, 216
  and shipbuilding risk, 152–3
  see also Lewinsohn, Turner's
    Asbestos Cement, Tweedale
Turner's Asbestos Cement,
  Clydebank, 2, 13–14, 122,
  184–5, 198–9, 203, 215
  asbestos exposure in, 64–79
  employers and management in,
    169
  and the environment, 201–3, 205–7
  trade unions in, 169
  see also Clydebank, Turner &
    Newall
Tweedale, Geoffrey, 8, 148, 151, 157,
  158, 213–14

United Turkey Red Co., Vale of
  Leven, 42
Upper Clyde Shipbuilders, 95

ventilation at work, 69–70, 75–6, 85,
  90–1, 125, 128–30, 234–5
Victoria Infirmary

asbestos study, 116–17

wages, 34–5, 154
Walsh, Jack, 65, 205
Watson, Mike (MP), 175
Weil's disease, 57
welfarism, 31–2, 45, 77, 149
West Dumbartonshire Council, 224
West of Scotland Cancer Surveillance
  Unit, 119–20
white asbestos, 9, 72, 79, 90, 113, 120,
  134, 176
Wikely, Nick, 147, 213
Williamson, Thomas, 78, 188
women
  and asbestos-related disease, 143–4
  and occupational health, 61
  and mesothelioma mortality, 26,
    78, 119
woodworkers, *see* joiners
work
  attitudes to risk, 220–1
  intensification of, 33–4
  meaning of, 31
  see also individual occupations
Workmen's Compensation Acts (1897;
  1906), 39, 41, 47, 51, 121; *see
  also* National Insurance
  (Industrial Injuries) Act
World War One
  and asbestos use, 81
  and occupational health, 49–51
  see also Health of Munition
    Workers' Committee
World War Two
  and asbestos exposure, 6, 22, 66,
    70, 83, 86–7, 141, 143, 178
  and occupational health, 49, 55
Wormald's Insulation, 140
Worthington, Tony (MP), 175
Wright Insulation, 140

Yarrow Shipbuilders, Glasgow 133